M W Thwing

Jan 1961

PRACTICAL IRONMAKING

DEDICATED TO GEOFFREY WELLS

PRACTICAL
IRONMAKING

By

G. D. ELLIOT

AND

J. A. BOND

SHEFFIELD

THE UNITED STEEL COMPANIES LTD

1959

Made and printed in Great Britain by
PERCY LUND, HUMPHRIES & COMPANY LIMITED
LONDON AND BRADFORD

CONTENTS

Contents

James Bond died shortly before this book went to press. It is hoped that the volume will serve as some small memorial to the tremendous help and assistance which Mr. Bond's co-author received during an association of very many years.

INTRODUCTION

THE LITERATURE OF IRONMAKING is peculiar in that most published works, both technical papers and text-books, are not directed to the man immediately interested in ironmaking. This means that the literature assumes in the reader either too little general knowledge or a large amount of specialised knowledge.

For the outsider, who will never have to make his living in an ironworks, this volume will be of little use or interest. There will equally be little of assistance to the scientist or research worker. An attempt has been made to interest and help the men in between—the interested student and the average operator. To that end, it is assumed that the reader has some knowledge of ironmaking but has not the ability or desire to delve into the more abstruse and highly scientific aspects of ironmaking.

In spite of the fashionable worship of such things as operational research, automation, cybernetics and the other catchwords which bedevil industry, it is believed that the ironworks will be one of the last places where the practical man will be king. This places a premium on practical experience, especially around the blast furnace itself, and this factor has been borne very much in mind during the writing of this small volume.

By adding much in the way of plant description, the volume could have been made larger, but the writers are addressing people who already have a plant and are trying to obtain the best from it. Similarly, little space is devoted to the raw materials of ironmaking; usually, operators are given a set of raw materials and have to make the best of them.

To write a long and over-comprehensive treatise is to ensure that it will not be read by the ordinary operator and student. The major problem was to decide on what to omit, rather than what to include.

The greater part of the book is written around experience at one ironworks. The results may not be directly applicable to all other plants and experienced operators may disagree with much that is written, but it is believed that the underlying principles do apply to all plants and practices.

If, in spite of so many obvious shortcomings, the book is of assistance to only one poor operator, the effort of writing will not have been in vain.

PREFACE

IRONMAKING IS PERHAPS THE oldest of the metallurgical arts and dates back to the days of Tubal Cain who was the first artificer in metals. After all these centuries there is still much confusion and much disagreement amongst ironmakers as to the best way of constructing their apparatus and of operating it. This is understandable when one remembers the diversity of raw materials involved and the only too frequent dependence of the operator on factors outside his control. It will be readily understood, therefore, that no two men can write authoritatively about such a complex subject.

Perhaps the greatest reward for serving in the most arduous and difficult section of the steel industry is the very real friendliness and helpful spirit which exists between one ironmaker and another. Although this volume makes no pretence at being authoritative, extensive use has been made of the many friendships enjoyed by the writers with their immediate colleagues and with a much wider circle of ironmakers throughout the world. The number of ironmakers whose experience has been so freely drawn upon is too large to permit individual acknowledgement. Nevertheless, the authors are very conscious of their indebtedness to their many friends.

Special mention must however be made to Mr. David King of the United Steel Companies, who gave valuable help in painstakingly reading and checking the script.

Finally, the authors thank the United Steel Companies, not only for permission to write this volume, but for many years of interesting and exciting work in the sphere of ironmaking.

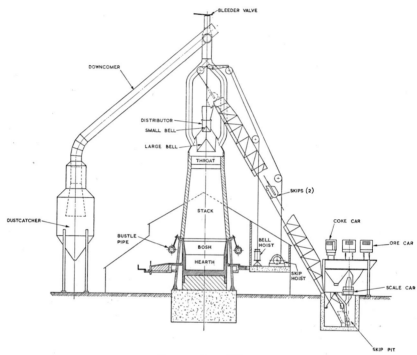

Cross-section of Furnace.

Chapter I

DESIGN OF THE BLAST FURNACE

LINES OF THE FURNACE

WHEN CONSIDERING blast-furnace design it is most important to take into account the history of the furnace. The blast furnace is the oldest metallurgical furnace known to man and its present state has been reached as a result of evolution rather than from deliberate design. Most metallurgical furnaces, for example, the open-hearth steel furnaces, were originally designed by one man to do a specific task. The descendants of that type of furnace today bear a strong resemblance to the initial design conceived by the inventor. The case of the blast furnace is quite different.

The beginnings of ironmaking are lost in history. Some authorities believe that iron was known in 4000 B.C. and it is generally agreed that it was known and used in 1500 B.C. At that time, prehistoric man took the stones of the field and built a small hearth with them in which a mixture of ore and charcoal was worked by natural draught until a small lump of pasty metal was obtained. Subsequent hammering separated most of the slag and produced wrought iron. All the reactions involved took place in the solid phase. This method of making iron, known as the Catalan Forge process, was used exclusively until the middle of the 14th century. In Central Europe about this time, the application of forced draught led to the production of iron in the liquid state and with a high carbon content—the first cast iron. This discovery soon led to the building of a new type of furnace. Again, the stones of the field were used but the furnace now took a shape strongly reminiscent of a modern blast furnace. In general, the internal lines consisted of two truncated cones placed one on top of the other. Ore and charcoal were charged through the narrow throat of the upper cone and the liquids collected in the narrow hearth of the lower cone. Openings for the admission of air and for the tapping of liquids were made at the lower level.

Thus, the modern blast furnace had its beginnings 600 years ago. From that time on, the basic design has slowly developed towards that known today. The major changes, naturally, have been increases in size dictated by the need for increased production; this has inevitably meant that engineering and constructional problems have had more influence in shaping the furnace than has scientific and metallurgical knowledge of the ironmaking process. This emphasis on engineering is understandable because it was, and still is, possible to operate a furnace and produce iron satisfactorily without knowledge of the science and metallurgy involved. Engineering developments have enabled the scale of operation to be greatly increased.

From the 14th century onwards, the furnace has steadily increased in size. From those early days when one fireback, or one tombstone, represented a day's output, the slow process of evolution has led to the furnaces of today when daily outputs of 2000 tons are not unknown. It is interesting to ponder on what would happen today if, in the light of current scientific knowledge, the problem of ironmaking had to be tackled without any knowledge of the blast furnace. It is possible that the blast furnace as it is now would never be used. Nevertheless, the blast furnace has evolved from these early beginnings into an extremely efficient machine for the handling of large tonnages and for the production of a satisfactory product at a comparatively low cost.

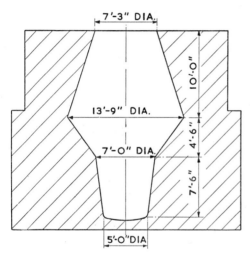

Fig. 1. Seventeenth century Blast Furnace. This furnace was operated by Abraham Darby who was the first man to use coke as blast-furnace fuel. Dynasty of Iron Founders – Raistrick.

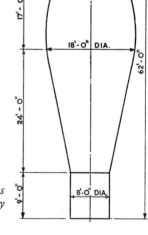

Fig. 2. Nineteenth-century Blast Furnace. This furnace was operated about 1870 at the Appleby Iron Company, Lincolnshire.

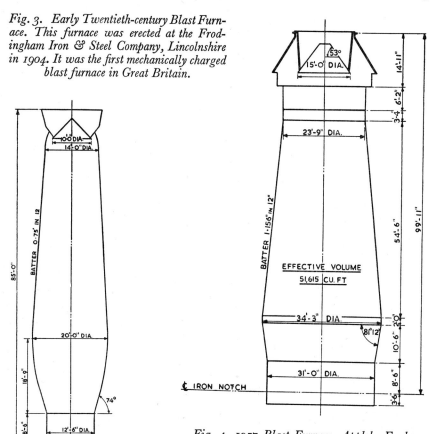

Fig. 3. Early Twentieth-century Blast Furnace. This furnace was erected at the Frod-
ingham Iron & Steel Company, Lincolnshire
in 1904. It was the first mechanically charged
blast furnace in Great Britain.

Fig. 4. 1957 Blast Furnace. Appleby-Frodingham Steel Company, Lincolnshire.

Until about 1880 the increase in size and, therefore, of production,
was very slow but after that time progress was rapid, especially during
the early years of this century. In American practice, modern engineering and constructional methods and the engineering inventiveness of
that period resulted in tremendous strides being made. Figs. 1–4 show a
furnace of the 17th century, the middle of the 19th century, the early
20th century and a furnace of today. It will be seen that there is a strong
family resemblance. The furnace of the 1950's still sits on mother earth
just as all its predecessors did; it is the only metallurgical furnace known
to man constructed in this manner. It is constructed of refractory bricks
which are not such a far cry from the stones of the field used by prehistoric man.

Knowledge of this process of evolution is important when considering the design of a new furnace today. For convenience, the blast furnace is divided into the following sections:

(*a*) Throat
(*b*) Stack
(*c*) Bosh
(*d*) Hearth

It is conventional to measure the size of a blast furnace by the diameter of the hearth; this, of necessity, presupposes conventional and accepted relationships between the hearth diameter and the remaining dimensions of the furnace. There is a trend to replace hearth diameter as a yardstick by effective volume, which is probably a more realistic measure, but this is not yet accepted universally.

With the changes in production rates, raw materials and fuels which have taken place over the centuries, it is probably not worthwhile to compare the furnace of today with furnaces earlier than about 1850. Table I gives the dimensions of furnaces erected within the last ten years in several parts of the world. Although the materials, fuels, and practices involved obviously vary a great deal, it will be seen that there is very little difference in the main dimensions of the furnace wherever it may be situated. But there are big differences from the furnace of 100 years ago.

What are the reasons for the blast furnace's distinctive shape?

Assume the throat to be the starting point of design. The relationship of throat diameter to the dimensions of the charging gear (bell and hopper) will be discussed later. When the furnace charge is dropped into the throat of the furnace it encounters modest temperatures which will lead to little change in physical characteristics and volume. In order to allow for the inevitably varying level of the stockline, it is usual, and probably desirable, to commence the upper part of the furnace with a small section of parallel.

The limitations of heat exchange from hot gases to colder solid materials and the speed of gas passage through a modern furnace demand a furnace height sufficient to permit absorption of the greater part of the sensible heat of the gases leaving the tuyeres. It is generally agreed that this height should be approximately 90 ft. from the centre line of the tuyeres to the top deck of the furnace. If the whole of this height took the form of a parallel shaft of the same diameter as the throat, the physical changes in the charge, together with the effects of wall drag, would almost certainly make such a furnace unworkable. It would also mean that the working volume of the furnace would be insufficient for satisfactory utilisation of the fuel. The necessity of

TABLE I

DIMENSIONS OF FURNACES FROM VARIOUS DISTRICTS

	Australia	South Africa	Spain	England	Scotland	U.S.A. Northern	U.S.A. Southern	India	Russia	Germany	Wales	Average
Hearth diameter—ft.	29' 0"	25' 0"	27' 0"	28' 6"	25' 9"	28' 0"	27' 3"	25' 0"	26' 3"	26' 3"	29' 9"	27' 1"
Bosh diameter—ft.	32' 2"	28' 3"	30' 3"	31' 9"	30' 0"	31' 0"	31' 5"	28' 3"	29' 6"	31' 0"	33' 0"	30' 7"
Throat diameter—ft.	23' 0"	20' 0"	20' 6"	22' 0"	21' 3"	21' 6"	21' 0"	20' 0"	20' 6"	21' 3"	22' 9"	21' 3"
Bell diameter—ft.	16' 6"	15' 0"	15' 6"	15' 0"	16' 0"	16' 6"	15' 0"	15' 0"	15' 6"	15' 6"	16' 6"	15' 8"
Bosh angle	82°15'	81°47'	81°12'	81°12'	80°21'	81°40'	82°0'	81°47'	81°07'	81°21'	81°57'	81°31'
Stack batter—in./ft.	0·981	0·952	1·136	1·136	1·016	1·000	1·150	0·952	1·110	1·017	1·056	1·042
Working volume—cu. ft.	54,189	39,437	41,370	44,350	44,700	47,550	49,092	37,633	42,900	46,000	53,975	45,563
Number of tuyeres	21	18	18	18	18	20	21	18	18	20	21	19
Taphole to bosh—ft.	9' 6"	9' 9"	9' 3"	8' 6"	9' 9"	9' 3"	10' 0"	9' 9"	10' 5"	9' 0"	9' 9"	9' 6"
Bosh height—ft.	12' 0"	11' 3"	10' 6"	10' 6"	12' 6"	10' 3"	14' 10"	11' 3"	10' 5"	15' 6"	11' 6"	11' 11"
Bosh parallel—ft.	10' 6"	9' 6"	6' 6"	10' 0"	10' 0"	9' 0"	6' 11"	8' 3"	6' 6"	3' 6"	8' 6"	7' 8"
Stack height (sloped)—ft.	56' 2"	52' 0"	51' 6"	51' 6"	51' 9"	57' 0"	54' 9"	52' 0"	48' 6"	57' 6"	58' 3"	53' 9"
Throat parallel—ft.	6' 9"	7' 9"	8' 6"	8' 6"	8' 0"	8' 0"	9' 6"	6' 3"	12' 5"	6' 6"	6' 0"	8' 5"
Height, taphole to bottom of closed bell—ft.	97' 0"	93' 9"	88' 11"	88' 1"	94' 0"	97' 0"	100' 0"	89' 6"	89' 0"	92' 9"	96' 0"	93' 3"
Taphole to slag notch—ft.	4' 6"	4' 6"	4' 0"	3' 3"	4' 6"	4' 8"	3' 9"	4' 6"	4' 6"	4' 6"	4' 6"	4' 3"
Slag notch to tuyeres—ft.	3' 3"	3' 6"	3' 6"	3' 6"	3' 6"	3' 8"	4' 3"	3' 6"	3' 6"	4' 0"	3' 6"	3' 7"
Tuyeres to bosh—ft.	1' 9"	1' 9"	1' 9"	1' 9"	1' 9"	11"	2' 0"	1' 9"	2' 5"	10"	1' 9"	1' 8"

departing from the parallel throat is emphasised further by the physical changes which occur in the charge.

With certain ores, carbon deposition takes place starting at temperatures of approximately 300°C.; it is known that this deposition is accompanied by an increase in solid volume. Laboratory work has shown that this increase in volume may be as much as 400 per cent. but, because of the speed at which the burden descends the stack of the furnace, it is extremely doubtful if expansion of this order is encountered in practice. The effects of carbon deposition and of wall drag therefore dictate that not very far down the furnace the parallel walls

TABLE II

EFFECT OF BATTER ON TRANSIT TIMES

AND SPEEDS IN THE STACK OF A 28 FT. 6 IN. FURNACE

Distance from commencement of batter, ft.	Area, sq. ft.	Downward movement relative speed	Relative time spent in zone
0	380	1·00	1·00
2	395	0·96	1·04
4	411	0·93	1·08
6	427	0·89	1·12
8	443	0·86	1·17
10	458	0·83	1·21
12	474	0·80	1·25
14	490	0·78	1·29
16	505	0·75	1·33
18	521	0·73	1·37
20	537	0·71	1·41
22	552	0·69	1·45
24	568	0·67	1·49
26	583	0·65	1·54
28	600	0·63	1·58
30	615	0·62	1·62
32	631	0·60	1·66
34	647	0·59	1·70
36	662	0·57	1·74
38	678	0·56	1·78
40	693	0·55	1·82
42	709	0·53	1·87
44	725	0·52	1·91
46	740	0·51	1·95
48	756	0·50	1·99
50	772	0·49	2·03

must give way to an outward taper. This taper is usually referred to as "Stack Batter".

There is some argument among operators on the correct amount of stack batter, but reference to Table I shows a remarkable unanimity of opinion that it should be approximately one inch to the foot. The effect of batter is to give an increased amount of volume at each succeeding lower level of the stack; this, of course, has an effect on the transit times and therefore on the residence times in the various zones (*see* Table II). It should also lead to more efficient utilisation of fuel.

Carbon deposition can take place at temperatures as high as 650°C. In certain practices, this temperature level may normally be some way down the furnace. In addition, all temperature levels vary from day to day in their vertical location. It is only when the solid ore charge is fully liquid that the decrease in volume necessitates a change in the diameter of the stack. At this level, outward stack batter is succeeded by inward bosh batter.

Fifty years ago, it was usual to make this change on a radius; today, it is universal practice to interpose a few feet of parallel between the top of the bosh and the bottom of the battered stack. The insertion of this parallel section is often said by operators to be in order to give the furnace a chance to make its own shape—an admission that no operator is sure where the top of the bosh or the bottom of the stack should be located. As any single ore is usually a mixture of different minerals, the change from solid to liquid may easily cover a temperature range of 300°C. This characteristic may justify the insertion of a parallel between stack and bosh. The use of a mixture of ores, especially when low grade ores are used, will promote a wide temperature range.

But it may be that the adoption of sinter burdens will lead to a change in the shape of the furnace. The future may well see a return to the high boshes of fifty years ago, but with a much steeper angle than was then the case. This is because of the narrow melting range of all sinters, and the fact that furnace operation is consistently more regular on sinter burdens than on ore burdens. Further evidence lies in the shape of all blown out furnaces; the bosh parallel has always been taken into the bosh. Table I gives the amount of bosh parallel used by designers in many parts of the ironmaking world. The figures range from 3 ft. 6 in. to 10 ft. 6 in.

Materials become fully liquid in the bosh and combustion of coke occurs in the upper part of the hearth. This means that less room is needed for the downward flowing solids which are rapidly contracting in volume and more room is needed for the ascending gases which are rapidly expanding due to combustion.

The height of the bosh is the dimension which has changed perhaps more than any other in the last half-century. Whereas the height of the bosh was usually over 30 per cent. of the total height of the furnace, the bosh of the modern furnace is only about half that. A further divergence from earlier design is seen in the angle of the bosh, which has steepened consistently over the last half-century: bosh angles of about 70° were universal then, whereas they are now usually about 80°. Literature shows that the troubles encountered in smelting the fine Mesabi ores of North America in the early years of the century led to a comparatively rapid change from high flat boshes to short steep boshes. The experience of the time was too uniform and too emphatic to be discounted. Nevertheless, many other changes were taking place during these difficult years and many changes in materials and practice have taken place

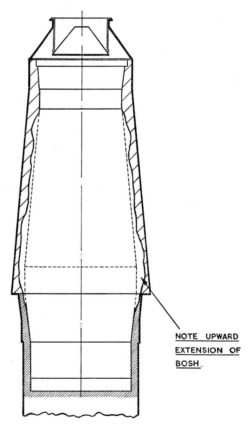

NOTE UPWARD
EXTENSION OF
BOSH.

Fig. 5. Typical lines of a blast furnace after blowing out.

more recently, but they do not seem to have had the same impact on the shape of the furnace as the early days of smelting Mesabi ore.

It may not be out of place here to examine the shape of a blast furnace after it has been in operation. Irrespective of the location, the practice followed, or the materials used, blast furnaces all over the world show a

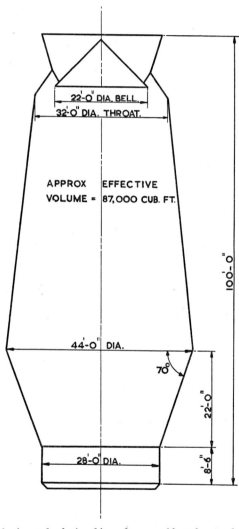

22-0" DIA. BELL.
32-0" DIA. THROAT.

APPROX EFFECTIVE
VOLUME = 87,000 CUB. FT.

44-0" DIA.

70°

100-0"

22-0"

8-6"

28-0' DIA.

Fig. 6 The horizontal relationships of a 1900 blast furnace have been scaled up to give the hearth diameter of 28-ft. Total height has been limited to 100-ft. and the relative proportions of height occupied by bosh, etc. have been maintained.

remarkably consistent wear line. Short of complete collapse of stack brickwork, all blown-out furnaces show fairly good retention of the hearth and bosh lines but a marked upward extension of the bosh. Above this cut-out of the lining, wear is usually slight and fairly uniform until a few feet below the throat parallel, where there is another pronounced cut-out. Fig. 5 shows typical blow-out lines. There is some evidence that this cutting out takes place within a few weeks of the furnace going into operation. If the lines of a new furnace of about the year 1900 and the blown out lines of a furnace today are compared there is a much greater similarity than between the new furnace of 1900 and the new furnace of today. It may be argued that this indicates the present-day lines are not correct. However, the evolutionary processes which have led to the present furnace shape must be considered. It would be a bold operator who disregarded the changes of the last fifty years and scaled up a small furnace of 1900 to a large furnace designed for the high tonnage of today. An attempt to do so has been made in fig. 6 in which a 1900 furnace has been scaled up to 28 ft. hearth diameter and 1900 relationships applied to such components as the bell and hopper. It is believed that these illustrations are important in indicating how the influence of engineering and construction has had a profound bearing on today's design.

In the orthodox furnace, the stack and top structure are carried by a heavy lintel and columns. The bosh and hearth are supported on the

TABLE III

LOADINGS ON THE FOUNDATIONS OF A 27 FT. BLAST FURNACE

	Tons
Brick lining and throat armour	920
Brick bottom	400
Salamander	530
Molten metal	525
Stock in furnace	1390
Mud gun and tuyeres	60
Bustle pipe	180
Structural steelwork and miscellaneous castings	1206
Hearth tuyere cooling castings	80
Skip bridge reaction	90
Cast house floor	1120
Concrete foundation	4264
Total ..	10,765

hearth jacket. The whole of the weight of the furnace, its contents, and the reaction from the charging mechanism, are carried on a very massive foundation. The weights involved can be substantial, as is shown in Table III. The orthodox type of construction has its limitations; the presence of columns does not give the most desirable access at the bottom of the furnace. The number and location of tuyeres, etc. are dicatated by the number and spacing of the columns. The heavy mantle ring is always the limiting factor when major alterations to the internal lines of the furnace are under consideration. To carry the weight of the top structure (which can be as much as 600 tons) on the steel tube comprising the shell, is satisfactory providing the shell is never over-heated. But in almost all practices, hot spots on the shell are encountered at some time or other, and fear of top collapse is always in the mind of the operator. The imposition of heavy top weights and the somewhat unsatisfactory means of support tend to make the designer chary of any increase in the size of top components. It may be that the ultimate limitation on the size of the blast furnaces built in this manner will be found in the magnitude of the top weights to be carried on the furnace shell. In any case, it is probably good practice to add a little to the capital cost of a new furnace of this type by having the shell stiffened by vertical ribs from the beginning. Too many cases are known where this has had to be done before many years have elapsed.

On the continent of Europe a rather different type of construction has been used for many years. The furnace itself is built along orthodox lines but the top structure is carried independently on another set of columns based outside the pitch circle of the furnace columns proper. This has a lot to recommend it, especially in the provision of platforms, to cover all parts of the stack. It does spare the operators much of the worry of an overheated shell.

FREE-STANDING FURNACE

In 1944, Bulle[1] described the construction of the first free-standing furnace as a "radical new design". In this, the top structure of the furnace was carried on independent columns so that the furnace shell had little or no load upon it. Instead of using a massive mantle and columns to support the stack the whole of the stack was supported on the bosh and hearth jackets (*see* fig. 7). This meant that the external profile of the furnace was altered and the internal shape was achieved in the brickwork. This design permits a very attractive layout around the bottom of the furnace. Tuyeres and slag notches can be positioned where most desired, as there are no columns taking up valuable room.

The design is achieving increasing popularity in Europe and it is considered eminently satisfactory for small furnaces. Whether it would be equally satisfactory for a 30 ft. furnace is probably a matter for argument.

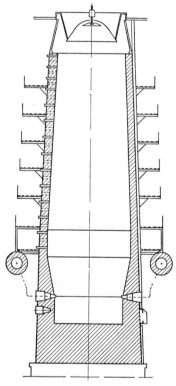

Fig. 7. Free standing furnace. Note how the external profile differs from the furnace shown in the frontispiece (after Bulle).

FUTURE TRENDS

As the size of furnaces increases, the limitations imposed by the weight of the top structure may lead to furnaces being built which are a combination of the three methods of construction outlined above, or to a concentration on the second type of construction. The furnace itself will be so big and heavy that the weight of the stack alone will demand the provision of a mantle ring and columns. The superincumbent load arising from bigger and more elaborate charging gear and from bigger and more elaborate gas extraction tubes, together with a greater reaction from the charging structure, may demand that this load be carried independently of the furnace.

The future may also see a radical change in the internal lines of the blast furnace. Certain small but highly efficient furnaces in Sweden, of free-standing construction, are now built with a bosh angle of 90°. In other words, the conventional bosh has disappeared (*see* fig. 8). If this

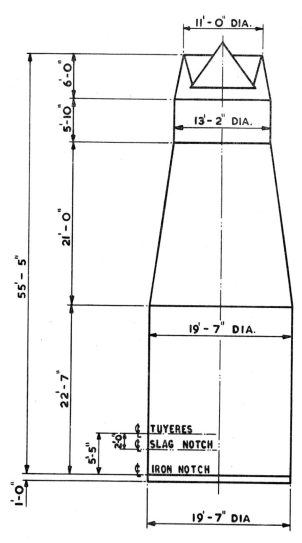

Fig. 8. Swedish blast furnace of 1956. Note the absence of bosh. This furnace is producing about 450 tons of iron per day with a coke consumption of 13 cwt. per ton.

radical development is followed, the reconciliation of structural demands to a new internal shape will add further emphasis to the remarks above.

THROAT ARMOUR

It is conventional to cover the top few feet of the blast furnace inwall with metal. This is necessary, because with most bell and throat designs, some of the burden will impinge on the furnace wall. This will lead to excessive wear and tear of the brickwork unless it is protected; the charging of scrap will aggravate this problem. Formerly, protection usually took the form of flat steel bars built into the brickwork. This practice has fallen out of favour for two reasons:

(a) Reaction with blast-furnace gas led to carbon deposition around the bricked-in bar in approximately the middle of the wall. Examples are known where this carbon deposition has been so excessive as to lead to lifting of the brickwork and splitting of the furnace shell.

(b) The overhanging flat bars quickly warped and distorted at service temperatures.

Then a design became popular in which bars of a heavier section and with a much shorter overhang were employed, the bars being anchored into a solid ring of concrete behind the brickwork by means of attached rods. Mechanically, this was a much stronger job than the flat steel bars but when it is realised that concrete tends to deteriorate at elevated temperatures, unless made of heat-resisting cement, and that heat-resisting cements are not very resistant to carbon deposition from blast-furnace gas, the limitations of this type of armour can be imagined.

Hanging throat armour has been used for very many years on the Continent and in certain parts of the U.S.A. In this design, a steel ring is suspended from the top deck of the furnace, an arrangement which has much to commend it. However, the preferred design of throat armour is shown in fig. 9. Here, the armour is regarded as part of the furnace separate from the stack lining; the armour is in sections, suspended quite independently on a false lintel round the furnace. The lintel is non-continuous to allow for movement due to expansion. Each piece of armour has some freedom of movement and is rugged enough to withstand a lot of abrasion. The material employed is cast steel or hematite iron.

Gas is able to circulate between and behind the section of armour, although slag wool is used to fill the spaces. The furnace shell is protected from over-heating by a brick lining behind the armour.

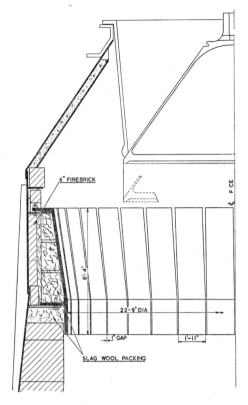

6" FIREBRICK

F CE

6'-4"

22'-9" DIA

1" GAP

1'-11"

SLAG WOOL PACKING

Fig. 9. A design for independently supported throat armour.

STACK CONSTRUCTION

In orthodox furnace design the stack casing is the container for the refractory lining (which is expected to withstand the arduous and irregular service conditions of several years) and the structural support of a heavy top gear. If either casing or lining suffer premature failure, the other will suffer. Usually, the stack casing has also to act as anchorage for a large number of coolers. There is, therefore, a good reason for separating the construction, and reducing the chances of failure.

To complicate matters further, there is considerable diversity of opinion as to whether the stack refractory should be built tight to the shell or whether an expansion space be provided; in other words, whether the refractory should be cooled or insulated. Finally, the shape

of the blast-furnace stack brickwork is such that the chimney-like structure is completely unsupported if failure occurs in the lower portion, as
it can and sometimes does.

In recent years, operating and design opinion has varied considerably. Many experiments are now in hand all over the world. What
follows, therefore, is subject to argument and the views expressed may
well prove to be ill-founded.

It seems that no available refractory is capable of withstanding operating conditions in the stack in all practices with hard-driven furnaces,
unless the refractory is efficiently cooled. Overall surface cooling is more
efficient than inset coolers. This means that the shell plates should be in
the closest possible contact with the refractory lining. It then follows
that the orthodox packing, or expansion space, is undesirable. It is
suggested that the multiplicity of joints in a lining afford sufficient
expansion allowance in themselves, which is another reason for advo-
cating that the lining should be built tight to the shell. As rivet heads
will break the continuity of such brick-steel contact, the stack should be
welded to form a continuous steel surface.

The non-self-supporting construction of the brickwork points to the
desirability of built-in supports. In view of the temperature conditions
involved in service, any such supports must be water-cooled, which
calls for a large number of inset coolers. In view of the possibility of
vertical expansion, the casing must be strong enough to afford good
anchorage for this multiplicity of coolers.

A conical steel tube is not the ideal structural support for a heavy top
gear; in a large furnace the deadweight on the stack casing is about
600 tons. Any local overheating of the shell, arising from refractory
failure, can lead to distortion and buckling of the steel with consequent
alteration to the relative levels of the top gear, which can affect the
settings of bells and bell operating gear with harmful effects on operation as well as on the safety of the structure. The casing should therefore
be stiffened with vertical ribs or flanges. Alternatively, the load of the
top gear should be carried independently.

The present orthodox design has given good service, but the number
of furnace shells which have had to be stiffened, and the number of
furnaces which have had to resort to spray cooling in mid-campaign,
point to the necessity to change stack design to meet the increasingly
arduous conditions of the furnace of tomorrow. The furnace of today is
a result of centuries of evolution and its successor must be the result of
rational design. It must be capable of standing up to increasingly
heavier duty, because there is yet no metallurgical limit to the production possibilities of the blast furnace.

BOSH CONSTRUCTION

As with so many other things about the blast furnace the history of bosh construction has a habit of repeating itself. A study of the early text-books, or indeed the early drawings of a company, shows how bosh construction has generally progressed from a very thick, totally un-cooled construction to the present-day standard of about 27 in. of fireclay brick. This mass of masonry is usually cooled by a large number of inset copper cooling plates so that the final result is a complicated mixture of pipes, copper and interlocking brickwork.

This type of construction has given admirable service in very many installations, but that in itself is not an argument against seeking something better; anyone who has carried out the "witch-hunt" usually necessary to identify a leaking bosh plate will appreciate that something simpler might be very desirable. It is suggested that this can be achieved by reverting to a design which was popular many years ago, the simple shower-cooled steel plate bosh jacket encasing a comparatively thin refractory lining.

This particular design fell into disrepute for several reasons, the more important being:

(a) The limitations of riveting which led to the use of jackets which were neither gas-tight nor water-tight. Obviously these defects could only lead to operating trouble.

(b) Ceramic refractories were generally not good enough to stand up under the prevailing conditions of service. The low thermal conductivity of fireclay refractories demanded inset cooling for preservation.

(c) Failure to maintain a continuous water film over the bosh which led to such troubles as hot spots and bosh breakouts. This failure was largely due to the riveted construction.

The advent of welding and the adoption of carbon refractories have removed these disabilities.

By the use of welding, it is now a simple matter to construct a steel plate jacket which is completely water and gas-tight. A welded jacket has no projections, such as lapped joints and rivet heads, to interfere with the uniform flow of water. Theoretically, providing they are protected from air and water, carbon refractories would work without cooling in the bosh of a blast furnace but the shell temperatures would be so high as to lead to warping and splitting of the casing, which in turn would cause infiltration. For these reasons, carbon in the bosh must be cooled. Because of its comparatively high thermal conductivity, a greater thickness of carbon can be cooled by shower cooling than could ever be achieved with normal fireclay refractories.

The general effect, therefore, is as shown in fig. 10. It is cheap, simple and virtually foolproof in that water leaks no longer occur.

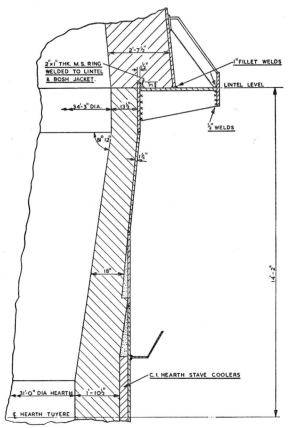

Fig. 10. Spray cooled bosh construction.

Note that the jacket is welded tight at top and bottom. Indeed, many furnaces now consist of a continuous steel jacket from the top deck to the foundation, a method of construction which has eliminated many troublesome points of gas leakage. Compared with orthodox design, this type of bosh is low in capital cost and lends itself to rapid construction.

TUYERE BELT CONSTRUCTION

The necessity of introducing tuyeres into the side of a furnace must involve a weakening of the brickwork mass. In view of the high temperature generated at the tuyeres, the refractory wall must be protected by water cooling. Advantage is taken of the necessary tuyere openings to provide efficient cooling by means of the tuyere cooler, which must be inset because of the design of the tuyere opening.

For many decades, cooling between the tuyeres has also been by inset coolers—plate coolers. The introduction of many apertures for these plate coolers inevitably has meant a structural weakening of the masonry, while few furnaces have given no trouble by way of gas leaks or slag breakouts round the plate coolers. A typical construction of this type is shown in fig. 11.

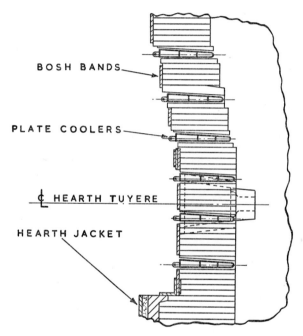

BOSH BANDS

PLATE COOLERS

HEARTH TUYERE

HEARTH JACKET

Fig. 11   Bosh and tuyere belt construction using plate coolers and bands.

In 1952, at the No. 10 furnace at Gary, Illinois, of the United States Steel Corporation, a new type of tuyere belt construction was introduced. This is regarded as an important improvement. Because of tuyere openings, external spray cooling in the tuyere zone is always messy and may be dangerous in case of burnt blowpipes.

The new construction (*see* fig. 12) employed a cast iron cooling stave to back the refractory lining. The whole was encased in a steel retaining jacket. Inlet and outlet pipes of the coolers were led through the retaining jacket and welded in place to render the joints gas-tight. This construction is much neater and stronger than that employing inset plate coolers. Fig. 13 shows the same section of a furnace with the old and the new types of construction.

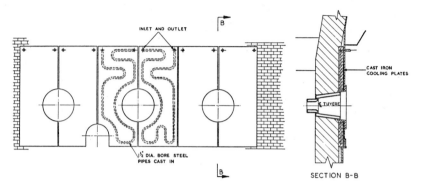

Fig. 12. Gary design of tuyere belt.

During a four-year campaign of a 25 ft. furnace prior to changing over to the Gary design, a total of 144 hours was lost because of leaking plate coolers. During the subsequent campaign of four years, the same furnace, fitted with the Gary type of tuyere belt cooling, had no downtime for troubles in this part of the furnace.

HEARTH CONSTRUCTION

The hearth of a blast furnace is defined here as all that part lying below the centre line of the slag notch. Broadly speaking, this section contains only the results of the ironmaking process, but a failure here is probably more dangerous and costly than a failure in any other part. Largely because of the highly corrosive nature of the liquids contained in the hearth, together with the heavy mechanical loading on the hearth, water cooling is always essential to protect the refractory lining. And it cannot be over-emphasized that an infinitely strong steel hearth jacket does not give strength to the refractory lining unless accompanied by efficient cooling.

There are two accepted methods of hearth cooling:

(*a*) Heavy cast iron stave coolers. Iron castings, about 15 ft. long, 4 ft. wide across the chord and up to 6 in. thick, incorporating steel cooling pipes, are used to back the refractory lining. The whole is encased in a welded steel jacket. A typical arrangement is shown in fig. 14. This type of construction is used on the majority of furnaces today.

Fig. 13. The upper photograph is of a 25-ft. furnace with orthodox copper plate cooling in the tuyere belt. The lower photograph shows the same furnace after relining and adoption of Gary tuyere belt design.

(*b*) External shower cooling. The refractory lining is built tight to a welded steel jacket which is covered by a continuous film of water delivered from spray pipes located at the top of the jacket. Fig. 15 shows such an arrangement. Although it is not so popular as the stave cooler arrangement, it is suggested that it is the better design.

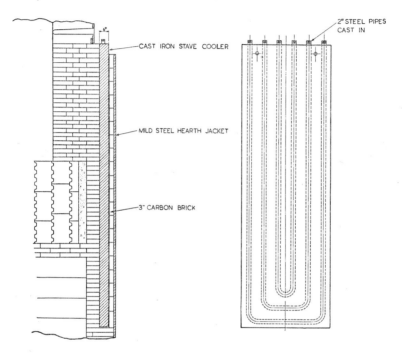

Fig. 14. Typical hearth construction using stave coolers. Note the 3″ carbon brick safety wall between the cooler and hearth jacket.

With both designs, it is necessary to pierce the ordinary jacket (and therefore the "wall of cooling") in order to make the tapping hole. Consider the relative merits of the two designs, remembering that the main object is to cool the refractory wall of the hearth efficiently and that in both cases the cooling medium is cold water. With shower cooling, the cooling is visible at all times and is evenly applied. In stave coolers, only the discharge water is visible and the cooling is applied unequally to the iron casting. Dirty water can lead to a reduction in cooling efficiency without this being obvious; this is not possible with shower cooling.

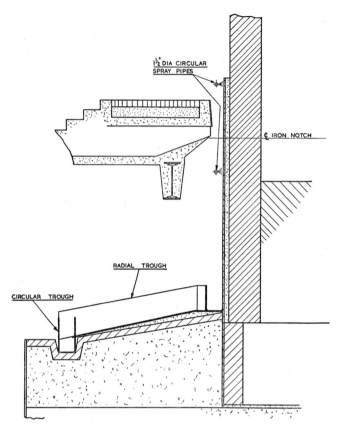

Fig. 15. Typical spray cooled hearth construction.

CHARGING MACHINERY

Most furnaces built in the last two decades employ double skip hoists and McKee tops as their charging gear. With automatic charging control, such as Freyn design charging panels, this set-up is remarkably flexible and reliable. Recent installations permit the charging of sufficient raw materials to produce 2000 tons of iron per day.

Again, high top pressure operation has influenced top design. The McKee revolving distributor has now been engineered so as to be gastight at a top pressure of 15 lb. per sq. in., and is now standard equipment for large furnaces operating under orthodox conditions (*see* fig. 16). Similarly, one-piece hoppers are rapidly becoming standard on all furnaces.

Compressed air bell-operating gear is another standard piece of

Fig. 16. Heavy duty McKee distributor.

equipment. Air is drawn from the cold blast main, backed up by a connection to the plant compressed air system which automatically comes into operation if blast pressure falls below a predetermined level.

Almost all hoist installations are driven by a two-motor winch, with Ward Leonard control. It is usual to be able to operate at reduced speeds on one motor. Safety protection is incorporated with such features as overspeed and overtravel limits and slack rope switches are also standard.

Generally speaking, except for wear and tear of such things as ropes, the charging gear of today's blast furnace is extremely trouble free.

But however sound the design and however rugged the construction of the gear, the operator still has responsibilities. A hard-driven furnace means fairly rough service conditions, so that regular inspection and checking of the gear are essential.

A broken hoist or bell rope can cause such havoc that it is not worthwhile to risk a damaged rope. Each rope should be inspected weekly and its condition reported. The revolving distributor should be checked weekly for accuracy of angular rotation and for condition of the seal ring. Distributor rollers must not be allowed to freeze and it should always be remembered that the lubrication system on top of a blast furnace is not in the easiest of situations. Whenever the furnace is off blast for an hour or more, the opportunity should be taken to inspect big and little bells and hoppers. A big bell which is not fully closing will soon lead to major trouble. Neither steel bell nor hopper is designed to withstand the extremely abrasive action of hot dust-laden gas moving at high velocity, and changing either of these in mid-campaign is not the most pleasant of jobs.

Similarly, a small leak at the seal ring of the distributor will soon be a big leak unless given attention. Besides wasting blast furnace gas, a leaking distributor will soon lead to a dirty furnace top.

As with so many troubles about a blast furnace, gas leaks on top are self-aggravating. A tight blast-furnace top is usually a sign of good maintenance.

Under certain circumstances, a really gas-tight top may lead to gas kicks (or explosions) between the bells. On lowering the big bell, the space between the bells will fill with gas at a temperature appreciably higher than that of the surrounding atmosphere. Before the big bell is again lowered, this gas will be reduced in temperature and therefore in volume. The resulting tendency to create a vacuum may result in air being drawn in through the space between big and little bell rods and the formation of an explosive air-gas mixture, which may be detonated by incandescent particles arising from the next lowering of the bell. In order to avoid this, it is good practice to maintain a slight positive pressure of steam between the bells at all times. It is certainly an inexpensive and effective insurance against explosions. The provision of a steam jet directed below the bell is a further means of preventing explosions in the top of the furnace which sometimes occur if a furnace is off blast for some hours, especially if the stock line is low.

STOCK RODS ·

For obvious reasons, it is necessary to know the level of the stock in the furnace at all times. This is usually achieved by having a rod, carried by wire rope from a winch at ground level, resting on the top of the burden. The rod must be withdrawn when the big bell is being dumped in order to avoid its being bent by falling burden. The principle is well-established, and extremely reliable gear is available which gives a continuous record of stock depth. It is also possible to interlock the test rod mechanism with the bell-operating gear so that burden depth can influence charging. The weakest part of the arrangement is always the rod itself and the gland through which it passes into the furnace. A rod will easily jam in a tight gland, while a loosely fitting gland is a source of unwanted gas leakage. A long stiff rod may bend and jam if a furnace slips and a flexible rod may bend and give a false reading.

All these problems were aggravated wherever high top pressure operation was introduced. To overcome the trouble, a fully enclosed rod was designed by Messrs. Ashmore, Benson, Pease & Co. In this, the rod is in a loosely fitting gland but the whole length is encased, only the suspending wire rope moving through the casing (*see* fig. 17). This design is extremely satisfactory and is recommended for all furnaces whether working at high top pressure or not.

Experimental rigs employing the principle of supersonic testing have been tried with little success. The use of radioactive isotopes, suitably mounted below the throat of the cupola, is a promising development in foundry work. Its application to blast-furnace work is now being tried.

BLEEDER VALVES

As furnace production rates have increased, many well-proved items of equipment have begun to cause trouble. Furnace bleeders are a case in point, and in common with other items, the solution of engineering problems associated with high top pressure operation is proving helpful in orthodox operation. The name "bleeder" is really a misnomer because they should never be used now for their original purpose—to bleed surplus gas to atmosphere. To discharge dirty gas does not help

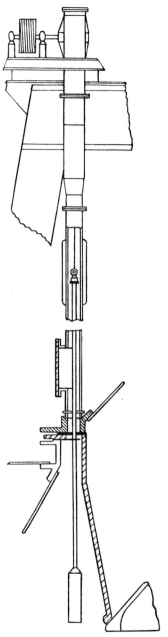

(Courtesy of Ashmore, Benson, Pease & Company.)

Fig. 17. Enclosed test rod developed for high top pressure operation.

neighbourly relations, nor does it help to make a clean plant or locality. When it is necessary to bleed gas, the discharge should be from the semi-clean main (after the washing towers).

Hot dirty gas will cut a bleeder valve in a short time. When a furnace slips, the main bleeders act as relief valves and pass abnormally hot and dirty gas at extremely high velocities. This is often a justification for hard surfacing the exposed sections with tungsten carbide or other wear-resistant materials. Because of the obvious difficulties in the way of maintaining a valve subjected to such onerous duty, especially when it is located more than 200 ft. above ground level, there are good reasons for giving close attention to design. It may be that power-operated valves are justified, as in high top pressure operation, but operators are naturally loath to trust their explosion relief to relatively delicate control gear. When such bleeder gear is fitted, there is always one bleeder which works independently and directly. It is desirable that a bleeder valve should close on a line of contact between valve and seat rather than on surface contact, which indicates the suitability of a solid ball valve.

Because of the highly corrosive conditions, all bolts, pins, etc. in the assembly should be of stainless steel. Changing a valve becomes an easier and safer job if a goggle plate is fitted in the uptake below the bleeder.

DUSTCATCHERS

Gas from the furnace is led by the downcomer to the dustcatcher. The downcomer is usually brick-lined, but unlined mild steel tubes are used in some plants. If correctly designed, the dustcatcher should have an efficiency of up to 70 per cent.

The inlet tube is led through the top of the dustcatcher; the tube flares out to its termination about one-third down the main vessel (*see* frontispiece). As the gas changes direction to leave *via* the top of the catcher, its velocity drops owing to the expansion and the dust settles out of the gas stream and collects in the cone-shaped bottom of the dust-catcher. From this position, the dust can be transferred to wagons. Usually, there is provision for wetting or conditioning this dust in order to reduce the dust nuisance about the area and to make it suitable for use in the sintering plant.

It is normal safety practice to introduce steam into the dustcatcher when the furnace is off blast. A leaking steam valve can lead to the dust accumulating on the sides and bottom of the dustcatcher to a serious degree. It is good practice, therefore, to control steam by means of two valves—one to regulate quantity (which will soon leak as it is usually

(Courtesy of Ashmore, Benson, Pease & Company.)

Fig. 18. Primary and secondary dustcatchers on a 28 ft. 6 in. blast furnace. Note tangential entry to the secondary dustcatcher.

only partly open) and a master valve behind, which is always either fully open or fully closed.

The main dustcatcher may be followed by a secondary dustcatcher. In this case, the gas to the secondary catcher will be introduced tangentially, as the average particle size of the dust is much smaller than that entering the main dustcatcher. The use of primary and secondary dustcatchers can lead to the extraction of 80 per cent. of the intitial dust content in an economical manner. Fig. 18 shows an arrangement of primary and secondary dustcatchers.

CAST HOUSE

The work of many people in mines, coke ovens and ore preparation plant culminates in the activities of about six men on the cast house floor at the blast furnace; it is at this point that lost time can never be made up. This places a premium on the design and layout of the working area around the tuyere platform and floor. It is also the area where, in case of trouble, there is less dependence on mechanical aids, and progress depends on brute strength and stamina where hammer, bar and shovel are the principal tools in use. The wheelbarrow will never be entirely displaced in the cast house.

The duties of the cast house crew should be considered in relation to all aspects of design and layout. A few examples can be mentioned to illustrate this point:

(a) The frontside crew have to clean up after every cast. Such materials as scrap and slag must be removed and the runners made good with sand, clay, etc. All runners should be steep enough to be self-draining as flat runners mean heavy skull scrap. A cast house crane should desirably span all runners. The disposal points for scrap and for rubbish should be easily reached.

(b) The snort wheel is the main control and is liable to be used at any time for any one of many reasons. It must be located so as to give the maximum possible visibility; it must always afford a good view of the taphole and, at the same time, the operator must have ample protection from flying metal. The taphole gun should be sited so that it does not stand between the snort wheel and the taphole.

(c) Every building such as control rooms and workmen's shelters must be provided with two means of exit.

(d) All water discharges should be clearly visible from floor level.

(*e*) It should be possible to wheel a loaded barrow to any part of the cast house and completely round the furnace. Too often, this is not possible because design starts by providing the best possible access at the back of the furnace. Here, the cast house floor is at the generally agreed level of 5 ft. below tuyere centres. If this is done, a working floor can only be achieved in the taphole section of the runner by inserting steps in the floor along a line at right-angles to the runner, located across the tapping hole. These steps make cleaning up difficult and, in case of trouble, make a hurried departure from around the taphole less easy than is desirable. It is better to provide a stepped plinth for access to all tuyeres (*see* fig. 19).

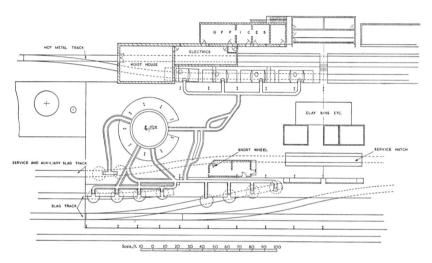

Fig. 19. Typical arrangement of a furnace cast house where slag is disposed in ladles.

(*f*) Good lighting and ventilation, as well as protection from inclement weather, are essential. This means that the cast house must be high.

(*g*) Because of the nature of the job, the furnace crew have to remain in the immediate vicinity and must eat when the job permits. Good facilities must be provided for this in the furnace area.

(*h*) Provision must be made for storing tuyeres, coolers, blowpipes, etc. and for the pipe fitter to carry out the preparatory work necessary for changing these members.

(Courtesy of Ashmore, Benson, Pease & Company.)

Fig. 20. Plunger type clay gun of 13 cu.ft. capacity.

Fig. 21. Hand operated bin gates and scale car.

(Courtesy of Ashmore, Benson, Pease & Company.)

Fig. 22. Power operated bin gates and scale car.

(*i*) Bins are needed for sand, clay, skimmer bricks, etc.

(*j*) Unless sensible tool racks are provided, the crew cannot be blamed for an untidy cast house.

(*k*) As much floor space as possible should be provided, consistent with good runner and railway layout.

Attention to these and other details is well worth while. A cast house is never a drawing room, nor an easy place to work in. But some cast houses are much better than others.

CLAY GUN

Undoubtedly, the introduction of the remotely controlled electric clay gun for stopping tapholes did more to easing the life of the furnace man than any other piece of apparatus. Operation of today's large furnaces would be impossible without such a gun. Anybody who has experienced the labour and danger of hand stopping, when the gun has been out of order, will have some idea of what furnace life was like before Vaughan invented the steam piston gun about 1900. The introduction of the electric rotary gun about twenty-five years later began a new era in frontside work. The furnace man now had at his disposal a clay gun which could be operated from a position of safety, and sufficiently robust to stop the tapping hole against a full flow of iron—only furnace men can appreciate what that meant. The rotary gun is now virtually obsolete and plunger type guns are almost standard equipment. Fig. 20 shows a Bailey plunger gun with a barrel capacity of 13 cu. ft.

The clay gun is a self-contained unit consisting of a large clay barrel and a plunger actuated by a motor-driven power screw. This unit is suspended from a carriage which in turn is supported on a pedestal sleeve revolving about a fixed pedestal post. The gun is swung into position on the tapping hole by two independent motions controlled by two separate motor drives. The first motion swings the gun carriage about 180° in a horizontal plane into position in front of the tapping hole by means of a drive on top of the pedestal and the carriage is automatically locked to the furnace front in this position by means of a latch. The second motion lowers the gun from a horizontal position down into the tapping hole and forces the nozzle into the hole by means of a powerful drive mounted inside the carriage, the power being transmitted through a heavy crank lever which supports the gun. The nose is guided down to the hole by means of two suspension levers fastened to the front of the clay barrel. The gun is held in position on the tapping hole by a self-locking worm gear so that it cannot back away while the plunger pushes the clay into the hole at a pressure of 450 to 500 lb. per sq. in. The plunger is actuated by a power screw driven by a motor through a helical gear drive.

STOCKHOUSE

It is usual practice for iron ores, sinter, etc. to be stocked in a line of bunkers, each of comparatively low capacity, equipped with bottom discharge gates. A scale car, whose hopper capacity is matched to that of the charging skip or bucket, draws the correct weight of burden from these bins. Because of their simplicity and low maintenance cost, hand-operated gates are preferable. With dry, free-running materials (such as sinter) no troubles are to be expected, but if the ores are sticky and wet, there is probably a case for the use of power-operated bin gates. An installation of hand-operated bin gates and scale car is shown in fig. 21. Power-operated gates are shown in fig. 22.

In order to reduce spillage, the capacity of the scale car should be a few cubic feet less than the capacity of the charging skip.

Coke is not handled by the scale car. It is stocked in two bunkers which are situated one at each side of the skip bridge centre line. By means of a weigh hopper, the correct amount of coke is transferred to the skip. As the weigh hopper can be filled whilst the scale car is otherwise employed, the use of weigh hoppers has considerably speeded up blast furnace charging.

A screen is interposed between the main coke bunker and the coke weigh hopper, which is used to reject the small coke breeze (usually −1 in.) at the last point before charging. Vibrating or oscillating screens are normally employed for this purpose. The rejected small coke is usually gathered into the skip of a small skip hoist and tipped into a storage bunker, which is emptied as necessary into railway wagons.

If a furnace is being built to smelt only one type of free-running ore or sinter, the principle could be extended so that the total furnace charge could be dealt with by way of four weigh hoppers. A scale car would no longer be necessary.

Scale cars and weigh hoppers must be checked frequently. Inaccurate weighing of either coke or ore can lead to exasperating blast-furnace difficulties.

REFERENCES

[1] BULLE, G. Stahl u. Eisen, 1944, 64.

Chapter II

COOLING THE FURNACE

BLAST-FURNACE COPPER

ALMOST WITHOUT EXCEPTION, those cooling members of a blast furnace that are inserted into the brickwork are made of copper and the blast-furnace man usually refers to all coolers by this name. Bronze, gunmetal and aluminium coolers have all been tried but it is now universal practice to use copper because of its very high thermal conductivity, which is second only to that of silver. Unfortunately, the conductivity of copper falls rapidly with slight amounts of impurities; for example, the presence of 1 per cent. of tin will decrease the conductivity of pure copper by 50 per cent. and 0·5 per cent. of arsenic will reduce it by 60 per cent. The manufacture of virtually pure copper coolers and tuyeres is not an easy matter and the addition of extremely small amounts of impurities make copper casting much easier. However, recent developments now permit tuyeres to be made with a purity of 99·9 per cent. Some operators favour the use of forged tuyeres but it is doubtful if the difference between a good cast tuyere and a forged tuyere is very great. With virtually pure copper, the failure of tuyeres and coolers arises much more from furnace conditions and water than from limitations of the copper itself. Dirty water and poor coke are undoubtedly the most prolific causes of copper losses.

Quite apart from abnormal tuyere losses, tuyere changing is usually the major cause of stoppages in blast-furnace operation. On occasion, the tuyere in a particular position will be lost much more frequently than tuyeres in other positions. In this case, the use of a tuyere longer than standard is very often effective in checking this increased rate of loss. Refractory-nosed tuyeres are a useful palliative in this connection, and in the last resort, the tuyere should be plugged for some days.

With a normally vigilant furnace crew, a leaking tuyere is usually detected almost as soon as it occurs. There is usually sufficient time to cast the furnace before coming off blast to change the defective tuyere. But if the leak is obviously serious, so that all the feed water is entering the furnace, the feed must be turned off. The tuyere may be held for an hour or so by fitting a previously prepared circular spray pipe to shower water on to the back of it.

TUYERE DESIGN

Tuyeres can be designed in a great many different ways; in most cases, the design reflects the operator's desire to cover a particular set of circumstances. They have been made with square noses, bevel noses, heavy noses, refractory noses and double compartments. Work with models indicates that the shape of the tuyere has little effect on the shape of the resulting combustion zone. A standard and well-tried design of tuyere is shown in fig. 23.

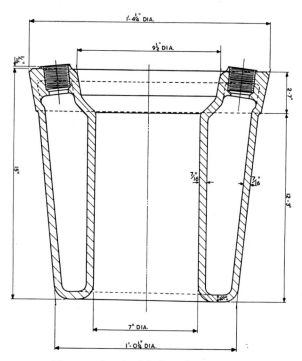

Fig. 23. Standard design of copper tuyere.

One important variation should be mentioned—the angle tuyere. It is believed that this was first invented by Stoecker with the intention of installing the tuyeres so that the blast was directed in a sideways direction, giving a spiral air flow. Today, this design of tuyere enjoys a certain amount of popularity but is invariably used to give a downward deflection to the blast (*see* fig. 24). Angle tuyeres are useful in keeping the furnace hearth clean when an accumulation of breeze follows from charging soft coke.

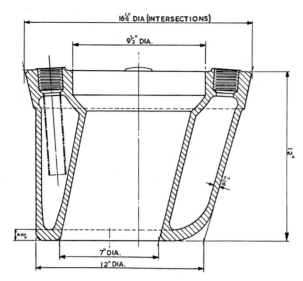

Fig. 24. Angle tuyere.

In recent years, more and more attention has been directed to efficient water flow in the tuyere. It now seems that the inlet water should be so directed by an internal tube that it gives sufficient swirl to ensure that there is no stagnant water at the tuyere nose.

All tuyeres should be fed from the bottom and discharged at the top. Ideally, these pipes should be at the exact top and bottom of the tuyere but this is not always possible in practice because of the proximity of the blow pipe to the feed and discharge water pipes. Any necessary deviation should be kept to a minimum.

TUYERES

The desirable number of hearth tuyeres for a given furnace is still a matter of some argument. The ideal, of course (which is impossible to attain), would be for the furnace to be blown through a continuous slot situated round the hearth of the furnace. The nearer that tuyere arrangements can be made to approach this ideal, the better the air distribution will be.

There are, however, limitations to the number of tuyeres which can be introduced into the circle of masonry which constitutes the furnace hearth. It is most essential that the openings in the masonry should be mechanically strong, which means that, for preference, each opening should be in the form of complete rings of arched brickwork. If the rings are allowed to touch each other it will be obvious that the resulting masonry will not be as strong as when rigid pillars exist between the openings.

The problem is further complicated in orthodox furnaces by the proximity of the furnace columns. Tuyeres should be at equi-angled intervals but as they cannot be installed immediately behind columns the number in a given hearth is always a compromise between sound masonry and column spacing.

There is a fairly strong feeling today that as many tuyeres as possible should be installed. Too many examples are now known of unsatisfactory furnaces whose operation has been considerably improved when more tuyeres have been fitted. It may be argued that to increase the diameter of a fewer number of tuyeres will give the same effect as using a larger number of smaller diameter tuyeres. This reasoning is erroneous. If tuyere area is achieved by using large tuyeres, few in number, the distance between the tuyeres will be so great that individual combustion zones will not touch or overlap. In this case, there will be a dead column of material between each pair of tuyeres, which is obviously undesirable. Many experiments have been made with large tuyeres, but it is safe to say that, all over the world, the diameter of hearth tuyeres is seldom less than 6 in. and never more than 8 in.

The following table shows what is considered to be the desirable number of tuyeres for a given hearth diameter.

Hearth diameter (ft.)	No. of hearth tuyeres
18	14/15
22	15/16
26	20/21
28	24/25
30	26/27

PLATE COOLERS

There are almost as many designs of plate coolers as there are of tuyeres, but it is believed that attention to correct water flow and the avoidance of stagnant water within the cooler are the two most important aspects of design. A satisfactory design of cooler is shown in fig. 25. It will be noticed that the internal baffles are so arranged as to ensure that there shall be no stagnant water at the cooler nose. Plate coolers,

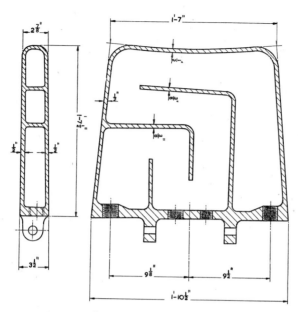

Fig. 25. Typical design of copper plate cooler.

unlike tuyeres which are always fed individually, are usually fed in a series of four or five from a single source. Many operators prefer to make the water flow uphill from cooler to cooler, but a neater arrangement of pipework is obtainable if the flow is from cooler to cooler at the same level, that is, in the same horizontal row.

It was formerly general practice to locate a plate cooler inside a cast iron holder. This practice has rightly fallen into disrepute. The box enabled a slightly shorter cooler to be used, so saving copper, but distortion of the box frequently occurred in service. This led to so much trouble in changing a leaking plate that the practice of setting a full-length plate cooler in brickwork alone is now universal.

It was also general practice to use plate coolers of such a length that the nose was protected by several inches of brickwork, but it was found that this protecting brickwork disappeared quite quickly. For that reason, copper-plate coolers are now used so that the length of the cooler is equal to the wall thickness of the brickwork to be cooled. Even when so used, a plate cooler which has been in service for some years is often very difficult to extract when leaking. A common fault is for the nose of the cooler to split so that distortion of the copper leads to jamming of the cooler in the brickwork, To save time when this happens, the back of the cooler may be cut away by pneumatic chisel, and the interior rammed with clay. A loop of 1 in. diameter pipe is inserted into this clay thus restoring some measure of cooling.

TUYERE COOLERS

The blowing tuyere invariably projects from a cooler which occupies the full thickness of the hearth brickwork. The projecting tuyere affords some protection to the nose of the cooler because it assists the formation of a scab in front of the cooler nose which, in turn, prevents direct contact with molten iron. The service duty of the hearth cooler, therefore, permits some liberty in regard to water flow and permits the feed and discharge pipes to be introduced more from the viewpoint of neat pipework than from efficient water flow.

The presence of the protective scab at the nose of a hearth cooler also gives some latitude in changing in case of failure. If a tuyere fails, the furnace must be taken off blast as soon as possible in order to change it, but if a tuyere cooler fails, it is usually possible to leave it with a much reduced flow of water until a stoppage can be arranged to cover other maintenance jobs.

STACK COOLERS

(a) PLATE COOLERS

In addition to being used in the tuyere zone and bosh of the blast furnace, copper plate coolers are commonly used for stack cooling. In the latter case, they may be located either horizontally or vertically. Frequently, the actual width of the cooler is considerably less than the thickness of brickwork to be cooled and long necks are cast on to the cooler in order to save copper. While coolers made of copper are more efficient, they are not preferred for stack cooling. They must be fed in a closed system and this may make it difficult to detect a leaking cooler. Once detected, the changing of a copper stack cooler is always difficult and sometimes impossible.

(b) CAST IRON COOLERS

The importance of conductivity of the cooler metal is obviously less important when service temperatures are much lower than those obtaining in the hearth and bosh. For that reason, cast iron can be used for cooling stack brickwork. Where this is done, open gravity-fed coolers are used, either of round or square section. A typical cooler of round section, the so called "cigar cooler" is shown in fig. 26. Apart from lower first cost, the gravity-fed cast iron cooler has much to recommend it. In case of failure, a leak advertises itself because furnace pressure will blow gases and steam outward and give visible warning. This type of cooler is much easier to change if it fails and it is possible to adjust the length of coolers progressively to match a decreasing lining

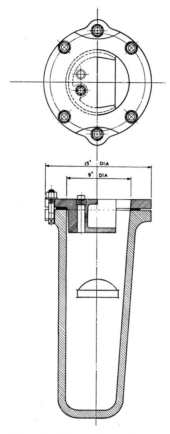

Fig. 26. Cigar cooler and cover.

thickness during the campaign life of a furnace. The circular shape of the cooler is not ideal, but the principles can be applied to square section coolers.

(c) STEEL COOLERS

Cast iron has been used satisfactorily for very many years and the practice is now being adopted of using the same principles of an open gravity-fed cooler but with a fabricated steel box cooler. This has much to commend it in that the coolers are easier to make in the more desirable square shapes needed to fit into the brickwork. It has been general practice in Germany for many years to use a greater amount of stack cooling than in any other ironmaking countries. Stack coolers are installed very close together from the stockline to the bosh. Fabricated steel coolers have been used successfully in several furnaces cooled in this way.

SLAG NOTCHES

Nowadays it is general practice to equip a blast furnace with two slag notches; on large diameter furnaces, a strong case may be made out for the installation of three notches, especially where slag volumes are high.

The location of slag notches in relation to the taphole is often governed by factors other than the desirability of having notches and taphole equally spaced; railroad layout is often the determining factor. If, as is usually the case, it is desired to have slag ladle tracks at one side of the cast house and metal ladle tracks at the other, there are immediate limitations in locating the slag notches.

It is a long way across a 28 ft. diameter furnace, which often makes it a physical impossibility to get slag out in times of trouble; at such times, a third slag notch is extremely valuable. Where two or three slag notches are used, the one farthest from the taphole should always be at a level approximately 6 in. higher than the others. This small difference in elevation can give a valuable extension of time when a furnace is chilling. The size of slag tuyere used is determined by the amount and analysis of the slag. On many furnaces with a low volume of fluid slag a $1\frac{1}{2}$ in. diameter slag tuyere is satisfactory. With high slag volumes a $2\frac{1}{2}$ in. slag tuyere may not be too big. The general practice today is to employ a three-member set-up at the slag notch. The slag tuyere is contained within an intermediate cooler which in turn is contained within a larger cooler, the length of which is equal to the thickness of the refractory lining. Fig. 27 shows a typical slag notch set-up.

It is important that all members of the slag notch system should be securely anchored so that they cannot be blown out of the furnace if an explosion should occur from iron passing over the slag notch (*see* fig. 27).

Until recent years slag notches were always stopped, or "botted", by hand, but mechanical slag notch stoppers are now being built which will operate satisfactorily. The early trouble with all equipment of this kind arose from dimensional changes in the gear resulting from wide temperature fluctuations. The gear is usually mounted above the slag notch and, if the clearances are correct at room temperatures, they will

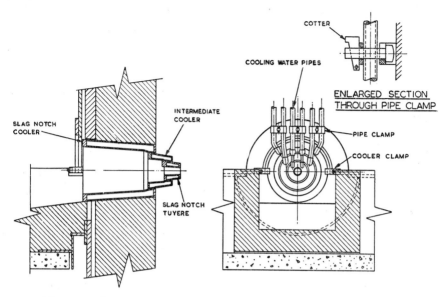

Fig. 27. Typical arrangement of coolers and slag tuyere showing clamps.

be incorrect when the apparatus has been heated up by the slag running below it. In the same way, if the slag notch stopper is mounted on the horseshoe main, temperature changes in the main itself may lead to trouble. The design and setting up of slag notch stoppers call for care and accuracy.

It is dangerous to run slag over a bare cooler. It is impossible to line the slag tuyere itself, but the intermediate and big coolers should be protected by a refractory lining which may consist of carbon ramming or clay. This lining should be inspected when cleaning up after every flush and patched or replaced if necessary. When a furnace is flushing dirty slags, or even passing iron through the slag notch, this precaution is especially necessary. An exploding slag cooler is not a trifle.

SLAG TUYERES

A slag tuyere is probably the most hard-working member of the cooling system of a blast furnace. At one plant, operating with a slag volume of 1·3 tons of slag per ton of iron, a daily iron production of 1200 tons means that nearly 1600 tons of slag are discharged through three slag tuyeres, each of $2\frac{1}{2}$ in. diameter. Normally, slag is flowing for 18 hours in each day. This means that slag is passing through a bare copper slag tuyere at the rate of $1\frac{1}{2}$ tons of slag per minute. When it is remembered that the slag is at a temperature of something over 1400°C., some idea is obtained of the conditions which a slag tuyere must withstand. Because the nozzle size must be limited (rarely is it greater than $2\frac{1}{2}$ in. inside diameter), the slag tuyere is small and the water space somewhat restricted. The influence of copper purity is probably felt more with slag tuyeres than with anything else. The feed and discharge pipes must be at the top of the slag tuyere in all cases to save them from damage from molten slag.

There is no doubt that the cooling effect of the intermediate and big coolers leads to the formation of a massive scab at the nose of the big cooler and that this scab is the main protection for the slag tuyere. When a big slag cooler has been changed, it is very helpful, therefore, if that particular slag tuyere is not used for 24 hours, giving time for the reformation of the scab in front of the cooler nose.

BLAST PIPES

Blast pipes are usually made of hematite iron with a wall thickness of $\frac{1}{2}$ in. to $\frac{3}{4}$ in. This material is quite satisfactory where blast temperatures are low and the quantity of air blown is high, or when blast temperatures are high and air flow is low. In the manufacture of ferro-manganese, blast temperatures of 900°C. are regularly used. Because the quantity of air blown (rarely more than 33,000 cu. ft. per minute) is comparatively low, hematite iron is quite satisfactory for the blow pipes. But blast temperature as low as 650°C. on a practice blowing 100,000 cu. ft. of air per minute will demand better materials for the blow pipes.

Some operators have long had a preference for cast steel pipes though it is believed that they offer little advantage over hematite iron or over heat-resisting malleable iron. The use of heat-resisting (stainless) steels is becoming increasingly popular because of their strength at high temperatures.

A blast pipe usually fails for one of the following reasons:

(a) Cracking due to variations in temperature. This is aggravated if water drips on to an iron pipe.

(b) Bowing, or distortion, arising from insufficient strength at high temperatures.

(c) Burning as a result of iron, or iron-bearing slag, flowing back down the pipe.

This latter trouble is known in all practice but is much more prevalent in high slag volume practice. In this connection, the use of refractory lined blast pipes is finding favour. There is a theoretical case for saving fuel by the use of an insulated blast pipe, but considerations of

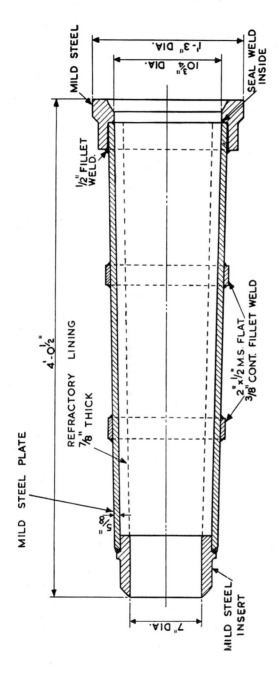

Fig. 28. Refractory lined blast pipe.

safety and the prevention of stoppages are giving the impetus to their present adoption. There are two general designs of insulated blast pipes. One is a normal steel or iron pipe with an inner sleeve of thin sheet metal, the space between being packed with an insulating material. The second, and probably more effective design, is a fabricated steel pipe lined with specially shaped tubular bricks, or with a lining of refractory concrete. When a blast pipe is insulated in this way the desired mechanical strength can be attained by a reasonable thickness of mild steel plate (*see* fig. 28).

WATER PIPING

A big furnace probably has to circulate rather more than 4000 gallons per minute through its complicated water cooling system. There will be hundreds of joints in the 35,000 ft. of pipework. On blowing-in the furnace it is expected that this system should be trouble free for some years, which obviously places a premium on good workmanship and sound design. But to design all the pipework for a furnace correctly is an almost impossible task. When set out on the drawing board, the arrangement of piping may look neat and tidy, but to the operator it may turn out to be inconvenient and even dangerous. It is so easy to set a feed cock immediately above a blowpipe, or to feed members from a point situated so that feed pipes are in the way of something else or with the discharge invisible from the cock. A piping drawing should never be prepared, except to site the manifolds and mains. All furnacemen have had the annoying experience of having to dismantle many yards of piping in order to draw a leaking plate cooler or having to go dangerously near a stream of iron or slag in order to operate a watercock. One other point is often overlooked—the provision of wash-down points and spare water feeds. It is doubtful whether any furnace ever goes through a campaign without extra feed-points being called for.

Discharges should be as evenly spaced as possible around the waste water trough and should be easily visible from the working floor. If the piping is done by furnace pipe-fitters in close collaboration with the furnace operators, a convenient and tidy arrangement can always be made. Feed cocks to all tuyeres and all members of the slag notch set-up should be clearly marked. In times of stress, the ability to lay hands on the water supply to a tuyere or "monkey" quickly is very useful. The use of flexible hose (either metallic or non-metallic) should be discouraged strongly. Flexibles encourage carelessness in permitting tuyeres and other members to be connected when they are not fitting correctly into the cooler. A ball union on rigid pipe gives all the flexibility that should be necessary.

Where cooling water is very soft and contains a lot of oxygen, or when salt water is used, there is probably a case for using copper pipes. But whatever the water or the cooling system, routine washing out is essential. Coolers, staves, etc., should be flushed at regular intervals. Staves should be flushed with high pressure water at least every two weeks and other types of coolers at least every six months. With coolers, this flushing should be accompanied by the removal of sludge and foreign matter via a sludge plug. Water manifolds on the furnace should be flushed and sludged regularly in a similar manner. In some cases, especially where hard water is used, chemical cleaning or acid washing is probably desirable at intervals of two years. Failure to observe routine attention to cooling systems can lead to disastrous results. A hearth breakout will lose much more time than is spent on routine attention to the stave coolers.

Feed and discharge pipes to the big slag coolers are subject to onerous conditions in service. As the cooler usually has a long life, it is good policy to change the pipes at regular intervals. Few things are more annoying than to lose a big cooler because the pipe-work to it has corroded.

Chapter III

FURNACE MAINTENANCE

GENERAL MAINTENANCE

WHEN BLOWN IN, a blast furnace is expected to operate night and day for some years. Down-time means the loss of iron which can never be made up, so that an efficient operating practice may be seriously impaired by excessive down-time. The necessity for efficient maintenance is obvious, especially when it is realised that complete overhaul of the gear is only possible at widely separated relinings.

The avoidance of excessive down-time is achieved by attention to several separate factors.

1. *Design and Construction:* If there is ever a case for over-designing in design engineering, it is around a blast furnace. It is an old and true saying that normal factors of safety should be trebled for everything attached to blast furnaces.

2. *Relining Repairs:* The only occasion when many items can be properly inspected and overhauled is during a reline. Literally every inch and item of the furnace and its attachments must be inspected and repaired at this time.

3. *Inspection:* Because so many troubles rapidly grow from minor to serious, a rigidly maintained inspection system is essential. Every accessible part of the furnace must be inspected at regular intervals. Such a system soon discloses the necessity for frequent inspection.

4. *Stoppage Reports:* Accurately timed reports of all stoppages serve to disclose where attention, and possibly design modification, is required.

5. *Utilisation of Stoppage Time:* Most stoppages of a blast furnace, such as the changing of tuyeres and notch tuyeres, are unpremeditated, but the actual stoppage time should be used to deal with minor faults uncovered and known by the inspection system. This factor alone justifies the retention around the cast house of a nucleus crew of all trades likely to be involved—pipefitters, mechanics, boilersmiths and electricians.

6. *Spares and Tools:* It is often quicker to replace an item rather than repair it, and the provision of improved tools and methods must be a

continuing preoccupation of the operating staff. Unfortunately, as furnaces get bigger, items of equipment get heavier and the cost of down-time increases. Much remains to be done to improve the tools necessary in so many off-blast jobs, especially as at most plants the most frequent cause of down-time is the need to change copper—often a most refractory job; it is still impossible to burn or cut copper with the ease that steel can be burnt or cut. To clean up a mess of iron or slag is a painfully slow process because most mechanical aids for "muck shifting" are of little use when dealing with hot slag and iron.

The future must see as much thought devoted to the avoidance of down-time as has been devoted to securing maximum production rates. This will certainly mean that many now accepted materials and methods of construction will be superseded. The development of new alloys, of new refractory materials, and of new methods of combining one with the other can and must make an important contribution to securing more operating hours per month.

RELINING

A blast furnace represents a large capital investment and its output is usually a large percentage of a company's production. When furnaces were smaller, it was usual to have a standby furnace so that relining could be done in a somewhat leisurely manner. But the size and cost of today's units make the provision of a spare furnace prohibitive. Especially is this so when consideration is given to the amount of other plant (coke ovens, ore preparation plant) which is often geared to supply a single large furnace. Relining must therefore be done as quickly as possible and must be considered when a new furnace is still on the designer's drawing board.

Top gear must be designed for easy dismantling and provision must be made for the lifting of large, awkward loads in dismantling. The cast house roof should be designed so that bells, hoppers etc. can be lowered to rail wagons or ground without elaborate preparation. The location of the downcomer should also facilitate lifting and lowering items of top equipment. There is no real virtue in locating the furnace, downcomer and dustcatcher on a common centre line if it interferes with relining operations.

Whether the furnace stack is cooled through all its height or not, platforms should be provided giving easy access to the whole area of the stack. Long before the furnace becomes obsolete, it is certain that structural repairs, such as replacement of isolated shell plates, will become necessary. Bricklaying in the stack can be greatly impeded if the only access is from the top deck or from the hearth tuyeres.

Unless absolutely impossible because of site condition, the hearth of a blast furnace should be open. It should be possible at all times to inspect the whole of the hearth jacket (*see* frontispiece). With this open type of construction it becomes possible to tap the bear at the conclusion of the blowing-out operation, which is much easier and quicker than having to remove it when solid by means of explosives. Indeed, without tapping it, bear removal is usually the longest single operation in relining.

To build taphole, cooler arches etc., specially shaped bricks are worthwhile. The time needed to cut standard squares in order to build a cooler arch is prohibitive, especially as refractories get harder. The use of correctly designed specials enables the partial prefabrication of what were formerly the slowest items of brickwork, without sacrificing the quality of the masonry.

It should be possible to modify the main skip hoist temporarily so that it can serve to feed bricks to a special brick hoist operating inside the furnace.

The provision of a large amount of special gear and tools can be justified by the saving in time to be obtained.

The following extracts from a paper on the relining of a blast furnace[1] give some idea of the gear and tackle used in successful and speedy relinings.

REMOVING BELL AND HOPPER

After the reception hopper, distributor gear, and top seal had been removed, in that order, two 12 in. × 8 in. joists were thrown across the top of the hopper, one on each side of the bell-rod. Links were fastened to the joists to hold the big bell by means of the lifting lugs on the bell. When the bell was secured, the bell rod was dismantled and removed to the ground. A stub rod about 3 ft. long was then fitted to the bell. The top trolley, which had already been reeved, picked up the bell and hopper together by means of this stub rod. As soon as the bell and hopper were clear of the furnace top, six 12 in. × 8 in. joists were placed across the top of the crown casting. The bell and hopper were then lowered on to this temporary platform.

The four-piece hopper was then split into two sections. The front section was lowered to the ground, followed by the bell and then by the second half of the hopper. It was impossible to have a vertical descent from the end of the furnace-trolley beam. A 10-ton travelling crane used as a winch took the free end of the block rope, and another crane was used to pull the load clear of the cast-house structure.

Four sets of 5-ton chain blocks were used. Two sets were hung in 28 ft. × 1 in. diameter wire-rope slings on each side of the big-bell rod, with an 8 ft. × 1 in. diameter sling on the rod for lifting the rod out of the big bell complete with the small-bell rod and wearing cones. Two sets were hung in 34 ft. × 1 in. diameter slings for transferring the big-bell rod, etc., on to the furnace platform before lowering it to ground level. One set of ⅝ in. wire-rope blocks, reeved 2 and 1, with 600 ft. of rope, were hung from the 40-ton trolley for lowering all material to ground level, with the exception of the big-bell rod, the big bell, and similar heavy lifts. These blocks were also used for lifting most of the material required on top.

The 40-ton trolley blocks were reeved with 1250 ft. × 1 in. diameter 6/37 wire rope, reeved 4 and 3. The fall of the wire passed through a single block with a safe working load of 10 tons anchored to the bottom of the dustcatcher supports, and then to the drum of a 10-ton steam crane, which was used as a winch. One set of ⅝ in. wire-rope blocks, reeved 3 and 2, with 1000 ft. of wire, were used for pulling out lifts when lowering or hoisting, so as to clear the cast-house structure. These blocks were also anchored to the dustcatcher legs, with the fall of the wire passing through a snatch block to another 10-ton steam crane. A set of 8 ft. × 1⅛ in. endless slings were anchored on to the lifting brackets inside the main hopper. For safety reasons, a ⅞ in. diameter wire-rope was passed over the block sling and through the bottom hole at each corner of the hopper section, so that the hopper was lifted level for easy decking on top.

BRICK HANDLING AND BRICKLAYING

Experience has shown that bricks can be laid as fast as they can be supplied to the bricklayers. The number of bricklayers available was limited and outside help was not sought in this connection. Most of the bricklayers had had experience of several relinings, so that the laying rate was fairly high.

In the upper stack, where the work is straightforward, the average number of bricks laid per 8-hour shift per bricklayer was 800. Of these 800 bricks, about 500 were 13½ in. × 6 in. × 3 in., with equivalent compass, and the remainder were 9 in. × 6 in. × 3 in., with equivalent compass. With eight bricklayers per shift, the supply of this large number of bricks to the stage inside the furnace called for special arrangements. Wagons of bricks from the stockpiles were brought in predetermined order to the steel unloading wharf that had been set up parallel to the scale-car track. This wharf was about 12 ft. wide and about 90 ft. long. Telephonic communication was established between this wharf and the foreman bricklayer inside the furnace.

Bricks were unloaded from the wagons into Warry barrows. These self-locking easy-dumping barrows will take 28 13½ in. bricks. The main furnace skip, which had previously been modified with a covering platform and extended bail, will accommodate two of these barrows.

On arrival at the top of the furnace, the barrows were wheeled along the temporary platform, shown in fig. 29, and thence to the cage of the relining hoist. This cage took two Warry barrows down to the extending swinging platform on which the bricklayers were working. From the cage, the barrows were wheeled and dumped to a point on the platform where the bricklayer could pick up bricks without walking from the point at which he was laying them. The winch for handling the brick hoist was stationed on the top deck of the furnace (*see* fig. 29).

The extending stage was designed by Appleby-Frodingham engineers after the design of Trexler[2] (*see* fig. 30). The stage was suspended from the top of the furnace by wire ropes attached to four Matterson 10-ton blocks. Control of the blocks was by four push-buttons on the swinging stage. As the winch drums would accommodate only 18 ft. of rope, previously prepared ropes of suitable lengths were used, to be joined or shortened as required. As a safety precaution, the stage was clamped to four hanging wire-ropes, which were anchored to the top structure. The swinging stage was designed to operate from a minimum diameter of 18 ft. to a maximum diameter of 29 ft. All the wooden decking planks were match-marked for rapid fitting. This stage was used for all the bricklaying from the lintel upwards

Dry jointing clay was taken to the top of the furnace by either passenger lift or the main skip, as opportunity offered. The clay was mixed in a large tub on the furnace top. The mixed jointing clay was then lowered to the bricklayers' stage in buckets as required.

When bricklaying was transferred to the hearth of the furnace, a temporary wooden platform was erected on supports when the working height became too high for the men to stand on the hearth floor. This platform was used until the top of the hearth was reached.

For bricking the bosh, a light wooden scaffold, manipulated by chain blocks suspended from four wire ropes anchored to the top of the furnace, was used. A hatchway was cut in the centre of this light platform, through which a small skip could pass. The skip was lifted by a rope passing over a cathead on the lintel platform to a winch situated on the cast-house floor. Bricks were fed to this skip by means of roller conveyors or a polished steel channel leading from tapping hole and slag notches (*see* fig. 29).

The swinging stage was suspended by 14 ft. × 1½ in. diameter wire-rope slings. Four of these were fitted with galvanised thimbles spliced at

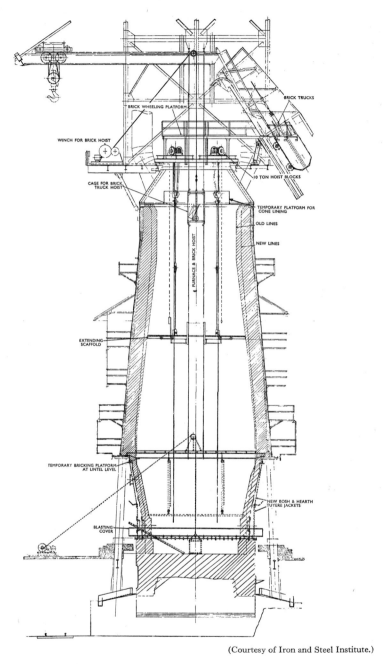

(Courtesy of Iron and Steel Institute.)

Fig. 29 Cross-section through a furnace showing relining gear.

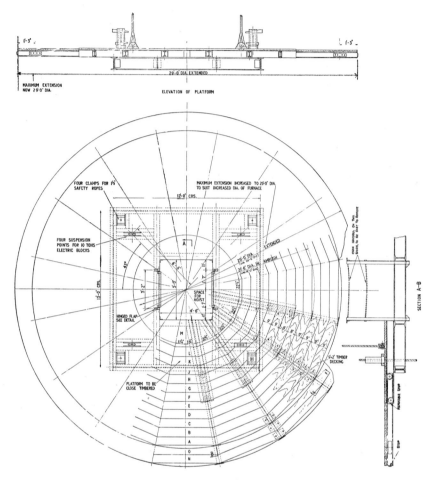

Fig. 30. Extending stage used in relining.

one end for hanging on to the Matterson winch hooks. The others were fitted with solid-steel eyes to take a 2 in. diameter pin. The remaining eight slings were fitted with solid-steel eyes in one end and an open conical socket in the other end. The safety ropes for the scaffold were also $1\frac{1}{2}$ in. diameter and $\frac{3}{4}$ in. locked-coil ropes were used as guides for the brick cage.

During blowing-out, on the cessation of charging, one of the main skips was fastened by means of wire slings and shackles at ground level; this was to give slack wire in the hoist-house, so that the hoist-house motors could be passed over the hoist drum."

Using methods and gear as described, it is possible to carry out a normal relining in less than 53 days. It is believed that the world's fastest relining was at Pretoria, South Africa when a furnace was completely relined in 19⅔ days. The fastest time in Britain was 23 days at Scunthorpe.

REFERENCES

[1] "Relining and Enlarging No. 9 Blast Furnace at Appleby-Frodingham Steel Company" by G. D. Elliot and others. *J. Iron & Steel Inst.*, 1953, *174*, 156.

[2] "Relining and Enlargement of No. 7 (G) Blast Furnace, Bethlehem Steel Co." by W. E. Trexler, *A.I.M.E. Blast Furnace Raw Materials Committee*, 1943, *3*, 98–116.

Chapter IV

EFFECT OF COKE QUALITY ON BLAST-FURNACE OPERATION

COKE

I T IS NOT within the province of this volume to deal with the manufacture of coke, but no treatise on blast-furnace practice can omit a
reference to the important subject of coke quality. While there is a
general agreement that the coke used in the blast furnace must be of
sufficiently good quality for the practice, there is much divergence of
opinion as to the assessment of that quality. The authors have found
that the standard $1\frac{1}{2}$ in. shatter test gives a very good indication of the
suitability of coke for large furnaces, though this does not rule out the
importance of other tests.

One or two assertions can be made with confidence. The bigger the
furnace, the greater the necessity for high quality coke, if the best
furnace results are to be obtained. Furnaces of 25 ft. hearth diameter or
more should be charged with coke having a $1\frac{1}{2}$ in. shatter value of
over 86. Coke of 90 shatter is very desirable. No furnace will operate
successfully if the coke contains a large percentage of breeze. The
general principle is that all coke charged to the furnace should be
screened as near to the charging point as possible and that all coke less
than approximately 1 in. in size should be rejected. At a large majority
of plants, this screening is carried out at the bottom of the skip bridge,
but at one or two European plants, the coke screen has been installed
above the charging hopper on top of the furnace.

Inferior coke undoubtedly causes serious trouble in the blast furnace.
The following are some of the symptoms and troubles arising when coke
quality deteriorates:

I. COPPER LOSSES

If the number of burnt tuyeres increases suddenly and abnormally,
the first thing to examine is coke quality. Small coke is a more frequent
cause of burnt copper than any other. The reasons for this burning are
associated with the explanation of other troubles described below.

2. LONG CASTING TIMES

All furnaces settle down to a fairly consistent time from beginning to end of cast. There will be the odd exception when the taphole is stronger than usual or when the opening of the hole has not been as complete as usual so that casting occupies rather longer than average. If casting times become unduly prolonged, however, taking two or even three hours from beginning to end of cast, the presence of abnormal quantities of small coke in the hearth should be suspected. A useful operating trick in these circumstances is to use a taphole drill of larger diameter than usual. In one plant, the normal taphole drill of 3 in. is replaced by one of 4 in. diameter. The larger hole so obtained permits the discharge of excess breeze through the taphole.

3. BURNING OF BLOW PIPES

In good practice, especially with low slag volumes, it is rare for more than a very little slag to run back from the tuyeres down the blowpipes; it is equally rare for iron and slag to run back in sufficient quantity to cause burning of the blowpipe. If blowpipes are being burnt, it can only mean that iron or a very ferruginous slag is running back on to the blowpipe. Experience indicates that soft small coke is the most frequent cause of this trouble on a furnace which is not at the end of its operating life. A high slag volume aggravates this trouble.

4. COKE BREEZE AT SLAG NOTCHES AND TAPHOLE

In normal operation coke should never survive much below the tuyere level. If coke does pass below the tuyeres, it cannot be burnt and can therefore play no useful part in furnace operation. If it passes the tuyeres, it is almost certainly due to the fact that at that point the coke is so small that it becomes enveloped in slag and therefore cannot be burnt by the air blast. When average sized coke arrives at the tuyeres, the surface area of each piece is so large that it is virtually impossible for it to become slag-encased in its passage through the bosh. Once rapid combustion commences in the tuyere zone, the combustion reaction is so fast that slag cannot envelop the individual piece. But if soft coke or coke with a large amount of breeze is charged to the furnace, the smalls become slag-wrapped when passing through the sticky bosh slags so that they do not burn at the tuyeres. If small coke is seen leaving the taphole or slag notches in quantity, therefore, it is a sign that coke quality has deteriorated. The following is an interesting theory of how small coke behaves in the hearth:

When it is remembered that all the coke charged to the furnace must pass through the combustion zone, it is difficult to reconcile accepted views of this zone with the presence of small coke below it. It is known that there is a raceway in front of the tuyeres (the active combustion zone) in which the solids are circulated until combustion of the individual pieces of coke is completed and the drops of slag etc., are in effect centrifuged out of the raceway. How can small coke be centrifuged out of the raceway before combustion is complete, when big coke is kept in the raceway until combustion is complete?

Consider a container being rotated at fairly high speed. Half fill that container with oil of a given viscosity, and then introduce a proportion of sand into that oil. Because of the small particle size of the sand, it will act as a liquid under these circumstances and the viscosity of the vessel's contents will be increased.

If, instead of introducing sand, an equal weight of fairly large pieces of sandstone is introduced to the oil, the viscosity of the contents of the vessel will still be the viscosity of the oil. If this analogy is at all correct it suggests that small coke escapes the combustion zone because it behaves as part of the slag and imparts an increased viscosity to the slag. On this assumption, the thrown-out coke represents a loss of heat to the process so that there is less and less heat available to meet the increased viscosity of the slag.

5. CHILLED HEARTH

The four points already mentioned are given in the approximate order of their importance and occurrence as symptoms of inferior coke. There is considerable evidence that these troubles can be cumulative; that is, small coke can pile up in the hearth of a furnace faster than it can be discharged through the only openings available—taphole and slag notches. If coke deterioration persists, the accumulation of small breeze in the hearth of the furnace will ultimately lead to a chilled hearth. The unburnt coke passing the tuyeres represents a serious loss of heat to the process because, with efficient operation, the margin between sufficient heat and insufficient heat is very small. The presence of small coke in the hearth prevents the iron and slag flowing as freely as usual through the taphole and slag notches and, in a bad case, slag billows up until it blinds the tuyeres. The breeze makes it more difficult for slag to flow to the slag notch, and finally, neither slag nor iron can be drawn from the furnace, all the tuyeres becoming filled with slag and ceasing to take the blast. This condition, only too familiar to experienced operators, is known as a chilled hearth.

6. BREEZE EXTRACTION

The quantity of breeze extracted at the furnace screens is a useful measure of coke quality. If the breeze percentage increases, a change of coke quality should be looked for. It must also be remembered that, with normal commercial screening installations, a serious increase in the amount of breeze contained in the coke will not be counteracted by screening, because the screen will become overloaded and some of the additional breeze will pass to the blast furnace. In other words, if breeze extraction is normally, say, 6 per cent. and suddenly increases to 9 per cent., it is almost certain that the true content of breeze is much higher than 9 per cent. and that the excess is going into the furnace where it can accumulate and lead to the troubles described above.

COKE ANALYSIS

Apart from a high physical strength, as measured by the shatter test, the chemical analysis of the coke is of importance. As the major part of the sulphur load in the furnace comes from the coke in all practices, the value of a low sulphur coke is obvious. If sulphur in coke is above about 1·2 per cent., trouble can be expected in meeting iron specifications.

Coke ash has to be removed as slag so the advantage of a low ash content lies in reduced slag volume. A reduction of ash, however, should never be sought at the expense of strength. Generally, ash in furnace coke ranges from 9 per cent. to 11 per cent. although as much as 17 per cent. is encountered in some districts. Fortunately, these districts smelt rich ores with a low slag volume, so that the effect of the high ash is not so serious.

The other important impurity in coke is moisture. Good plant practice should ensure that moisture is rarely higher than 3 per cent.

Chapter V

PREPARATION OF ORES – I

CRUSHING

IRON ORE IS rarely won in a condition suitable for smelting in the blast furnace, or, more correctly, it is rare that the iron making practice is able efficiently to smelt iron ores in the as-mined condition. At many plants, some or all stages of ore preparation are carried out at the mines and a prepared raw material delivered to the ironworks. At other plants, the as-mined ore is delivered to the ironworks where all treatment is carried out as part of the ironworks processes. In some cases, crushing is carried out at the mines followed by further treatment in the works. The principles are universal, however, and crushing is the first step in nearly all processes of ore preparation.

THE NEED FOR CRUSHING

Mined ore is usually loaded as a mixture of lumps and fines. Pieces of ore larger than about 6 in. are usually unsuitable for the furnace burden for the following reasons:

(a) Large pieces of ore are more difficult to smelt than smaller pieces. Furnace efficiency therefore dictates an upper limit to size.

(b) Materials handling equipment on scale cars, bin gates and furnace charging gear usually imposes an upper limit on the size of lump to be handled.

If mining machinery is to be efficient, it must be designed to load a wide range of sizes in order not to restrict loading rates; a 4 ft. lump of ore is no obstacle to loading by a large face shovel but would be an impossible proposition for the charging equipment of a furnace. Yet lumps cannot be broken without producing fines.

Crushing is a highly specialised subject which cannot be dealt with fully in a text-book about ironmaking. Nevertheless, the crushing plant is so often an integral part of the ironworks, especially in Great Britain, that the subject cannot be ignored. It is proposed, therefore, to deal briefly with the specific subject of British ores.

Fig. 31. Primary Crusher for British ores. Note slugger teeth.

The bedded ironstones of Britain are delivered from the mine or quarry in a very mixed range of sizes. Large face shovels can and do load lumps of up to 4 or 5 ft. in one dimension. The use of explosives in the mining operation inevitably leads to the production of much fines. With any type of crusher, there is a limit to the reduction ratio possible in one operation, so that if crushing is intended to provide the blast furnace with lump ore, two stages are necessary. If the crushing process is to provide the feed for a sintering operation, three or even four stages will be involved.

(a) PRIMARY CRUSHING

There is little doubt that the most suitable type of crusher for this operation is the Hadfield two-roll crusher with one slugger roll (fig. 31). This is particularly suitable because of its ability to deal with the wet sticky clay-bearing ironstones of the Midlands. A crusher with rolls of 6 ft. diameter and 5 ft. wide is generally used for primary crushing. The rolls revolve at approximately 160 revolutions per minute, and when set to crush down to a nominal 6 in. or 7 in. can attain production rates of 1000 tons per hour. Satisfactory operation demands that the nobblers and slugger teeth are maintained to design dimensions and profile. This demands a careful and rigidly maintained schedule of routine building-up by weld metal. Examples are known where a pair of rolls maintained in this manner have had a useful life of over 12 years, having dealt with about 15 million tons of iron ore.

As with all crushing operations, scalping before crushing is desirable. Fig. 32 shows an arrangement of a drop bar feeder and two-roll screen, together with a primary crusher. The gathering machinery after the crusher must be of ample capacity; it is too often forgotten that, although a crusher may be designed for say, 600 tons per hour, a big lump passing through the crusher may increase the feed rate for a few seconds to two or three times this figure. If this factor is overlooked, the belt conveyors will inevitably be overloaded on occasion, leading to considerable spillage.

A crusher of the type shown in fig. 31 is quite easily capable of absorbing lumps 3 ft. 6 in. in one dimension. On some installations, a second drop bar feeder has been installed below the primary crusher in order to level out the peak loading arising from the crushing of lumps, and to give some regularity of feed on to the belt serving the secondary crushers.

Jaw crushers and gyratory crushers are used with other ores as primary crushers, but they are not recommended for British ores.

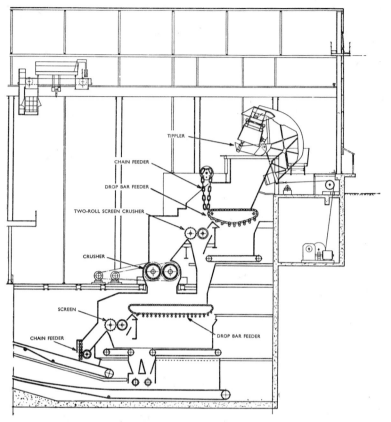

TIPPLER

CHAIN FEEDER

DROP BAR FEEDER

TWO-ROLL SCREEN CRUSHER

CRUSHER

SCREEN

CHAIN FEEDER

DROP BAR FEEDER

(Courtesy of Ross Engineers Limited.)

Fig. 32. Cross-section through a primary crushing plant.

(b) SECONDARY CRUSHERS

The secondary crushing of the Jurassic ores of Britain presents a somewhat unusual crushing problem. Generally, the ores are slabby and often sticky and clay-bearing. Jaw crushers, single-roll crushers and plain two-roll crushers are generally not as satisfactory as a cone crusher and the latter is usually used for the secondary crushing of iron ores. If a cubical product is desired, a cone crusher must be choke fed, that is, the feed box should at all times be full. Providing it is the correct size for the job, this type of crusher is noteworthy for its trouble-free operation. The selection of the right size is a matter of importance—if it is too large, the product will almost certainly be slabby; if it is too small, it may be prone to choking.

THE DESIRABLE SIZE OF LUMP ORE

When a blast furnace is operated on lump ore, the size of the lump is the major control available to the operator in dealing with the different characteristics of the several iron ores used. British ores are soft, easily reduced and prone to break down at comparatively low temperatures. In order to maintain as open a stock column as possible, it is suggested that British ores should not be crushed much smaller than about 5 in. This size would be undesirable for hard dense magnetites. The harder and denser the ore, the smaller it should be when charged to the blast furnace. For example, the magnetites of Northern Sweden should be crushed to 1 in. or, at the most, $1\frac{1}{2}$ in. The soft ores of the Mediterranean coast can safely be charged in lumps as big as 6 in.

When both hard and soft ores are involved, there is a very good case for installing duplicate secondary crushers, one to be reserved to crush hard ores to approximately $1\frac{1}{2}$ in. and the other for soft ores.

TERTIARY CRUSHING

Where the ore preparation process includes sintering it is just as necessary to prepare the charge to the sinter plant as to the blast furnace with one important difference. In the blast furnace, there is a minimum size for every ore below which operation will suffer because of decreased voidage in the stock column. In the sintering process, on the other hand, there is a maximum size above which sintering cannot take place efficiently. Unfortunately, the lower limit for the blast furnace and the upper limit for the sinter plant rarely coincide.

Experience indicates that, with British ores, nothing smaller than $\frac{1}{2}$ in. or $\frac{5}{8}$ in. should be charged to the blast furnace, whereas with richer, harder ores it is permissible to go as low as $\frac{3}{8}$ in. On the sinter plant, however, British ores as big as $\frac{1}{2}$ in. are an almost impossible sintering proposition; in fact, everything for sintering should be smaller than $\frac{1}{4}$ in. With rich ores, it is possible to sinter at $\frac{3}{8}$ in. but a much better product is obtained if the ore is reduced to $-\frac{1}{4}$ in. Some authorities go so far as to say that nothing bigger than $\frac{1}{8}$ in. should be charged to the sinter plant. In order to meet the demands of the sinter plant, tertiary crushing becomes necessary.

SWING HAMMER MILLS

Swing hammer mills are universally used for tertiary crushing. Mills with moving breaker plates on each side of the rotor have been developed for sticky ore (*see* fig. 33). This type of crusher has been found extremely satisfactory. It must be emphasised, however, that the

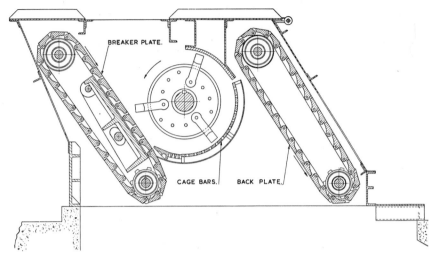

BREAKER PLATE.

CAGE BARS.   BACK PLATE.

(Courtesy of Fraser & Chalmers Limited.)

Fig. 33. Cross-section of a hammer mill used for tertiary crushing. This mill is equipped with a moving breaker plate and a moving back plate.

maintenance costs of a hammer mill are very high because of the severe wear on the hammers which must be hard-faced with some material such as tungsten carbide. If the product of the mill is to be maintained regularly at the correct size a strict routine of hammer maintenance and changing is essential. With this type of mill, feed rates may be as high as 300 tons per hour.

GRINDING

If the iron ore is to be subjected to a concentration process, material as large as $\frac{1}{4}$ in. is rarely suitable. With the taconite ores of North America, for example, concentration can only be achieved when the ore is reduced to about 350 mesh. This degree of reduction cannot be achieved in an orthodox crusher but must be carried out in some type of grinding mill. Ball mills, rod mills, and tube mills are all used for this duty. (Rod mills are discussed in more detail in the section on "Sintering".)

SCREENING

In all ore preparation processes, screening is an essential operation, having two main purposes:

(a) *Scalping:* It is logical to prevent the entry to a crusher of material already smaller than the size at which the crusher is set. This operation is generally known as "scalping". After crushing, the fines scalped out usually join the main flow from the crusher to the next operation. Screening efficiency in a scalping installation is not as important as trouble-free operation. As the scalping screen must handle material in the wide range of sizes delivered from the mining or quarrying operation the necessity for robust construction will easily be appreciated.

(b) *Sizing:* In this operation, the flow of ore is separated into two or more sizes. As the object is usually to produce a clean lump ore fraction for blast-furnace use, a high degree of screen efficiency is necessary. If screening is not efficient, the blast-furnace operation will inevitably suffer.

SCALPING

Several types of scalping or grizzly screens are available. The drop bar screen and two-roll grizzly (*see* fig. 32), are used extensively in the treatment of iron ores and are extremely rugged in construction. These two types are preferred for iron ores because they are self-cleaning to some extent. The movement of alternate bars of the drop bar conveyor on the return run ensures that material adhering to the rolls in their closer setting is discharged. The two-roll screen consists usually of one grooved roll and one ribbed roll. A comb cut to suit the profile of the grooved roll is used to keep the grooves clean.

SIZING SCREENS

There are many screen designs available, but vibratory or shaking screens are universally adopted for the treatment of iron ores. As efficiency of screening is of prime importance, considerable emphasis is placed on the provision of ample screen area. The time available for a screen to do its work is so short with commercial rates of operation that generous design for screen area is usually a good fault; this is especially important where the ores being handled are in a wet or sticky state. Two screens in tandem are preferable to a double-deck screen with this type of iron ore; on the latter it is unavoidable that the first third of the lower deck should be virtually unused. Fig. 34 shows an installation of gyratory screens in tandem, fitted with screens of $\frac{1}{4}$ in. $\times 2$ in. mesh and dealing with 250 tons of ore per hour. An elongated mesh of this nature is always employed for smaller sizes although square mesh may be quite satisfactory for coarse screening.

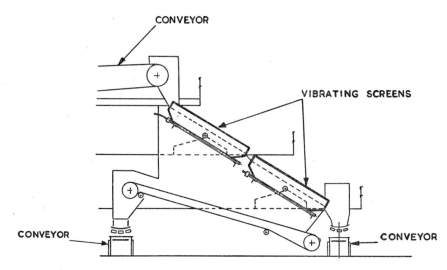

Fig. 34. A typical arrangement of tandem screens with gathering conveyor beneath.

Wet ores will tend to adhere and build up on all types of screen. This leads to blinding of the screen, reduction of screening area, and general inefficiency of the operation. In addition, such a build-up will throw a screen out of balance and cause premature failure of the screen cloths. To overcome these troubles, heated screens are becoming increasingly popular. Electrical heating has been successfully developed for small screens but the difficulties in maintaining uniform distribution of the current on a large screen mat make it somewhat unreliable. A simple installation of gas burners below the screen has been found extremely effective in preventing blinding of large screens.

It is not necessary to raise the temperature of the screen cloth to much more than 100°C. Iron ore fed at the correct rate for the screen will not adhere to a screen cloth so heated. Quite apart from the improvement in screening efficiency, gas heating can often be justified by the resultant improvement in the life of screen mats and therefore the reduction of down-time. This problem of sticky ores persists beyond the screen, and the gathering chutes below it must be designed with steep valley angles to prevent building-up.

With some British ores, building-up will still take place even where the valley angle is 60°. It will be appreciated that a 60° valley angle demands considerable height in the gathering chute; to avoid a related increase in the height of the screening station building a wide belt conveyor is installed below the screen to gather the material from the screen for delivery to a normal belt conveyor (*see* fig. 34). This unusual application of belt conveyors considerably reduces the head-room necessary for a screen and completely eliminates the problem of material building up in gathering chutes.

ORE DRYING

Orthodox apparatus can be used to rough crush almost any type of iron ore without modification or alteration; this is also true of screening at fairly large mesh sizes. But the fine crushing and fine screening of many ores is almost impossible with orthodox apparatus. Gas-heated screens can be of considerably assistance when dealing with wet and sticky ores, but some ores demand additional treatment. Prominent among these are the siliceous clay-bearing ores of the British Midlands. The preparation of these ores, first for the blast furnace and later for the sinter plant, has led to the introduction of ore drying as an important section of ore preparation. It seems probable that ore drying will be applied increasingly in the future and almost certainly to ores other than those for which the practice was originated. The principles, however, can be explained by reference to the Northampton Sands ore.

Ores of this type may contain more than 20 per cent. of moisture and 7 per cent. of alumina. In its natural state, the ore is sticky and cannot be screened efficiently at any mesh size. Similarly, it is quite impossible to crush it in its natural state down to $-\frac{1}{4}$ in. for sintering, whatever the crushing machinery employed. All machines quickly plug with Northampton ore in its natural condition. When the moisture is reduced to round about 10 or 12 per cent., however, the ore becomes manageable. As drying can only be carried out on the surface of the ore, larger pieces will retain a larger proportion of their original moisture. Sufficient drying must be carried out, therefore, to prevent trouble in the hammer mills when such pieces are being crushed.

ORE DRYING MACHINERY

The Buttner system ore drier is the most generally used for iron ores. Fig. 35 shows the arrangement of a typical installation. In this system, ore is fed by means of a scraper feeder from the reception hopper to a chute which discharges the ore into a rotary drum, the chute passing through the stationary flue connecting the combustion chamber to the drum. The chute is located in the hot gas stream and is maintained at dull red heat to prevent the ore from sticking. Blast-furnace gas and primary air are supplied to the burner, the products of combustion and secondary air being drawn through the brick-lined combustion chamber and the drum by means of an exhaust fan.

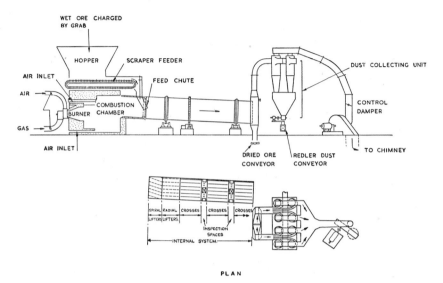

(Courtesy of Buell Combustion Company Limited.

Fig. 35. Arrangement of ore drying plant.

The drum consists of a steel shell, the interior incorporating a system of lifting vanes and crosses by which the ore discharged into it is distributed across the path of the gas flow (fig. 36). The discharge end is enclosed in a hood and seals are provided between the rotating drum and the stationary entry flue and discharge hood. The outgoing ore passes into a hopper from which it feeds through a counterweighted flap on to a gathering belt and the waste gas passes through dust cyclones before entering the exhaust stack. The drum is carried on steel tyres running on rollers, the angle of the drum being 5° to the horizontal, with thrust rollers to arrest drum "creep". Measuring 43 ft. long by 8 ft. 7 in. diameter, the drum is equipped with gear boxes to give rotational speeds of 3·75, 5·00, or 6·25 r.p.m.; at top speed it yields over 60 tons per hour.

The operator can adjust the drum inlet temperature by varying the gas consumption, and the outlet temperature by means of a damper control on the exhaust fan inlet.

Enough gas is burnt to ensure that the inlet chute is kept clear and that ore freely enters the "honeycomb" inside the drum. The inlet temperature varies according to the condition of the ore but normal operation results in sufficient gas being burnt to maintain an inlet temperature of 800°C. with the fan damper control adjusted to maintain

Fig. 36. Feed end of an ore dryer showing ore delivery chute and arrangement of lifters inside the drum.

Fig. 37. *An installation of Van Tongeren cyclones at the discharge end of a sinter machine. Lurgi-Frodingham sinter coolers are also shown.*

the exit temperature between 100 and 120°C. Typical winter operation results in the consumption of 200,000 cu.ft./hour of blast-furnace gas when operating at a throughput of about 60 tons per hour and reducing the average moisture in the ore from 20 to 12 per cent. Drying time at the fastest rotational speeds is about 15 minutes.

DUST EXTRACTION

The drying of ore is inevitably accompanied by the production of dust and the same is true of the sintering process. The adoption and extension of these stages of ore preparation, coupled with the increasing desire to reduce atmospheric pollution, has led to the introduction of dust extraction equipment at many points in an ironworks. Dust extraction, as exemplified by gas cleaning, has long been practised at the blast-furnace plant, but it is a rather different problem on the ore preparation plant. On some sintering plants, local conditions have compelled the adoption of electrostatic cleaning plants. Generally, however, satisfactory performance has been achieved by the use of cyclone dust separators. Fig. 37 shows a typical installation of Van Tongeren cyclones at a large ore drying plant. The dust collected in such cyclones is generally pugged with water in a small mill before being introduced as raw material to the sintering plant. Van Tongeren multi-cyclone installations have an efficiency of about 95 per cent., which gives a gas discharge from the ore drying plant chimney of about 0·7 grains of dust per cubic foot. On sinter plants, density of dust in the chimney discharge is as low as 0·15 grains per cubic foot. The air in a dust collecting system must be maintained at a temperature above dew point; this can be achieved by the provision of stoves to supply hot air into the ducting. Blast-furnace gas is burnt in a stove and enough secondary air is induced to reduce the temperature of the waste gases to about 400°C.

It is probable that the future will see a considerable extension of dust extraction. Such places as ore crushing plants, coke screens at the furnace skip pit, discharges into bunkers containing sinter, coke, and other dry materials are all points at which dust extraction may be usefully applied.

Chapter VI

PREPARATION OF ORES – II

AGGLOMERATION

IN ALL METHODS of ore treatment the end products are invariably classified as roughs and fines. The accepted division between the two varies with the materials and with the blast-furnace practice to be followed. A broad rule-of-thumb guide is that for hard, rich ores $+\frac{3}{8}$ in. may be regarded as rough; with soft, low-grade ores $-\frac{3}{4}$ in. must be regarded as fines.

As all the ore treatments mentioned are purely mechanical, and as no concentration process is being considered, the chemical quality of roughs and fines is basically similar; it is certainly never so different as to justify the discard to waste of the fines.

THE NECESSITY FOR AGGLOMERATION

An important objective of blast-furnace operation is to blow as large a volume of air as possible through a given furnace. In doing so, the maximum amount of coke will be burnt and therefore the maximum, or nearly the maximum, amount of burden will be smelted. The speed at which air can be pushed through a bed of broken solids is almost entirely controlled by the permeability of the bed. In most ironmaking practices, coke provides most of the permeability. There are two reasons for this: a satisfactory coke is in itself porous and retains its shape and size until it is actually burnt at the tuyeres; in addition, the volume of coke in the furnace is usually twice the volume of the burden, except when very lean ores are being smelted. Coke volume is one of the fundamental differences between rich ore and lean ore practice.

All iron ores in the as-mined condition vary considerably in particle size. Usually, the large pieces of ore are too big to be handled in any blast-furnace plant and the number of such pieces is far too great for them to be broken individually. It follows, therefore, that the ore must be crushed. The desired size to which it should be crushed is immaterial to this discussion; the important consideration here is that the lump of ore cannot be broken without producing fines. There is sufficient data available to demonstrate that the size grading of a bed of broken solids has a profound influence over the permeability of such a bed.

Crushed iron ore has been compared to a mixture of sand and marbles in which the sand occupies the interstices between the marbles. If the sand is discarded, the permeability of the remaining marbles will be much higher than the permeability of the mixture. Furnace operation will therefore benefit if the ores are screened and the fines discarded; but it would be wholly uneconomical to discard to waste the iron ore fines arising from crushing and screening. When it is decided to screen crushed ore in order to secure a clean oversize it follows automatically that a process of agglomerating the fines is necessary. At the moment, the most successful method of agglomeration is sintering.

To summarise, it may be said that sintering is forced upon the operator as soon as screening is accepted and that sintering is the price to be paid initially for securing a clean oversize ore. The amount of sinter to be smelted under these conditions is therefore a function of the amount of fines arising during the pre-treatment of the ores. This amount, of course, varies with the ores concerned and with the practice.

Once sintering is adopted it becomes an important part of the ironmaking process.

The desirability or otherwise of preparing all the ore by sintering is discussed in a later chapter. At this point, it is sufficient to re-emphasise that sintering stems initially from the demands for a clean lump ore. The only exception to this is when the ore can only be obtained as a concentrate of small particle size.

There are three main agglomerating processes practised today. These are nodulising, which employs a rotary kiln; pelletising, with subsequent heat treatment in either a vertical shaft kiln or possibly a sintering grate; and sintering. Most of the agglomerate produced throughout the world is obtained by a sintering process.

SINTERING

The history of the blast furnace and the history of the sinter plant have much in common. It was a long time before it became generally accepted that it was necessary to prepare the burden for the blast furnace. Similarly, it was a long time before the importance and desirability of preparing the burden for the sinter plant was appreciated.

It is the practice at many plants to take the fines arising from ore screening and to supply them directly to the sinter plant. This means that the minimum size of ore used at the blast furnace dictates the conditions for the associated sintering practice. Rarely can this be done without detriment to either ore or sinter. Coke breeze as screened out of the coke going to the blast furnace is unsuitable for sintering until it has been crushed. In the same way, the purpose and importance of the correct circulating load is very often overlooked. It must be appreciated that each set of raw materials for sintering imposes its own conditions on the preparation of the sintering mixture.

Fines have previously been defined as $-\frac{3}{4}$ in. in the case of lean ores and $-\frac{3}{8}$ in. in the case of rich ores. It is possible to manufacture a fair quality of sinter from rich ores $-\frac{3}{8}$ in. in size, but it is quite impossible to make good sinter from lean ores $-\frac{3}{4}$ in. in size. Hard and fast rules cannot be laid down; they must be established for each set of conditions. As a general indication, however, lean ores should be wholly smaller than $\frac{1}{4}$ in. before sintering and it is desirable that rich ores should be of the same size. Except when the particle size is below approximately 100 mesh, the smaller the material to be sintered the stronger will be the final product. Reconciliation of the various factors involved becomes a matter of economics.

The necessity for presenting the material to be sintered in the correct size range is better appreciated by practical consideration of what happens in sintering.

Sintering is a process of incipient fusion in which the components must be taken up to their melting points for a brief space of time. The ores are usually a mixture of many minerals. As the ore is heated, moisture, combined water and carbon dioxide must be driven off, in that order, before true sintering can commence.

The fuel to do all this work must be very small pieces of coke or anthracite coal. If the coke is larger than $\frac{1}{8}$ in. trouble with patchy irregular sintering and high grate bar losses will be encountered. The margin between too little fuel and too much fuel is a very narrow one. If there is insufficient fuel, it will have exhausted itself before preliminary calcination has been succeeded by sintering. If there is too much fuel, the ores will be raised to too high a temperature for too long a time, resulting in abnormal liquefaction. This will yield an undesirable sinter or may even lead to slagging of the bed on the grate and so to a cessation of sintering through loss of permeability before the whole of the bed has been processed.

The same practical reasoning may be applied to the question of return fines. At all plants, the finished sinter passes over a screen and the undersized material is returned to the process. This fraction is generally known as return fines. At first thought, return fines might be regarded as the product of inefficiency in the process. Ideally, all the material going on to the sintering grate should leave at a size greater than the setting of the final screens after the machine. In practice, this is never achieved; even if it were, the sinter would leave the machine in such large pieces that a crushing process would be necessary and the fines resulting from the crushing would have to be returned to the process. Practice everywhere, however, indicates that the return of some of the product to the process is accompanied by real operating advantages. Within limits, output increases with the amount of return fines, the optimum percentage varying with the materials being sintered. The strength of sinter also increases with the amount of return fines.

When sintering rich ores the desirable circulating load is usually around 20 per cent.; low grade ores may need up to 40 per cent. The circulating load increases the permeability of the bed and also reduces the average sintering loss. In the case of carbonate ores, the sintering loss may be as high as 30 per cent. and the amount of work involved in driving off volatiles in the time available is too much for the production of strong sinter.

In addition to increasing the strength of the sinter and raising the permeability of the bed, a third and important function of return fines in many practices is the formation of a hearth layer for the protection of the grate bars. Suitably sized ore is used in some plants for this purpose, but sinter is a better material for forming a hearth layer and is more commonly employed. Hearth layering and protection of the grate are discussed under "Feeding the Machine".

MIXING

Water is added to all sintering mixtures because it is a cheap and effective method of increasing the permeability of the mixture. A simple analogy is that of sand. Dry sand will flow almost as a liquid, and in bulk will have low permeability. The addition of water will give the sand some mechanical stability and in bulk it will have high permeability. But if too much water is added, mechanical strength will disappear, permeability will drop to zero and again the sand will behave as a liquid. Exactly the same can happen with sintering mixtures, so that control of moisture is always critical. The margin between optimum moisture content and excessive moisture is small. Fig. 38 shows the effect of moisture additions on the permeability of a sintering mixture.

Long-held views on mixing have had considerable influence on the design of the necessary apparatus. The following types of mixers have been used:

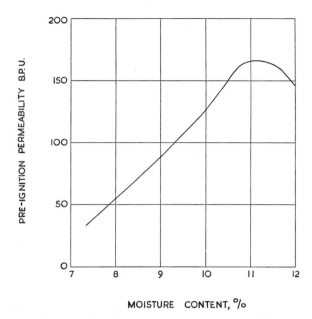

Fig. 38. The effect of moisture on bed permeability.

(*a*) trommel mixers;

(*b*) trommel mixers with paddles;

(*c*) stationary bodied mixers with paddles.

The development of pelletising processes in recent years has directed attention to improving the permeability of the sintering mixture by pelletising.

In attempts to agglomerate exceedingly fine materials—too fine to be sintered by orthodox methods—much research has been concentrated on "balling together" the fines in order to make pellets, usually of ½ in. to 1 in. diameter. After heat treatment, the pellets are a suitable blast-furnace material. This work also demonstrated to sinter plant operators that increased permeability of the sintering mixture could be obtained by some measure of pelletising, only small pellets of ¼ in. and less being desired for this purpose.

Pelletisation has led to modified views on the most suitable type of machinery for mixing. It seems probable that the next few years will see a return to the old-fashioned drum or trommel mixer, modified in line with the experience gained in true pelletising of fine materials.

It is now usual to have two stages of mixing, whatever machinery is being used. The problem is to produce as intimate a mixture as possible of the ores, flue dust, return sinter, coke breeze and water; and all these materials have very different characteristics. When it is considered that the production flow of the plant may permit only about 30 seconds for mixing time, the desirability of two-stage mixing becomes obvious.

As a rule, the first mixing is designed to yield a mechanical mixture without all the water necessary for sintering. Conveyance of the mixture from the primary to the secondary mixer gives some time for the moisture already added to spread itself evenly. This enables moisture control to be carried out much more accurately in the secondary mixer where the final water additions are made.

In other words, the first stage should consist of true mixing, which may involve the violent movement associated with paddles, while the second stage should be one of moisture control and balling, calling for rotating drums without paddles. This process would perhaps be better described as granulating, to distinguish from a true balling or pelletising process.

FEEDING THE SINTER MACHINE

The method of delivering the sintering mixture to the grate will depend on whether or not a separate hearth layer is considered necessary, a matter on which there is a considerable division of opinion. On the one hand, the provision of a separate hearth layer necessitates more complicated machinery. On the other hand, if all the material to be sintered is very fine (*e.g.* concentrates), it is doubtful whether excessive losses through the grate can be avoided unless a hearth layer is used. With fairly coarse materials, say, $\frac{1}{4}$ in. maximum size, satisfactory protection of the grate can normally be achieved by segregation from a swinging spout to deliver coarse sinter from the return fines to the grate (*see* fig. 39). This permits a simple and comparatively inexpensive layout at the feed end of the machine. By altering the speed of movement, the length of the spout, and the angle at which it delivers to the machine, it is possible to influence the distribution of the materials on the grate to produce a satisfactory segregation. The bottom of the bed will contain more coarse material than the top and the top of the bed will contain more coke than the bottom. At all levels, the size distribution and carbon distribution must be the same across the width of the machine.

A further advantage of the swinging spout is that, with careful design of the conveyors, any permeability achieved by mixing can be maintained on the grate.

The other common system of feeding a sinter machine, especially when a hearth layer is used, is by means of roll feeders. Roll feeders are very good for delivering the mixture but the passage of material through

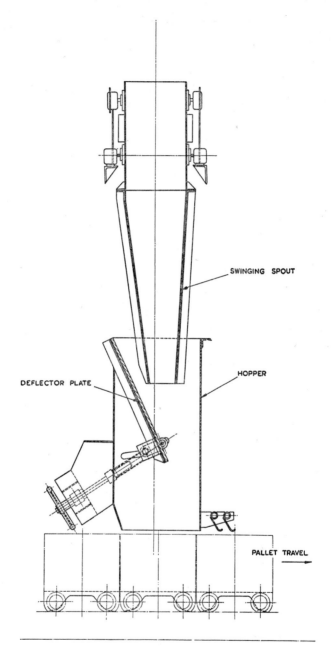

Fig. 39. Arrangement of swinging spout.

the gate above the roller must lead to some compression and therefore to some reduction in permeability.

Other means of feeding, such as jigging feeders and horizontal swinging spouts, have been employed with success in the last few years.

It is important for the level of the mixture below the spout to be maintained as constant as possible. Generally, the bed should be laid so that the top is very little above the cut-off plate, *i.e.*, the stationary plate under which the pallets pass to the ignitor. If the pallets are over-filled, the surplus feed will be held back by the plate and will fall down the slope of the material below the spout. This obviously gives an incorrect distribution of sizes (*see* fig. 40).

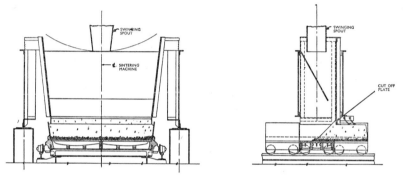

(Courtesy of American Institute of Mining and Metallurgy.)

Fig. 40.   Correct feed from a swinging spout.

IGNITION AND FUEL

Ignition of the sinter bed should be as fierce as possible. It is not sufficient merely to ignite the coke breeze in the top of the bed; the ignition must supply sufficient heat to simulate sintering conditions existing lower down the bed.

Blast-furnace gas alone is seldom satisfactory and a mixture of coke-oven and blast-furnace gas with a calorific value of about 150 B.Th.U.'s is generally employed. If gas is not available, oil is used.

The design of ignition hoods and burners varies a great deal. A typical igniter is shown in fig. 41.

The effectiveness of ignition is improved by correct preparation of the sintering mixture and of the top of the bed. Material of small particle size will give a smooth surface to the bed and consequently a better ignition. This emphasises the importance of maintaining the feed to the sinter machine at the correct level below the swinging spout. Typical arrangement of the feed end of the machine is shown in fig. 39.

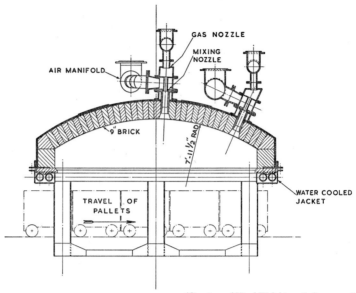

(Courtesy of Head Wrightson & Company Limited.)

Fig. 41. Ignition furnace for a sintering machine.

As sintering commences at the top of the bed and proceeds downwards it will be appreciated that the speed of travel of the flame front influences the production rate. In recent years, a great deal of research work has been carried out on the mechanics of flame front travel. It may be easier to understand some of the difficulties of producing satisfactory sinter if the problem is expressed in somewhat oversimplified terms. The mixture of ore fines, coke, and water has to be converted into a sinter which has been raised for a short time to the highest melting point of the mixture. Moisture, combined water and CO_2 must be driven off; only when this has occurred can the material be raised to the melting point, so securing the necessary agglomeration by bonding. As the moisture is driven off from the top of the bed, it will temporarily increase the moisture in the level immediately below that in which combustion is taking place. A zone of increased moisture will travel down through the bed in front of the actual flame front. It has been demonstrated that sulphur driven off in the top of the bed is first of all absorbed in this wet zone before being driven off again by the following flame front. Unless these various fronts can proceed evenly and in step with each other, sintering can never be correctly controlled.

The coke particles must be fine enough to mix intimately with the ore fines. If the coke is too fine, the heat it generates will be dissipated before it can be usefully employed. If the coke is too large, the heat generation will occupy more time than the uniform progression of the flame front can permit. Because the lower part of the bed is preheated by the hot gases from the higher level, ideally there should be more coke in the top of the bed than in the bottom. This desired segregation can be obtained from a swinging spout, with coke of the correct size range.

Opinion throughout the world is almost unanimous that the desirable size grading for coke breeze in all sintering practices is $-\frac{1}{8}$ in.

If the ore fines are too large, the evolution of CO_2 and water may actually encase the centre of the particle with an insulating layer so that the flame front will pass before the centre of the particle has been raised to sintering temperature. The maximum particle size must therefore be reduced to $\frac{1}{4}$ in. Especially with carbonate ores, it is desirable that the larger particles should be segregated on deposition from the spout to afford some protection to the grate bars. It follows that the ore fines used should be so graded in size as to permit this to happen without the material on the grate becoming so big that sintering is impossible for the reasons outlined above. This ideal is seldom attainable, however.

Conversely, if all the ore fines are reduced to a very fine particle size of say, 150 mesh, it will be impossible in normal practice to retain this material on the grate; the effect will be to pull the mixture through the grate. This is one of the reasons why it is necessary to return a certain amount of sinter to the process. Generally speaking, the size segregation vertically through the bed is controlled by a suitable addition of somewhat larger sized returned sinter. This has the further advantage of reducing the average volatile losses of the mixture and thus offsets some of the difficulties outlined earlier.

As the flame front descends through the travelling bed the temperature at each successive wind box will rise. The aim should be to attain maximum temperature at the penultimate wind box. This means that virtually the whole of the machine is being used for sintering and the last wind box (approximately 6 ft. of machine length) provides a margin to ensure that incompletely sintered pallets do not reach the end of the machine.

Experience has shown that wind box temperature control is much more effective than control by means of wind box suctions.

GRATE BARS

Grate bar maintenance is of importance; apart from the wastage of sintering effort arising from a grate in poor condition, the life of the main fan impeller can be shortened by a significant amount.

There are two main types of grate bar (*see* fig. 42):

(*a*) plate bars;

(*b*) finger bars.

In the long run, the plate bar is probably better, although when a bar is burnt, the failure of a small area leads to the scrapping of a much larger area. On the other hand, the normal wear and tear on finger type bars soon leads to the pallets being filled with slightly undersize bars. Until there is room for one additional bar to be fitted, there is a general deterioration in that section of the grate.

Malleable cast iron has been used for grate bars for many years with considerable success. In the last few years, special steel bars have been introduced for this purpose. Special heat-resisting steels containing up to 30 per cent. chromium are standard at several plants. Which type of material to use is a question of economics. If the sintering practice employed leads to heavy grate bar losses, the use of expensive special steels may be attractive. But attention to the grading of the sintering mixture and to the way it is deposited on the bars may enable malleable iron to be used with success. No grate has yet been designed which eliminates the need for some form of hearth layer. Whether that hearth layer is obtained by segregation from a swinging spout or is deposited separately depends on the characteristics of the mixture being sintered.

Coke containing large pieces, such as domestic breeze, can cause grate bars to burn as the breeze tends to segregate at the bottom of the layer.

SURGE CAPACITY

In good sintering practice the sintering machines should be maintained at a constant speed. This can only be achieved if the operator has surge capacity at his service which can be used to correct changes in material flow without altering the speed of the machine. Surge capacity is also necessary where a pair of machines is fed by a single gathering belt from the raw material bunkers. Similarly, in order to avoid frequent and serious fluctuations in the circulating load, there should be ample surge capacity in the return fines system.

Where two machines are fed from a single gathering belt, surge capacity can be utilised to avoid segregation, especially of coke, between the machines. A good arrangement is for the correct proportions in the sintering mixture, including return fines, to be delivered on to a single gathering belt. After primary mixing, the total mixture is conveyed to a reversing belt conveyor serving two bunkers, each of 100 tons capacity. From each of the 100 ton bins, the mixture for one machine is drawn *via* a feeder table and passes through a secondary mixer before delivery to the grate. Each of the surge bins should be kept about half

Fig. 42. Feed end of a sintering machine showing finger type and plate type grate bars.

full. On a suitable time schedule, the reversing conveyor will deliver its total load alternately to the two bins and therefore no problem of segregation will arise. As the machine operator notices the surge bin rising or falling with a constant machine speed, he should at all times ensure that there is sufficient material in the bin to allow him to vary the delivery on to the first gathering belt. In other words, if the surge bin is falling he should have time to increase the delivery from the raw material bins before it is necessary to vary the speed of the machine. This point is considered to be important.

Without surge capacity behind the machine, the rate of sintering often has to be speeded up to deal with a temporary increase in delivery, when it would be more desirable to slow down the machine in order to deal with the changed conditions.

After the sinter is finally screened, the undersized material should pass to a large capacity surge bin. The provision of 1000 tons capacity for two machines is not too much. Again, the bin is maintained approximately half full.

If trouble on the machine leads to an increase in undersized sinter, this increased tonnage can be absorbed without resorting to panic measures on the machines. If the reduction of return sinter falls below normal, the level in the surge bin may be allowed to fall temporarily. The provision of this generous surge capacity means that the returns can be added as part of the mixture and changes in the amount of returns need only be made at infrequent intervals of three or four days.

When the sinter plant is connected to another part of an ore preparation plant, such as a crushing plant, surge capacity between the two processes is necessary. An ample stockyard for sinter plant raw materials with a capacity large enough to operate the sinter plant for three days is desirable. It is impossible to have a good sintering operation if its production rate has to vary to suit the production rate of the plant feeding it.

SINTER COOLING

The primary purpose of sintering is to convert fines to lumps. All sinters, whatever their composition, are essentially brittle materials although sinters of low iron content are invariably weaker and more brittle than sinters of high iron content. All are made at a high temperature (more than 1100°C.) but in most ironworks they have to be cooled before they can be transported to the blast furnace. In certain Swedish works, hot sinter is transported in steel skips by an aerial ropeway to the top of the furnace, but this type of layout is rarely possible, especially when high tonnage rates are involved.

To use the sinter machine for completely cooling the sinter it produces is an extremely wasteful process. A sinter machine should be used to make sinter and the product should be discharged hot—at an average temperature of 700°C. or more. Formerly, it was general practice to water quench hot sinter but this practice has rightly fallen into disrepute. Not only does water quenching lead to considerable size degradation, but the resultant steam and dust cause intolerable working conditions in the quenching area, and if the sinter is to be conveyed by rubber belt, the belt will have a short life because it will be either burned by hot sinter or rotted by water.

From every viewpoint, therefore, air cooling of sinter is both desirable and necessary. The first successful sinter cooling system was designed by the Lurgi Company in 1952.

After discharging from the end of the machine, the sinter cake passes through a sinter breaker which reduces the size to about 8 in. maximum (*see* fig. 43). The broken sinter passes next over a screen which rejects

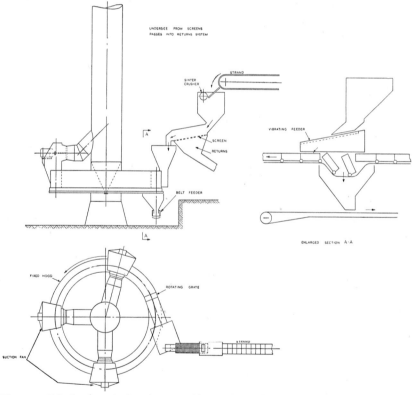

Fig. 43. Discharge end of a sinter machine and Lurgi-Frodingham sinter cooler.

the undersize sinter for circulation as return fines. The oversize sinter then passes to the cooler, which consists of a line of lightly constructed pallets with louvred bottoms through which air is drawn by means of equi-spaced suction fans. The pallets may be in a straight line, as in a sinter machine, or, in the preferred construction, on a circular track. At the end of the machine, fully-cooled sinter is discharged to a hopper from which a vibrating feeder transfers the sinter to a rubber belt conveyor. Control of cooling rate is affected by a variable speed drive to the cooler.

It is important that the sinter should be screened before being transferred to the cooler, an operation which considerably increases the permeability of the mass, so reducing the power required for the suction fans. Screening before cooling also removes much of the dust so that the suction fan impellers are not subject to severely abrasive conditions.

Fig. 43 shows a typical arrangement of a circular sinter cooler.

COKE CRUSHING

For good sinter, it is essential that the coke breeze should be smaller than $\frac{1}{8}$ in. in particle size but it should not contain a high proportion smaller than 100 mesh. To secure this mesh size, especially with the varying moisture usually found in breeze, a rod mill is the most suitable apparatus. Coke is so abrasive that roll crushers set to crush as small as $\frac{1}{8}$ in. are quickly worn to give an irregular product containing much oversize. Abrasion in a rod mill results in reduction in diameter of the rods but this is quickly compensated by adding a proportion of new rods. The necessary weight of rods varies with the size of the mill; for example, a rod mill with drums 14 ft. long × 7 ft. 6 in. diameter requires a rod load of about 15 tons. As charged, rods are a mixture of $3\frac{1}{2}$ in. and 3 in. diameter but they wear down to less than 1 in. before being scrapped.

The principle of scalping before crushing is observed in the grinding of coke. In this case, a gas-heated screen is essential because wet coke breeze is an impossible screening proposition at the small mesh sizes involved.

Chapter VII

SINTER PLANT CONTROL

SINTER PLANT CONTROL

THE OPERATOR of a sintering plant has three main demands to satisfy.

1. *Production rate:* to provide the tonnage of sinter required at the blast furnace.

2. *Physical quality:* to produce sinter which will enable the furnace to operate at high rates of production.

3. *Chemical quality:* to produce sinter making possible the production of pig iron of the desired composition with the lowest possible coke consumption.

To satisfy these often conflicting demands is not easy. Generally, the stronger the desired sinter, the lower is the permissible production rate. It follows, therefore, that optimum operation is always a compromise obtained by using the several methods of control available. The plant should be designed to give maximum flexibility with a high degree of quickly applied control.

The following are the principal factors which are capable of being varied so as to establish a satisfactory basis of operation.

(Throughout, reference is made to continuous machines, but the principles are applicable to all types of sintering apparatus.)

(*a*) MACHINE SPEED

It is not possible to correlate output of furnace sinter and machine speed without reference to the production of return fines. An increase in machine speed is accompanied by a proportional increase in output only when there is no increase in the proportion of returns rejected by the screen. If the machine is operating near to the optimum sintering time, a faster speed may so reduce sintering time that increased amounts of returns will be produced from the weaker sinter.

(b) BED DEPTH

Changes in bed depth will be reflected in production rates because of the change in total resistance to air flow. A change in bed depth is another way of altering the sintering time.

(c) AIR VOLUME

The amount of air required per minute varies with other factors, but it is virtually constant when expressed as air per ton of sintering mixture.

(d) ADDED WATER

The permeability of the mixture, and therefore its resistance to air flow, is generally controlled by the amount of water added to the mixture.

(e) CARBON CONTENT OF THE MIXTURE

Too little carbon will lead to the production of soft dusty sinter, yielding a large amount of returns. Too much carbon will give a hard sinter but will demand a long sintering time. If the carbon in the mix is very excessive, sintering will not progress through the full depth of bed. Slagging of the mixture will occur because it has been held too long at sintering temperature and this will effectively seal off all air space, so bringing the process to a stop.

(f) RETURN FINES

Over a long period, usage of returns must be the same as production. Indeed, a major operational aim is to achieve this. But short-time changes may be made to influence the process. Generally speaking, an increase in returns added to the mixture will produce a harder sinter.

(g) IGNITION

The intensity of ignition can be varied by adjusting gas and air volumes. A weak ignition will lead to excessive dusting in the top part of the bed.

The above control factors ignore any changes in the characteristics of the mixture to be sintered. Change in particle size, in the amount of flue dust in the mixture, in the amount of volatile matter in the ores, etc. all have effects on operation. The combinations and permutations possible are so large in number that plant operation is never an easy matter.

APPLICATION OF CONTROLS

As a general principle, operators should aim to exercise sufficient control over all the variables involved to enable the sinter machine to operate at a constant speed. Steady operation is never possible unless this aim is met.

1. *Production rate:* When the required tonnage is known the necessary, strand speed should be calculated. This must take into account the amount of returns expected to be produced. Experience alone can give the basis for this calculation.

2. *Physical quality:* The definition of quality is a difficult matter. Each furnaceman has his own views and these depend on many factors connected with his practice and his raw materials. Three factors of importance apply to all sinters, however:

(*a*) Satisfactory size range, with the minimum proportion of fines.

(*b*) Sufficient mechanical strength to enable the sinter to withstand handling without major breakdown.

(*c*) Freedom from unsintered material.

For a given set of raw materials, sinter quality is principally affected by sintering time and by the amount of returns in the mixture. The necessary sintering time is primarily determined by tonnage demands, but it must be long enough to allow completion of sintering just before the product is discharged from the machine. Sintering time is mainly affected by:

(*a*) Permeability of the bed.

(*b*) Fuel content.

(*c*) Depth of bed.

The higher the permeability, the shorter will be the sintering time. But quality will suffer with high permeabilities if bed temperatures are too low or are not maintained for a sufficient length of time. With a given raw material mixture, permeability can only be controlled by water additions and by careful attention to the operation of the swinging spout or other device feeding the machine. If the feed line is too high, permeability will suffer as the mixture is squeezed below the levelling plate (*see* fig. 40).

The fuel content must be adequate to raise the mixture to a temperature at which the necessary amount of incipient fusion can take place.

Having established permeability and fuel, a bed height suitable for the available fan power can be decided. It is perhaps in regard to fan power that the operator requires the greatest operating margin. In designing the plant, ample fan power should always be provided.

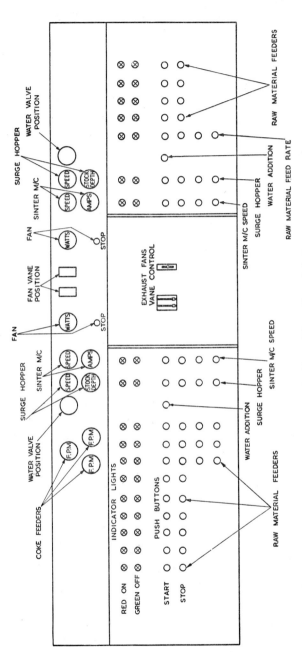

Fig. 44. Sinter Plant Control desk.

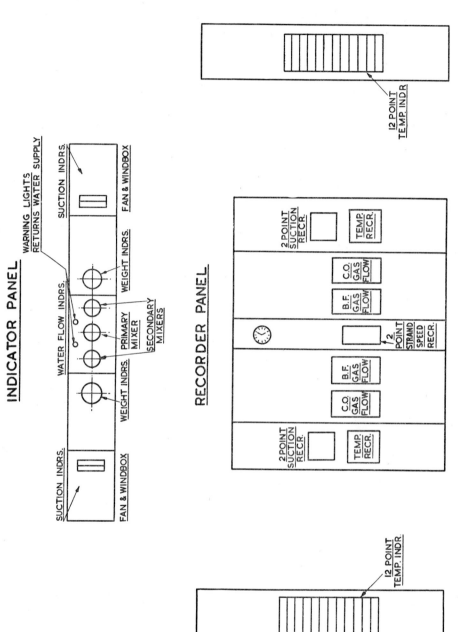

Fig. 45. Sinter Plant Instrument panel.

3. *Chemical quality:* This simply means that the correct proportions of the mixture constituents are fed to the machine at all times. Because of the well-known difficulties of maintaining uniform flow of fine ores, etc. from a feeder table, the amount of feed from each table should be checked at half-hourly intervals. This is usually done by allowing a tray of standard length to travel on the gathering belt so as to collect the total discharge from the table. The material in the tray is weighed on a spring balance. The mixture is usually ordered in pounds of each commodity, as measured by this simple tray method.

INSTRUMENTATION

Instruments may be broadly sub-divided into:

(*a*) *Operational instruments:* These are required for the minute-to-minute operation of the plant and are largely indicating instruments only.

(*b*) *Inquest instruments:* These are required as a check on personnel and to assist investigation of selected periods of operation. Recording instruments are used for obvious reasons. Figs. 44 and 45 show the arrangement of instruments and controls for a two-machine plant.

ROUTINE OPERATION

The layout of the control system should be such as to permit one man to control the process from the discharge of raw materials from the feeder table to discharge of the finished product from the end of the machine. This man cannot, of course, have visibility of the process at all stages, nor should he be expected to stop and start every item of plant in the flow line. But he should have sufficient control buttons within reach to stop or start the more important items. He should also have sufficient instruments to enable him to know what is happening and an efficient system of communication to permit him to receive information and then issue orders to any section of the process.

The major operational changes are dictated by instrument readings and instrumentation is becoming an increasingly important section of plant design.

Perhaps the best way of indicating how routine operational control is exercised is to quote freely from the standard operating procedures adopted at the plant equipped with the controls, etc. shown in figs. 44 and 45.

OPERATING PROCEDURE

1. The control room is to be manned at all times by the first operator, or in his absence, by the second operator.

2. Changes in sinter mixture (such as particle size, coke moisture, etc.) must be reported immediately.

3. Aim at continuity of operation. Any threat to this must be reported to the control room by the operator concerned.

4. The first step in securing continuity is to balance input to against output from the surge hoppers.

(a) Watching the surge hopper level indicators, alter the speed of the feeder table motor generator set to achieve a balance.

(b) Never stop individual feeds to maintain balance.

(c) Always leave enough room in the surge hopper to allow the belt system feeding it to be emptied in case it is necessary to stop the system after the surge hopper.

5. The second step in securing continuity is to balance surge hopper output against the consumption of the sinter machine.

(a) Watching the level of the feed below the swinging spout, use the speed control on the surge hopper table to maintain the top of the mixture on the machine at a level an inch or so above the cut-off plate.

(b) Ensure that the swinging spout and the back plate are cleaned regularly so that the feed is evenly distributed across the pallet.

6. Feeder tables must be started in the correct order so that no length of conveyor belt is devoid of any one constituent.

7. Changes in water additions at the primary mixer must only be made on instructions from the control room. Such changes are made to match other operational changes, such as an alteration in total raw material feed rate.

8. Other than momentary changes in surge hopper table speeds must be matched by changes in water flow to the secondary mixers.

9. The first operator must endeavour to maintain maximum permeability of the mixture. Observation of conditions under the ignition hood is a guide to this. He must adjust the water flow to the secondary mixers accordingly. Excess water (and therefore decreased permeability) will show by a deterioration in the quality of ignition or by a build-up of material in the swinging spout.

10. The highest wind box temperature should be attained at the penultimate wind box. If the peak temperature is reached earlier, the whole of the machine is not being used for sintering; if later, unsintered material will be discharged from the machine.

11. The main suction fan should be operating as near to full load as possible. This means that careful watch will have to be kept on the electrical load indicators.

12. Remember that the effects of a fan motor tripping out are felt for a much longer time than the actual stoppage.

13. Unless instructed by senior supervision, the operator must not alter the mixture proportions (excepting coke and water) or the bed height.

14. If the peak wind box temperature occurs earlier than the penultimate wind box, increased permeability is the probable cause.

(a) When this peak temperature is low (*e.g.* 250°C.) reduce the amount of water being added in the final mixer and then slightly increase the amount of coke. If this alteration results in an increase in the peak wind box temperature, and its transfer to the end of the machine, slightly increase the water addition to bring back the peak temperature to the penultimate wind box.

(b) Where the peak temperature is high (*e.g.* 400°C.) and earlier than the penultimate wind box, reduce the amount of air passing through the bed. Do not add coke or reduce water as either of these moves may lead to slagging or sticking of sinter to the grate bars. If the peak wind box temperature moves to the end of the machine, increase the amount of air passing through the bed before taking the next step (15).

15. If the peak wind box temperature occurs after the penultimate wind box, decreased permeability is the probable cause.

(a) If the peak temperature is high (*e.g.* 400°C.):
   (i) Reduce machine speed immediately by about 20 per cent. in case the bed is not sintering through.
   (ii) Increase water in the final mixer.
   (iii) Reduce coke slightly.

As the peak wind box temperature moves back to its proper position, steadily increase machine speed until normal speed is restored. If the correction is too drastic, reduce water slightly.

(b) If the peak temperature is low, and it moves to the discharge end of the machine, carry out the changes recommended above more drastically and inspect the discharge for signs of slagging.

16. A continuation of the reduced air flow recommended in 14b indicates that a compensatory increase in bed thickness may be necessary.

17. Should condition 15 persist, and the amount of coke is lower than normal, a decrease in bed thickness may be called for.

18. Whenever the coke feed is altered from the control room, the operator must ask the feeder table attendant to check the tray weight.

19. Changes in water and fuel often show in the appearance of the bed top below the ignition hood.

20. The level of the main returns bin (2000 tons) is to be reported each hour. A sudden change in level should be investigated immediately. An unexpected plant stoppage of some hours' duration may lead to a violent increase in the level of this bin. In this case, the proportion of returns in the mixture must be greatly increased. The new mixture should be sintered without altering the speed of the machine. When the bin level is again normal, restore normal operation.

21. Inspect the sinter cake at the discharge end at regular intervals to check for uniformity of sintering.

22. "Rat holes" in the sinter bed indicate broken grate bars, which should be changed at the earliest opportunity.

23. The gap between pallets at the discharge end must be checked each shift whilst the machine is operating normally. If the gap is greater than 9 in. or less than 5 in., it must be reported. (*N.B.*—This applies to machines 168 ft. long.)

24. Side boxes at the discharge end must be inspected and kept clear.

PLANT STOPPAGES

On any production plant, stoppages are at best a nuisance and almost always a costly item, but their effects are usually measured in relation to the actual time the plant is idle. But this is not the case on a sinter plant.

Every stoppage means a disturbance to the delicate balance of temperature, air flow and material mass which it is the aim of good operation to establish. The amount of air handled by the fan varies with the temperature (and therefore the density) of the air; a stoppage alters this temperature. Sintering entails the steady progression of various zones through the sinter bed; a stoppage distorts the usual pattern of these zones and this in turn distorts the pattern of air flow through the different wind boxes. The yield of furnace sinter, and therefore of return fines is affected. The effects of a stoppage lasting only a few minutes may be felt for hours. Certainly, one stoppage of two hours has far less harmful effect than six stoppages of ten minutes each.

Because of the effect of stoppages on the process, continuity of operation must be the basis of plant design. Design must be adapted to suit the particular needs of the materials to be processed and, in this respect, plants differ widely in their design requirements. The necessity to duplicate certain auxiliary items may arise on one plant but not on another simply because of differences in materials or operating hours.

The advantages of good initial plant design can only be perpetuated by efficient maintenance where the emphasis must be on scheduled replacement rather than "first aid" repair.

The effect of stoppages places a premium on efficient maintenance and on generous design. For example, if water additions are to be made in the mixer to secure high bed permeability, the risk of plugging or choking the mixer has to be accepted. A contingency of this nature appears to justify the provision of duplicate mixers, with facilities for changing from one to the other without closing down the sinter machine. To avoid spillage on conveyors, all belts should be wide enough to deal comfortably with more than the expected maximum flow rate. Pallet wheels should be grease-packed and each pallet serviced at scheduled intervals, to minimise the stoppages caused by frozen wheel bearings.

Chapter VIII

THEORY OF THE BLAST FURNACE – I

THE THEORY OF THE BLAST FURNACE

THE THEORY OF the blast furnace is extremely abstruse and is not yet fully explored. Understanding of what happens in a blast furnace demands knowledge of such sciences as thermo-dynamics, kinetics, chemistry, and physics, and the blast-furnace operator (to whom this chapter is specially addressed) is not, as a rule, expected to be a specialist in all these subjects. His principal preoccupation is to get as much good quality iron as possible from the furnace at the lowest possible cost. In Britain, coke is nearly always the most expensive component of the furnace burden, and as it is the one which usually gives the best chance of making savings, its efficient use is the most important study that the operator can undertake. Such a study involves consideration of the various thermal and chemical factors which affect the economics of ironmaking.

CHEMICAL REACTIONS IN THE BLAST FURNACE

The production of iron in the blast furnace is a thermo-chemical process, during which iron is produced from its oxides by a series of chemical reactions.

As it is intended to deal specially with the thermal aspect of furnace reactions it is desirable at this stage to consider how heat is generated and utilised and to define the factors used.

Various units are employed for measuring these reactions; metric units are frequently used in technical books, but as the blast-furnace-man is usually more familiar with British units, the unit of weight used here will be the pound, and the unit of heat, the British Thermal Unit. This unit (abbreviated to B.Th.U.) is the amount of heat which is required to raise the temperature of 1 lb. of water by 1°F.

It is well-known that heat is given off when the carbon contained in coal is burnt by the oxygen of the air in a firegrate. It is equally well-known that the application of carbon dioxide from a fire extinguisher will put the fire out. It is obvious, therefore, that the reaction between carbon and oxygen is of the type which produces heat, and the reaction between carbon and carbon dioxide of the type which absorbs heat. It is not so well known that all chemical reactions involve a transfer of heat either into or out of the system. For example, when iron (Fe) combines with oxygen (O) to form iron oxide (FeO) a certain amount of heat is given off for every unit of iron taking part in the reaction. Exactly the same amount of heat will have to be applied in order to decompose the same weight of this compound back into iron and oxygen. A list of the compounds which are decomposed in the blast furnace with the amounts of heat required for their decomposition appears in Table V.

TABLE V

DECOMPOSITION OF BLAST-FURNACE MATERIALS

Compound	Products of decomposition		Heat required for decomposition	Ref.
Ferric Oxide $2Fe_2O_3$	$4Fe$	$+3O_2$	3,162 B.Th.U./lb. Fe	1
Ferroso-Ferric Oxide Fe_3O_4	$3Fe$	$+2O_2$	2,870 B.Th.U./lb. Fe	1
Ferrous Oxide $2FeO$	$2Fe$	$+O_2$	2,051 B.Th.U./lb. Fe	1
Calcium Phosphate $(CaO)_3P_2O_5$	$3CaO$	$+P_2O_5$	4,761 B.Th.U./lb. P	2
Phosphorus Pent-oxide $2P_2O_5$	$4P$	$+5O_2$	10,451 B.Th.U./lb. P	1
Calcium Carbonate $CaCO_3$	CaO	$+CO_2$	1,738 B.Th.U./lb. CO_2	3
Manganous Oxide $2MnO$	$2Mn$	$+O_2$	3,012 B.Th.U./lb. Mn	1
Silica SiO_2	Si	$+O_2$	13,468 B.Th.U./lb. Si	1
Hydrated Iron Oxide $Fe_2O_3 H_2O$	Fe_2O_3	$+H_2O$ (liquid)	137 B.Th.U./lb. H_2O	8
Water $2H_2O$ (vapour)	$2H_2$	$+O_2$	5,780 B.Th.U./lb. H_2O	1
Water $2H_2O$	$2H_2$	$+O_2$	6,832 B.Th.U./lb. H_2O	1

None of the materials shown in Table V, with the exception of calcium carbonate and calcium phosphate can be decomposed in the blast furnace by heat alone. Their decomposition is brought about by a reducing agent, such as carbon, carbon monoxide, or hydrogen. Table VI lists the most important reactions occurring in the blast furnace and shows the amounts of heat which are given off or absorbed during the reactions.

TABLE VI

REACTIONS IN THE BLAST FURNACE

Reduction	Heat absorbed	Heat evolved	Ref.
$3Fe_2O_3 + CO = 2Fe_3O_4 + CO_2$		48 B.Th.U./lb. Fe_2O_3	
$Fe_3O_4 \ +CO =3FeO \ +CO_2$	68 B.Th.U./lb. Fe_3O_4		
$FeO \ \ +CO =Fe \ \ +CO_2$		95·5 B.Th.U./lb. FeO	
$FeO \ \ +C \ =Fe \ \ +CO$	862 B.Th.U./ lb. FeO		
$MnO \ +C \ =Mn \ +CO$	1,588 B.Th.U./ lb. MnO		
$P_2O_5 \ +5C =2P \ \ +5CO$	2,700 B.Th.U./ lb. P_2O_5		
$SiO_2 \ +2C =Si \ \ +2CO$	4,517 B.Th.U./ lb. SiO_2		
$FeO \ \ +H_2 =Fe \ \ +H_2O$	150 B.Th.U./ lb. FeO		
$H_2O \ \ +C \ =H_2 \ \ +CO$	2,842 B.Th.U./ lb. H_2O		
$2H_2O +C \ =2H_2 \ +CO$ (vapour)	930 B.Th.U./ lb. H_2O		
Combustion $C \ \ \ \ \ \ +O_2 =CO_2$ (coke)		14,550 B.Th.U./ lb. C	4
$C \ \ \ \ \ \ +CO_2=2CO$ (coke)	5,735 B.Th.U./ lb. C		4
$C \ \ \ \ \ \ +\frac{1}{2}O_2 =CO$ (coke)		4,407 B.Th.U./ lb. C	4
Solution Phosphorus in Iron	—	2,858 B.Th.U./ lb. P	3
Manganese in Iron	—	Nil	
Silicon in Iron	—	1,832 B.Th.U./ lb. Si	3
Carbon in Iron	1,800 B.Th.U./ lb. C		3

Reactions which give off heat are called "exothermic" and those which absorb heat are called "endothermic". Most of the reactions required to produce iron from iron ore are endothermic and therefore require a constant application of heat, which is generated by the combustion of coke.

It will be noticed that the reaction heats shown for the same compounds differ in Tables V and VI. This is because Table V simply shows the heat required for decomposition, no matter how this is achieved. In Table VI, the actual means of decomposition is shown, for example:

$$MnO+C=Mn+CO.$$

In this reaction, the normal amount of heat is required to decompose the manganous oxide, but heat is also generated by the conversion of carbon to carbon monoxide. The various heats involved are shown in the following example:

Equation 1 $2MnO=2Mn+O_2$, heat absorbed 331,019 B.Th.U.
Equation 2 $2C+O_2=2CO$, heat generated 105,768 B.Th.U.

The sum of the two equations is

$2MnO+2C=2Mn+2CO$, heat absorbed 225,251 B.Th.U.

The heat absorbed in equation 1 is 3012 B.Th.U. per lb. of manganese and the equation represents twice the atomic weight of manganese in pounds, i.e., 2×54.93. The total heat absorbed is therefore:

$$3012 \times 2 \times 54.93 = 331,019 \text{ B.Th.U.}$$

The heat generated in equation 2 is 4407 B.Th.U. per lb. of carbon and the equation represents twice the atomic weight of carbon in pounds, i.e., 2×12. The total heat generated is therefore:

$$4407 \times 2 \times 12 = 105,768 \text{ B.Th.U.}$$

When the two equations are added, the total heat absorbed is:

$$331,019 - 105,768 = 225,251 \text{ B.Th.U.}$$

As the sum of the reactions represents the decomposition of twice the pound molecule of manganous oxide, i.e., $2(54.93+16) = 141.86$ lb., the heat absorbed per lb. of manganous oxide is:

$$225,251 \div 141.86 = 1588 \text{ B.Th.U. per lb. of MnO.}$$

CHEMICAL REACTIONS AND EQUILIBRIUM

Some of the reactions are reversible, as, for example, that involving carbon, carbon monoxide and carbon dioxide.

Reaction in such a system can take two forms:

$$C+CO_2=2CO$$
$$2CO=C+CO_2.$$

These two reactions are directly opposed to each other, but they can proceed simultaneously.

If carbon is heated with carbon dioxide to a constant temperature in a closed vessel so that the gaseous products of reaction stay in contact with the reacting carbon, carbon monoxide will be produced rapidly by the reaction $C+CO_2=2CO$. At the same time, carbon dioxide will be produced slowly by the reaction $2CO=C+CO_2$. As the percentage of carbon monoxide in the gaseous mixture rises, the speed of its production will lessen and the speed of carbon dioxide production will increase. All reaction will finally appear to stop when the rates of production of carbon monoxide and carbon dioxide are equal.

Such a condition is described as a "state of equilibrium" and, as long as no external change takes place, the system will remain unchanged in its chemical composition, *i.e.*, it will consist of a certain percentage of CO and a certain percentage of CO_2.

The external changes which can influence such reversible reactions to proceed in one direction or the other are the temperature, pressure and the concentration of the two gases.

The proportions of CO and CO_2 have been calculated for all conditions of temperature, pressure, and concentration. Fig. 46 shows the equilibrium of the system at the pressure of the atmosphere ($14·7$ lb. per sq. in.)

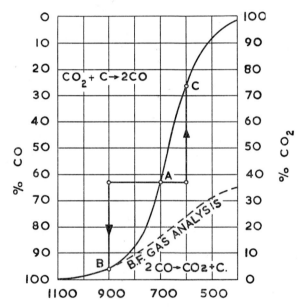

Fig. 46. *Equilibrium of the C. CO. CO_2 system (P—1 Atm.) (after W. Gumz, Gas Producers & Blast Furnaces. John Wiley & Sons.)*

This shows that at $700°$C. (Point A) the gas will contain 63 per cent. CO and 37 per cent. CO_2. At $900°$C. (Point B) the gas composition is 96 per cent. CO and 4 per cent. CO_2. An increase in temperature from

700°C. to 900°C. would put the system out of equilibrium and increase the speed of CO production:

$$C+CO_2=2CO.$$

This reaction would continue at slower and slower rates until the gas contained 96 per cent. CO and 4 per cent. CO_2 and at this point the speeds of production of CO and CO_2 would again be equal, *i.e.*, a state of equilibrium would be restored. A reduction in temperature to 600°C. would increase the CO_2 production rate until the gas contained 26 per cent. CO and 74 per cent. CO_2 when equilibrium would be re-established.

Thus, under equilibrium conditions, gas composition is fixed for any given temperature and pressure. If the system at 700°C., containing 63 per cent. CO and 37 per cent. CO_2 (*i.e.* in equilibrium), is disturbed by the introduction of CO_2 from an outside source, increasing CO_2 concentration to say 70 per cent., equilibrium will be re-established by the reaction:

$$CO_2+C=2CO,$$

the reaction ceasing when the proportion of CO_2 has fallen to 37 per cent.

Table V shows that the reaction

$$C+CO_2=2CO$$

is endothermic and the reaction

$$2CO=C+CO_2$$

is exothermic.

It has been shown that a temperature increase will promote the first of these reactions, *i.e.*, the endothermic one, and a temperature decrease will promote the exothermic reaction. This is so for all such chemical reactions, as laid down in Van't Hoff's law, which asserts that a rise in temperature promotes the formation of those products which are formed with an absorption of heat; a fall in temperature promotes the formation of products which are formed with an evolution of heat. In other words, if a reaction needs heat, the provision of that heat (by a rise in temperature) will promote it—and *vice versa*.

The law governing the effect of pressure shows the same kind of submission to outside influence, as an increase in pressure favours a reaction which produces a decrease in volume and *vice versa*.

Thus, the carbon, carbon monoxide, carbon dioxide reaction is influenced by pressure, as two volumes of carbon monoxide are produced from one volume of carbon dioxide. Increased pressure naturally resists increasing volume and causes the reaction to proceed in the direction of CO_2 formation and lower volume:

$$2CO=C+CO_2.$$

The conditions which govern the reaction can therefore be summed up as follows:

$$C+CO_2=2CO$$

is promoted by

(a) an increased temperature,
(b) a decreased pressure,
(c) a high ratio of CO_2 to CO,

and the reverse reaction

$$2CO=C+CO_2$$

is promoted by

(a) a decreased temperature,
(b) an increased pressure,
(c) a high ratio of CO to CO_2.

The range of pressure, temperature, and concentration of reaction components in the blast furnace is very wide. At the tuyeres, the burning coke releases gas at temperatures between 1900°C. and 2000°C. which passes out of the furnace top at 150–350°C. within a few seconds. The pressure at the furnace tuyeres may be as high as 35 lb. per sq. in. while at the top it has fallen to about 2 lb. per sq. in. The gas at the tuyeres consists entirely of carbon monoxide (nitrogen neglected) while at the furnace top the ratio of CO to CO_2 has fallen to about 2 to 1.

Within these wide limits of temperature, pressure, and concentration, reactions can and do proceed in contrary directions in different zones in the furnace.

REACTION RATES

It must not be assumed that chemical reactions automatically proceed until a state of equilibrium is reached. Equilibrium is the final state and all reactions proceed in that direction, but time is required for the transfer of the reaction components. For example, in the reaction

$$C+CO_2=2CO$$

the carbon monoxide formed must diffuse away in order to allow further carbon dioxide to come into contact with carbon.

Reaction velocities are influenced by such factors as speed of gas flow, particle size, temperature, contact time and how far a system is from equilibrium. If in the carbon, carbon monoxide, carbon dioxide system the gas mixture at a given temperature and pressure contains 90 per cent. CO_2 and 10 per cent. CO, and the equilibrium mixture for that temperature and pressure is 20 per cent. CO_2 and 80 per cent. CO, then the velocity of the reaction

$$CO_2+C=2CO$$

will be high. If, however, the gas analysis is little removed from equilibrium, say 25 per cent. CO_2 and 75 per cent. CO, CO will be produced quite slowly until the gas contains the required 80 per cent.

Reactions in the blast furnace rarely attain equilibrium. This is apparent from fig. 46 where the line showing the probable gas analysis at various temperatures only coincides with the equilibrium line of C, CO, CO_2 at the high temperature of the furnace hearth and bosh. At this temperature, the reaction velocity is very high and any carbon dioxide is immediately converted to carbon monoxide. As the gas temperature falls, reaction velocities also fall. The velocity of the gas through the furnace is extremely high; gas produced at the tuyeres passes out of the furnace top in a few seconds. Radio-active tracers introduced into the furnace tuyeres[5] and detected in the outflowing gas gave transit times of 3 to 7 seconds. At such a high velocity, contact time between gas and solid in the cooler parts of the furnace is too short for equilibrium to be attained.

REACTIONS OCCURRING IN THE BLAST FURNACE

The heat necessary to carry out the process of smelting the ores and to raise the resultant iron and slag to temperatures at which they will flow freely from the furnace is generated in front of the tuyeres by combustion of the carbon in the coke in a stream of preheated air. The carbon dioxide resulting from this combustion cannot exist in contact with carbon at the temperature of the furnace hearth and is almost immediately converted to carbon monoxide.

The gas rising from the tuyere zone contains carbon monoxide from carbon combustion, nitrogen from the air blast and a small amount of hydrogen from the reduction of the blast moisture

$$H_2O + C = H_2 + CO.$$

The temperature of the gas at the moment of complete combustion at the tuyeres is between 1900°C. and 2000°C. according to the temperature and the degree of humidity of the blast. As the gas rises from the tuyeres, it meets and imparts most of its heat to the descending stock and leaves the furnace at a temperature of the order of 150–350°C. At the same time, the gas undergoes chemical changes as it passes through the stock.

In order to follow the chemical and physical changes in the gas and stock it is convenient to divide the furnace into two zones. The furnace stack can be called the preparation zone and the hearth and bosh, the smelting zone. It must be realised, of course, that it is quite impossible to draw a sharp dividing line between the two zones because temperature levels are continually fluctuating and the functions of the two zones tend to overlap.

THE PREPARATION ZONE

The function of the preparation zone is to deliver materials to the smelting zone at a temperature and in a state of reduction suitable for final smelting. The temperature of the stock must be raised from atmospheric temperature to one at which the slag and iron will begin to melt, and iron oxide must also be reduced. It is not possible to give the precise order in which the stack reactions occur as most of them have a temperature range within which there are large variations. Table VII, taken from an unpublished work by Dawes and Ridgion of the British Iron and Steel Research Association, gives the probable temperature ranges of these reactions.

TABLE VII

	$°C.$
Removal of Moisture	100
Removal of Combined Water	100– 800
$Fe_2O_3 + CO = 2FeO + CO_2$	400– 700
$2CO = CO_2 + C$	450– 650
$FeO + CO = Fe + CO_2$	700– 800
$C + CO_2 = 2CO$	700–1000
$CaCO_3 = CaO + CO_2$	800–1000
$(CaO)_3 P_2O_5 + C = 3CaO + P_2 + 5CO$	900–1000
Carbon Solution in iron	1000–1500
$FeO + C = Fe + CO$	1200–1400
Phosphorus Solution in Iron	1200–1500
Slag Reactions	1300
$MnO + C = Mn + CO$	1350–1450
$SiO_2 + 2C = Si + 2CO$	1400–1500
Silicon Solution in Iron	1400–1500

The table shows the different functions of the rising stack gas. The volatile matter of the burden—moisture, combined water from hydrated iron oxide, carbon dioxide from limestone or any carbonate ore charged—is removed as the temperature rises. Iron oxide, usually in the form of Fe_2O_3 or Fe_3O_4 is reduced, through the FeO stage, to Fe. Calcium phosphate is decomposed and the resultant P_2O_5 reduced to phosphorus. This phosphorus and some carbon are dissolved in the iron which is liquefying at this stage. In the lower part of the preparation zone, the slag reactions occur and primary slag is produced.

THE SMELTING ZONE

There should be no solid material except coke in the hearth and bosh. The melting iron and slag, only partially separated, trickle through the bed of incandescent coke and any remaining iron oxide is reduced by the coke carbon:

$$FeO + C = Fe + CO.*$$

Silica, which requires a temperature of 1400 to 1500°C. for reduction, is probably reduced by coke carbon in this zone:

$$SiO_2 + 2C = Si + 2CO.*$$

The silicon resulting from this reaction is dissolved in the iron.

The amount of silicon involved depends on the temperature and basicity of the slag—a hot silicious slag will tend to increase the silicon in the iron.

Manganese is also reduced from manganous oxide by carbon in this high temperature zone:

$$MnO + C = Mn + CO.*$$

Some 50–70 per cent. of the manganese is reduced and passes into the iron. The proportion of the manganese in the iron is dependent on the slag temperature and basicity—a hot limey slag will encourage reduction of manganous oxide.

The iron and slag then pass through the zone of coke combustion—the hottest part of the furnace—and are raised to the temperature at which they will flow freely from the notches, i.e. 1350°C. to 1450°C.

Sulphur readily combines with iron—in fact, iron oxide is used to absorb sulphur in some desulphurising processes. Sulphur in the ore may be present as a sulphide or as calcium sulphate, the latter being reduced to sulphide by carbon at high temperature. The sulphur in the coke, which represents the major portion of the sulphur in the furnace, is usually in the form of iron sulphide. Whatever its source, the sulphide will dissolve in the iron and can only be removed by contact with slag in the presence of carbon at the highest temperature of the hearth:

$$FeS + CaO + C = Fe + CaS + CO.$$

Desulphurisation is never complete, some iron sulphide always remaining dissolved in the iron. The controlling factors are high temperature and high slag basicity. Most of the sulphur probably passes from the iron into the slag as the drops of iron trickle through the slag layer.

* It is, of course, possible that these are examples of the kind of indirect/direct reduction discussed on pages 116–118.

THE REDUCTION OF IRON OXIDES

The nitrogen in the gas arising from the tuyeres is almost chemically inert but serves to carry heat to the stock. The small amount of hydrogen produced from the decomposition of the blast moisture acts as a reducing agent, taking oxygen from iron oxide:

$$FeO + H_2 = Fe + H_2O,$$

but the water produced again reverts to hydrogen by the action of incandescent coke:

$$H_2O + C = H_2 + CO.$$

This is one form of "direct reduction" (*i.e.* reduction by solid carbon) as the summation of the two reactions is:

$$FeO + C = Fe + CO$$

and the hydrogen is free to go through the same cycle of events again. The final stage of such cycles is probably:

$$2H_2O + C = 2H_2 + CO_2.$$

This reaction takes place at lower temperatures in the furnace stack. All hydrogen produced at the tuyeres eventually passes out of the furnace as hydrogen. The thermo-chemical principle is that the net heat evolved or absorbed in a chemical process is the same whether the reaction takes place in one or several stages. Therefore, the intermediate reactions in the furnace involving hydrogen can be ignored.

So carbon is the basis of all the reduction reactions taking place in the furnace, either in the form of solid carbon (the so-called "direct reduction") or after combustion to carbon monoxide (the so-called "indirect reduction").

Direct reduction: $FeO + C = Fe + CO$

Indirect reduction: $FeO + CO = Fe + CO_2$

In 1870, Gruner[6] asserted that for maximum thermal efficiency all the carbon charged into the furnace should reach the tuyeres unaltered and that all the reduction of iron compounds should be effected by carbon monoxide produced by the combustion of carbon at the tuyeres. This is known as "Gruner's theorem" and is based on the fact that reduction by carbon monoxide is an exothermic reaction and reduction by solid carbon is endothermic. Moreover, any solid carbon used for reduction fails to reach the tuyeres and takes no part in heat generation.

Since Gruner's time many blast-furnace operators and research workers have expressed their views on this subject, some of them agreeing with the "theorem" and others maintaining that better thermal efficiency can be attained by departing from this "ideal working".

It is outside the province of this book to argue this question, the author having already expressed his view[7] that the furnace operator has very little influence over the amount of direct reduction taking place, except by thorough burden preparation, which is advocated here for a different reason. It is, however, necessary to know exactly what is meant by the terms "direct" and "indirect".

One of the most important furnace reactions involving carbon is the reversible reaction

$$CO_2 + C = 2CO$$

which has already been mentioned.

At temperatures above 700°C. the reaction proceeds to the right, *i.e.* carbon dioxide "dissolves" carbon and produces carbon monoxide. This reaction is usually referred to as "Solution Loss" which implies that the carbon involved is prevented from reaching the tuyeres and thus fails to reach its highest thermal efficiency.

At temperatures below 650°C. the reaction proceeds in the reverse direction in the presence of a suitable catalyst (such as iron or iron oxide) and carbon monoxide is dissociated into carbon dioxide and carbon, the carbon being deposited on the catalyst. With a dense ore burden the carbon will be deposited on the surface of the ore, but a porous ore can become impregnated with carbon to such an extent that swelling and, finally, complete breakdown occurs.

This reversible reaction has a profound effect on iron oxide reduction. As the gas leaving the tuyere zone rises through the furnace the reactions which proceed until the 700°C. temperature zone is reached are, first:

$$FeO + CO = Fe + CO_2.$$

Here carbon dioxide, being unstable in the presence of carbon in this temperature range, reacts with solid carbon

$$CO_2 + C = 2CO.$$

The summation of the two reactions gives

$$FeO + C = Fe + CO.$$

Although this is known as "direct" reduction, it has been brought about in a most indirect way, involving indirect reduction and carbon solution.

Carbon dioxide is produced from the decomposition of carbonates in the temperature range 800°C. to 1000°C. and is thus liable to dissolve carbon and reach the 700°C. zone as carbon monoxide. In this case, however, although carbon has been dissolved, the carbon concerned has taken no part in the reduction of oxides nor in the generation of hearth heat.

When the gas temperature has fallen to 650°C. the carbon deposition reaction occurs at an increasing rate and is at a maximum at about 450°C. When the ore is porous enough to become impregnated with carbon it is fairly certain that some reaction will take place between the carbon and iron oxide when the burden has descended to higher temperature zones. The iron oxide will be reduced and the resulting iron may be carburised. This type of reduction can hardly be called direct in the accepted sense of the term, as "direct" reduction always implies loss of carbon. In this case, the carbon which takes part in the reaction arises from the carbon monoxide generated at the tuyeres. The two equations

$$2CO = CO_2 + C$$
$$C + FeO = Fe + CO$$

can be expressed as

$$2CO + FeO = Fe + CO + CO_2.$$

Thus, the carbon arriving at the carbon deposition zone has reduced iron oxide with the production of CO_2 and no loss of carbon is involved.

It is improbable that much reduction by solid carbon takes place in any other way except for a small amount in the furnace hearth. There can only be surface contact between coke and solid ore and the gaseous-solid contact is so much better that it is reasonable to suppose that reaction between solids goes on only to a very limited extent. Contact between liquid iron and slag and the coke occurs in the bosh and hearth of the furnace where molten products trickle through the bed of incandescent coke. Here, any unreduced iron oxides will be deoxidised and silica, which requires a higher temperature for reduction, will be reduced by coke carbon, the resultant silicon dissolving in the iron.

Reduction by carbon monoxide at temperatures below 650°C.:

$$Fe_2O_3 + 3CO = 2Fe + 3CO_2$$

is an indirect reduction involving no loss of carbon, as the carbon dioxide is produced in the temperature range in which it is quite stable.

To sum up, it can be stated that:

(1) Reduction which takes place at temperatures higher than 800°C. (*i.e.* in the temperature range in which carbon dioxide is unstable in the presence of carbon) may become "direct" and prevent carbon from reaching the tuyeres.

(2) Reduction by carbon monoxide at temperatures below 650°C. is "indirect" and involves no loss of carbon.

(3) Reduction by deposited carbon involves no loss of carbon at the tuyeres.

REFERENCES

[1] *Contributions to the Data on Theoretical Metallurgy Part XII—Heats and Free Energies of Formation of Inorganic Compounds.* Bulletin 542 U.S. Bureau of Mines.

[2] "Thermodynamics of Substances of Interest in Iron and Steel Making from 0°C. to 2400°C. II. Compounds between Oxides", by F. D. Richardson, J. H. E. Jeffes and G. Withers. *J. Iron & Steel Inst.,* 1950, 213.

[3] "Thermodynamic Background of Iron and Steel Making Processes", by F. D. Richardson and J. H. E. Jeffes. *J. Iron & Steel Inst.,* 1949, 397.

[4] *Chemical Process Principles,* by O. A. Hougen and K. M. Watson. J. Wiley & Sons, Inc.

[5] "A Radioactive Technique for Determining Gas Transit Times in a Driving Blast Furnace", by E. W. Voice. *J. Iron & Steel Inst.,* 1949, 312.

[6] *Studies of Blast Furnace Phenomena* (English translation), by M. L. Gruner. Henry S. King & Co., London, 1873.

[7] *Iron & Steel Institue Special Report No. 30,* 227–230.

[8] *Warmewirtschaft, 1947.* V. D. E. Warmestelle, Dusseldorf.

Chapter IX

THEORY OF THE BLAST FURNACE – II

FUEL UTILISATION

THE BLAST FURNACE REQUIRES a minimum amount of heat compatible with making a ton of iron and its accompanying slag, heating these products to a free-flowing temperature, driving off all the volatile matter of the charge and providing for the heat which will be lost in the outflowing gas, in the cooling water and into the surrounding atmosphere. This heat, as has already been said, must be supplied by the burning coke and the heat of the blast.

Suppose the heat required is 12,000,000 B.Th.U., a convenient round figure, of which 2,000,000 can be supplied as blast heat. The remaining 10,000,000 B.Th.U. must be generated by burning the carbon of the coke. But there is more than one way of doing this. Table VI shows that 1 lb. of carbon burnt to carbon dioxide produces 14,550 B.Th.U., but only 4407 B.Th.U. when burnt to carbon monoxide. It is clear that if all the carbon is burnt to carbon dioxide, about 690 lb. will be enough to generate the 10,000,000 B.Th.U., but if burnt to carbon monoxide, about 2260 lb. of carbon will be required. Of course, the blast furnace will not produce a gas with all the carbon present as either carbon monoxide or carbon dioxide—there will be some mixture of the two.

In order that the blast-furnace gas can reduce the iron oxides of the burden, however, there must be preponderance of carbon monoxide. The limiting ratio is given by Colclough[1] as 1·86 to 1, *i.e.* 65 per cent. of carbon monoxide to 35 per cent. of carbon dioxide. At this ratio, 1 lb. of carbon would generate 7968 B.Th.U. so that the 10,000,000 B.Th.U. required would need 1257 lb. of carbon.

Nitrogen and hydrogen make up about 60 per cent. of the gas, leaving 40 per cent. of carbon monoxide and carbon dioxide combined. The 1·86 to 1 ratio quoted above gives 14 per cent. CO_2 and 26 per cent. CO, a ratio not achieved in many ironworks. There are many reasons why furnaces fail to produce such CO/CO_2 ratios—and the low coke ratios which go with them.

The burden for a given furnace contains a proportion of oxygen which does not vary much. This oxygen must be removed by the action of either carbon or carbon monoxide. If the ore is easily reducible, or

crushed to a size suitable to its particular reducibility, a large proportion of the oxygen will be removed by carbon monoxide, producing
carbon dioxide to improve the CO/CO_2 ratio of the gas. If the ore is
only reduced with difficulty (*i.e.* slowly) or charged in such large lumps
that the gas cannot penetrate to the centre of the lumps in the upper
part of the furnace, reduction may be by carbon, producing carbon
monoxide which will not improve the CO/CO_2 ratio.

Another common cause of poor gas ratios and high coke rates is poor
gas-solid contact in the furnace stack. If the distribution of the gas over
the cross-sectional area of the furnace is bad, a large proportion travelling up the furnace centre and little up the wall, the gas velocity in the
centre may be so high that little of the work of reduction can be carried
out and most of the CO generated at the tuyeres is still CO at the
stockline. The furnace stock will reach the hearth insufficiently prepared
and an unnecessarily large quantity of coke will have to be burnt
because the hearth must carry out work which should have been done
in the stack.

If the furnace burden is badly prepared for smelting or the size range
of the materials charged is too wide, this condition will certainly arise.

Any steps that can be taken to encourage a more uniform distribution
of gas over the cross-sectional area of the furnace will have the effect of
reducing the gas velocity and allowing more time for gaseous reduction.
The stock will be more uniformly prepared for final smelting and there
will be less likelihood of relatively cold unprepared material reaching
the hearth.

The most effective measure that can be taken to avoid segregation at
the stockline, utilise the whole cross-sectional area of the furnace, improve the CO/CO_2 in the gas, and reduce the coke rate per ton of iron,
is complete and effective ore preparation. The whole of the furnace
burden should be converted into self-fluxing sinter (any limestone
required for fluxing being added in the sinter plant) and the sinter
should be screened into two size ranges and charged in separate layers.

THE EFFECT OF USING SELF-FLUXING SINTER ON OUTPUT AND COKE RATE

Segregation at the stockline can be reduced to a minimum by crushing the ore to the correct size, screening out and sintering the fines and
charging the sinter and rough ore correctly (*see* section on "Distribution"). But the charging of a burden composed wholly of self-fluxing
sinter brings economies that can be achieved in no other way.

Essentially, sinter is composed of iron oxide crystals set in a silicate
matrix. The matrix is chemically similar to, although slightly more

basic than the resultant blast-furnace slag in an all-sinter practice. In other words, sinter is practically an iron-bearing preformed blast-furnace slag. The lime, silica, alumina, and magnesia are already in a state of combination, and therefore more easily smelted than the normal burden of ore and limestone. Self-fluxing sinter made from the Jurassic ores of Britain begins to soften in the furnace at just over 1000°C. and is fully melted at 1150°C. The "sticky" zone in the furnace caused by the resistance to gas flow of the partly melted burden is therefore short. The same ores, unsintered, begin to soften at about 800°C., but are not completely melted until they reach a temperature of about 1250°C. and have fluxed the calcined limestone. The "sticky" zone is obviously longer and gas flow will not be so free as with the sinter burden.

Good sinter is porous and of irregular shape and, after suitable screening, has a close size range. The ratio of surface area to weight is high. Good voidage is provided for the gas stream and heat absorption and reduction is efficient and rapid. Unlike many ores, sinter does not break down to powder under the action of carbon monoxide and therefore maintains an "open" burden all the way through the furnace stack.

The volatile matter in ore and limestone (carbon dioxide, combined water and moisture) requires heat for its evolution, and this evolution lowers the gas temperature and retards reduction. The carbon dioxide released from the ore or limestone is harmful in the furnace as it either dissolves carbon, preventing it from reaching the tuyeres, or, by dilution impairs the reducing property of the gas at the temperature levels at which a preponderance of carbon monoxide is most needed.

Sinter contains practically no volatile matter and for this reason alone the heat demand can be 15 to 20 per cent. less than with an ore/limestone burden.

All these factors lead to a saving in the coke rate per ton of iron. Part of the coke saved has, of course, already been used in the sintering plant, but the coke used for sintering is not metallurgical coke fit for the blast furnace—rather is it the coke discarded by the coke oven and blast-furnace screens. Moreover, it is more efficiently used in the sinter plant, being wholly converted to carbon dioxide generating 14,550 B.Th.U. per lb. of carbon, whereas in the furnace, even at the 1·86 ratio cited above, it will only generate 7968 B.Th.U. per lb.

Apart from the reduced cost of total coke per ton of iron, the principal benefit of the practice is greater furnace output.

If a furnace is capable under optimum conditions of burning 1000 tons of coke per day, a coke rate of 20 cwt. per ton will produce 1000 tons of iron. A saving of 10 per cent. in the coke rate will increase the iron make for the same amount of coke burnt to 1111 tons per day.

TABLE VIII
COMPARISON OF THERMAL BALANCES

	All-sinter burden $B.Th.U. \times 10^6$	%	Non-sinter burden $B.Th.U. \times 10^6$	%	Gain in sinter practice $B.Th.U. \times 10^6$
Heat generated					
Carbon burnt to carbon dioxide	5·820	48·59	6·577	38·36	
Carbon burnt to carbon monoxide	4·147	34·62	7·521	43·85	
Solution of silicon	0·029	0·24	0·058	0·34	
Solution of phosphorus	0·081	0·68	0·100	0·58	
Sensible heat of moist air	1·901	15·87	2·262	13·19	
Formation of slag	—	—	0·632	3·68	
Total	11·978	100·00	17·150	100·00	5·172
Heat expended					
For metal: Reduction of Oxides	6·546	54·65	6·791	39·60	
Decomposition of calcium phosphate	0·135	1·13	0·168	0·98	
Solution of carbon	0·151	1·26	0·149	0·87	
Sensible heat of iron	1·225	10·23	1·222	7·13	
Total	8·057	67·27	8·330	48·58	0·273
For slag: Sensible heat of slag	2·050	17·11	2·060	12·01	
Evolution of volatile matter					
Decomposition of calcium carbonate	0·035	0·29	0·678	3·95	
Decomposition of iron carbonate	—	—	0·115	0·67	
Decomposition of hydrated iron oxide	0·004	0·03	0·130	0·76	
Decomposition of burden moisture	0·062	0·52	1·004	5·86	
Evaporation of burden moisture	0·155	1·29	2·083	12·14	
Total	0·256	2·13	4·010	23·38	3·754
Sensible heat of dry gas	0·807	6·73	1·032	6·02	0·225
Decomposition of blast moisture	0·236	1·97	0·300	1·74	0·064
Heat loss in cooling water	0·550	4·59	1·270	7·41	0·720
Unaccounted for loss	0·022	0·18	0·148	0·86	
Grand total	11·978	100·00	17·150	100·00	

THE THERMAL BALANCE

Thermal balances (*i.e.* statements of heat generated and heat consumed in the furnace) drawn up for self-fluxing ore practice and for a practice using the same ores sintered are shown in Table VIII. The calculations have been carried out as accurately as possible and the figures rounded off to the nearest 1000 B.Th.U. in the final balance sheet. (It must not be assumed that the nearness of the balances is a measure of their accuracy. As determined by this method the unaccounted for loss may be as much as 250,000 B.Th.U.) A comparison of the two balances clearly shows the savings outlined above. (The details of the calculation appear in Chapter X.)

HEAT EXPENDED

Heat required for metal

The heat required for the reduction of oxides depends on the state of oxidation of the iron in the burden and the quality of the metal produced. Sintering has little effect on the degree of oxidation, but the sinter burden facilitates the production of low sulphur and low silicon iron.

The sulphur input to the furnace is much reduced by the use of sinter, because of the desulphurisation which occurs in the sintering process, and, what is more important, the lower rate of coke per ton of iron.

The sulphur inputs in the two cases were:

Sinter burden

| Net sinter | .. | .. | .. | 5630 lb. at 0·230 % S = 12·95 lb. |
| Net coke | .. | .. | .. | 1671 lb. at 1·300 % S = 21·72 lb. |

Total sulphur input = 34·67 lb.

Non-sinter burden

Net limey ore ..	..	..	3864 lb. at 0·315 % S = 12·20 lb.
Net siliceous ore	..	..	4034 lb. at 0·170 % S = 6·85 lb.
Net coke	..	..	..	2644 lb. at 1·300 % S = 34·30 lb.

Total sulphur input = 53·35 lb.

In the former case, 96·5 per cent. of the sulphur (*i.e.* 33·46 lb.) went into the slag, giving an average sulphur content in the iron of 0·054 per cent. In the latter case, only 94·5 per cent. of the sulphur (*i.e.* 50·44 lb.)

went into the slag and the iron contained 0·13 per cent. In order to keep the sulphur down to this figure, the furnace had to be unduly hot and the silicon rose to 1·40 per cent. Thus, the heat demand for the reduction of silicon was twice as great as for the sinter burden.

HEAT REQUIRED FOR THE EVOLUTION OF VOLATILE MATTER

Most of the volatile matter of the ores is driven off in the sintering process and the saving in furnace heat demand for this item is considerable when smelting sinter. The evolution of volatile matter required only 2·13 per cent. of the total heat consumption in the case of the sinter burden and 23·38 per cent. for the non-sinter burden.

OTHER ITEMS

Although the top gas temperature was higher when smelting sinter, the much lower volume of gas produced resulted in a reduction of heat demand for this item. The lower heat required for the decomposition of blast moisture with the sinter burden was the result of the lower coke rate and the consequent lower volume of air blown per ton of iron.

The heat loss in the cooling water is practically a constant value per unit of time irrespective of the amount of iron produced; on a furnace with a given blast volume, therefore, the heat loss is proportionate to the coke rate per ton of iron. The sinter burden, with its lower coke rate and higher output of iron, considerably reduces the heat loss per ton of iron.

HEAT GENERATED

The sinter burden shows a saving of over 5,000,000 B.Th.U. With the non-sinter burden, the solution of greater amounts of silicon and phosphorus and the formation of the slag provide some of the extra heat; the total heat from the blast, although at a lower temperature, was greater owing to a greater volume of blast, but a large proportion of the additional heat had to be provided by burning an extra 649 lb. of coke.

It is noteworthy that the amount of heat generated per lb. of carbon varies considerably in the two cases. With the sinter burden, the heat raised from 1346 lb. of coke carbon gasified was 9,967,000 B.Th.U., equivalent to 7400 B.Th.U. per lb. The 2314 lb. of coke carbon gasified when using ore raised 14,098,000 B.Th.U., or 6100 B.Th.U. per lb. The reason for this difference is obvious. The heat demand in the hearth and bosh is similar in the two cases, but the residual heat of the gas at the top of the bosh must be greater with the non-sinter burden because of the greater heat demand for the evolution of volatiles in the stack. The extra heat is generated by burning extra coke, principally to carbon monoxide, and most of this is used as a heat conveyor only and passes out of the furnace without further oxidation. Without this extra heat the reactions in the stack would so lower the gas temperature that all reactions would be delayed and the burden would reach the bosh in-adequately prepared for the final smelting.

Although the heat consumed in the sinter practice is almost as low as can be achieved, 84·38 per cent. being used for the production of iron and slag, the CO/CO_2 ratio of 2·23 in the top gas shows that further saving in the coke rate is possible. However, it should be remembered that the CO/CO_2 gas ratio in sinter practice is not strictly comparable with that in self-fluxing ore, or ore/limestone practice. In the former, all but 20 lb. of CO_2 was produced from the oxidation of CO while in the latter 585 lb. of CO_2 arose from the decomposition of carbonates.

REFERENCE

[1] "Considerations on Blast-furnace Practice", by T. P. COLCLOUGH. *J. Iron & Steel Inst.*, 1949, *150*, 359.

Chapter X

THEORY OF THE BLAST FURNACE – III

THE CALCULATION OF A THERMAL BALANCE

THE THERMAL BALANCE for an all-sinter burden is worked out in detail below. All the data necessary for the same calculation for a burden consisting of the same ores unsintered are also given. It is recommended that every blast-furnace operator should work out the balance for his own practice; such an exercise will certainly lead to the consideration of almost every factor in furnace operation and will probably give him a fresh view of the furnace he controls. Many furnace operators consider a blast furnace to be a most awkward and capricious piece of apparatus always ready to go wrong and to cause troubles which are both expensive and dangerous. But the more deeply one considers the chemical and thermal happenings inside the furnace, the less capricious it seems and the more amenable to the laws of cause and effect.

APPROXIMATE MATERIALS BALANCE

A thermal balance will not give a complete account of what happens in the furnace and can, at best, be only approximately correct. It is based on the weights of materials charged and recovered and their chemical analysis; on readings of recording instruments, and on thermal factors such as those shown in Table V.

All the bases of the calculation can introduce errors into the final result. This is well illustrated in the report of a test carried out on a furnace at the Clyde Ironworks.[1] For the test, which lasted a week, a team of 36 people were employed in sampling ores, coke, and gas, taking slag and metal temperatures and generally making sure that all the figures used in the materials and thermal balances were as correct as possible. Before the test, all the weighing machines and measuring instruments were overhauled and tested and during the test all materials, including every ladle of slag, were carefully weighed. Even with such an elaborate organisation the materials balance was not by any means accurate. In discussing the errors, the authors point out the difficulties of correctly sampling the large quantities of materials involved, and the inaccuracy of chemical analyses, which never add up to 100 per cent. It is common experience that a furnace does not always yield all its iron at cast and may carry as much as 100 tons from one week to the next if the deficiency occurs at the weekend. Under these conditions, some of the material included in the materials balance will not show any iron yield. To compensate for these errors the investigators at Clyde Ironworks stated that it must be assumed either:

(a) That the ingoing materials are correct and the weights of iron and slag must be adjusted accordingly, or

(b) That the weights of iron and slag are correct and the adjustment must be made to the weights of materials charged.

In order to calculate thermal balances to compare one working period or one type of practice with another on any particular furnace plant, it is not necessary and, indeed, scarcely possible to use such an elaborate organisation as that employed at Clyde Ironworks. Their test was indeed a scientific investigation which would have been impossible to carry out without costly preparation. But it is possible to get valuable information from calculations made on the data normally produced in the blast-furnace office. It is recommended that the period covered by the calculation should be not less than a month; the longer the period, the less important are errors of weighing and analysis of materials.

METHOD OF CALCULATION

Table IX, which shows the office records of all-sinter practice on a large modern furnace for a four-week period, contains all the data necessary for calculating a thermal balance. Table X gives the same data for non-sinter practice.

TABLE IX

TABLE OF FURNACE RECORDS—ALL-SINTER BURDEN

Burden	lb.	Moist. %	Fe_2O_3 %	Fe_3O_4 %	FeO %	Fe %	CO_2 %	C %	Combined H_2O%
Sinter	5654	1·0	38·1	—	13·2	—	0·37	0·22	0·5
Cinder	53	—	—	—	72·0	—	—	—	—
Scale	140	5·0	—	29·0	56·6	—	—	—	—
Scrap	23	—	—	—	—	75	—	—	—
Total burden	5870								

Coke	lb.	Moist. %	H_2 %	N_2 %	Total Carbon%
	1705	2·50	0·34	1·22	84·5

Gas % by volume	CO_2	CO	H_2	N_2
	11·5	26·7	1·8	60·0

Iron analysis	C %	Si %	S %	P %	Mn %	Fe %
	3·73	0·70	0·054	1·27	0·92	93·326

Flue dust

The flue dust loss was 274 lb. per ton of iron. It contained 10·6 per cent. of carbon equivalent to 12·5 per cent. of coke. The iron content was 31·6 per cent., so it is assumed that the 87·5 per cent. in addition to the coke, was wholly sinter. The 274 lb. of flue dust therefore contained 34 lb. of coke and 240 lb. of sinter.

The net burden was

$$5870 - 240 = 5630 \text{ lb.}$$

and the net coke

$$1705 - 34 = 1671 \text{ lb.}$$

The average atmospheric humidity for the period was 3·4 grains per cu. ft.

The average blast temperature was 668°C.=1235°F.

The average gas temperature was 223°C.=435°F.

The slag calculated from materials and analysis and checked by test weighing of slag ladles was 2770 lb. per ton of iron. The iron content was 1·1% and the average temperature 1440°C.

The iron produced averaged 8907 tons per week and its average temperature was 1415°C.

The cooling water used was 4500 gallons per minute and the average increase in the water temperature was 10·8°F.

TABLE X

TABLE OF FURNACE RECORDS—NON-SINTER BURDEN

Burden	lb.	Moist. %	Fe_2O_3 %	FeO %	Fe %	CO_2 %	Combined H_2O%
Limey ore	3894	10·5	13·5	6·9	—	12	12·2
Silicious ore	4064	11·1	24·2	8·1	—	3	11·8
Scrap	83	—	—	—	75	—	—
Total burden	8041						

	lb.	Moist. %	H_2 %	N_2 %	Total carbon %
Coke	2654	3·4	0·34	1·22	84·5

	CO_2	CO	H_2	N_2	
Gas % by volume	10·4	29·0	3·2	57·4	

	C %	Si %	S %	P %	Mn %	Fe %
Iron analysis	3·70	1·40	0·13	1·57	0·73	92·47

Flue dust

The flue dust loss was 70 lb. per ton of iron. It contained 12·5 per cent. of carbon (equivalent to 15 per cent. of coke) and 85 per cent. of ore.

The net burden was

$$8041 - 60 = 7981 \text{ lb.}$$

and the net coke

$$2654 - 10 = 2644 \text{ lb.}$$

The average atmospheric humidity for the period was 2·7 grains per cu. ft.

The average blast temperature was 510°C. = 950°F.

The average gas temperature was 175°C. = 350°F.

The calculated slag volume was 2750 lb. Its iron content was 1·1 per cent. and its average temperature 1430°C.

The iron produced averaged 4200 tons per week and its average temperature was 1405°C.

The cooling water used was 4400 gallons per minute and the average increase in the water temperature 12°F.

The specimen thermal balance which follows is based on these data and refers to the production of one ton of iron. No attempt has been made to give a complete materials balance showing all the elements and compounds going into and out of the furnace. All that is necessary for the present purpose is to produce a statement of the weights of the materials needed for the thermal balance.

The furnace input consists of burden, coke, air and water vapour in the air. The weight of burden and coke are given but those of air and water vapour will have to be calculated.

The output consists of iron, slag, flue dust, dry gas, and water vapour in the gas; again, the last two items will have to be calculated.

The weights of air blown and gas produced are derived from the carbon balance, *i.e.* the input from coke and sinter and the output in the gas.

The method of calculation of the approximate materials balance is set out below and the results are summarised in Table XI.

(i) *The carbon gasified in the furnace*

The first requirement is the amount of carbon actually gasified in the furnace. The carbon charged per ton of iron was from:

1705 lb. of coke containing 84·5 % of carbon   = 1441 lb.
5654 lb. of sinter containing 0·32 % of carbon   =   18 lb.

Total carbon charged = 1459 lb.

All this carbon was not oxidised in the furnace, some being lost in the flue dust and some going into the iron:

274 lb. of flue dust containing 10·6 % of carbon   =   29 lb.
2240 lb. of iron containing 3·73 % of carbon   =   84 lb.

113 lb.

The carbon going into the gas was therefore

$$1459 - 113 = 1346 \text{ lb.}$$

(ii) *Gas analysis*

The gas analysis is given by volume and must be converted to analysis by weight to give the weight of carbon per lb. of gas. The following table gives the percentage of the gas components by weight, calculated from the volume analysis at standard temperature and pressure (S.T.P.), *i.e.* 60°F. and 30 in. mercury pressure:

	% by volume	Wt./cu. ft. of component	Wt./cu. ft. of gaseous mixture	% by weight
CO_2	11·5	0·1163	0·01337	17·22
CO	26·7	0·074	0·01976	25·45
H_2	1·8	0·0053	0·00010	0·13
N_2	60·0	0·074	0·04440	57·20
			0·07763	100·00

Each lb. of gas contained 0·1722 lb. of CO_2 and 0·2545 lb. of CO. Carbon dioxide contains 12/44 and CO 12/28 by weight of carbon; therefore the total carbon per lb. of gas was

$$0·1722 \times 12/44 = 0·047 \text{ lb.}$$
$$0·2545 \times 12/28 = 0·109 \text{ lb.}$$
$$0·156 \text{ lb.}$$

The weight of gas was therefore

$$1346 \div 0·156 = 8628 \text{ lb.}$$

The 8628 lb. of dry top gas was made up of:

CO_2 17·22% of 8628 lb. = 1486 lb.

CO   25·45% of 8628 lb. = 2196 lb.

H_2 0·13% of 8628 lb. = 11 lb.

N_2 57·21% of 8628 lb. = 4935 lb.

Not all the carbon dioxide in the gas was the result of oxidation of carbon in the furnace. The decomposition of calcium carbonate produced 20 lb. of carbon dioxide, leaving

$$1486 - 20 = 1466 \text{ lb.}$$

from the coke carbon. The carbon oxidised to CO_2 was

$$1466 \times \frac{12}{44} = 400 \text{ lb.}$$

All the carbon monoxide in the gas was the result of the oxidation of carbon

$$2196 \times \frac{12}{28} = 941 \text{ lb.}$$

(iii) The weight of dry air blown

The weight of dry air blown can be calculated from the weight of gas on the basis of nitrogen content. The 4935 lb. of nitrogen in the gas came from the nitrogen in the air blown plus that evolved from the net coke. The nitrogen from the net coke was

$$1671 \times 0 \cdot 0122 = 20 \text{ lb.}$$

and that from the air was

$$4935 - 20 = 4915 \text{ lb.}$$

As dry air contains 76·7 per cent. of nitrogen by weight the 4915 lb. of nitrogen came from

$$4915 \div 0 \cdot 767 = 6408 \text{ lb. of dry air.}$$

If the figure for nitrogen content of the coke is not readily available it may be safely ignored as the error introduced would not be appreciable when comparing practices using the same type of coke.

Dry air at S.T.P. weighs 0·07622 lb. per cu. ft. and therefore the volume of dry air blown per ton of iron was

$$6408 \div \cdot 07622 = 84{,}072 \text{ cu. ft.}$$

The air blown, however, contained 3·4 grains of moisture per cu. ft. At 7000 grains to the lb. this is equivalent to:

$$3.4 \div 7000 = 0 \cdot 000486 \text{ lb.}$$

The total air blown per ton of iron therefore contained

$$84{,}072 \times 0 \cdot 000486 = 40 \cdot 9 \text{ lb. of moisture.}$$

(iv) Moisture in the top gas

Most of the moisture in the coke and burden charged passed into the gas as gas moisture, but a small proportion was decomposed in the upper part of the furnace. The hydrogen from this decomposition increased the hydrogen content of the gas. This is shown in the hydrogen balance in which the weight of hydrogen in the gas is greater than can be accounted for by the air blast moisture and the hydrogen of the coke. To calculate the weight of moisture in the top gas the weight of burden moisture decomposed must be deducted from that of the total water charged.

It is assumed that the moisture and combined water of the flue dust were evaporated in the furnace and therefore the total water charged was

In burden

Scale moisture	.. .. ..	5% of 140 lb. =	7·0 lb.
Sinter moisture	.. .. ..	1% of 5654 lb. =	56·5 lb.
Sinter combined water	.. ..	0·5% of 5654 lb. =	28·3 lb.

In the coke

Moisture	.. .. .. 2·5% of 1705 lb. =	42·6 lb.

Total water charged $=134\cdot4$ lb.

The hydrogen in the top gas was 0·13 per cent. and in the coke 0·34 per cent. The weight of moisture decomposed can be calculated from these figures:

Weight of hydrogen in gas, $8628 \times 0\cdot0013$	$=11\cdot22$ lb.
Weight of hydrogen in net coke, $1671 \times 0\cdot0034$	$= 5\cdot68$ lb.
Weight of hydrogen from decomposed blast moisture, $40\cdot9 \div 9$	$= 4\cdot54$ lb.
Weight of hydrogen from blast moisture and coke	$=10\cdot22$ lb.

The surplus hydrogen in gas arising from decomposed burden moisture was:

$$11\cdot22 - 10\cdot22 = 1\cdot00 \text{ lb.}$$

The water from which this hydrogen was evolved was:

$$1\cdot00 \times 9 = 9\cdot00 \text{ lb.}$$

The water passing out of the furnace in the gas was therefore the water charged less that decomposed:

$$134\cdot4 - 9\cdot0 = 125\cdot4 \text{ lb.}$$

(v) The source of the iron (Fe) in the metal

Table IX shows that Fe entered the furnace in the form of Fe_2O_3, Fe_3O_4, FeO and free iron. Fe_2O_3 consists of 112 parts of iron and 48 parts of oxygen, *i.e.* it contains 70 per cent. of Fe. Fe_3O_4 consists of 168 parts of iron and 64 parts of oxygen, *i.e.* it contains 72·4 per cent. of Fe. FeO consists of 56 parts of iron and 16 parts of oxygen, *i.e.* it contains 77·8 per cent. of Fe.

The total weight of Fe charged was:

As Fe_2O_3
    Net sinter   ..   5414 lb. $\times$ 0·381 $\times$ 0·7   =   1444 lb.

As Fe_3O_4
    Scale ..   ..   140 lb. $\times$ 0·290 $\times$ 0·724 =   29 lb.

As FeO
    Net sinter   ..   5414 lb. $\times$ 0·132 $\times$ 0·778 = 556 lb.
    „ cinder   ..   53 lb. $\times$ 0·720 $\times$ 0·778 = 30 lb.
    „ scale   ..   140 lb. $\times$ 0·556 $\times$ 0·778 =   61 lb.
                                          ————— 647 lb.

As Fe
    Scrap ..   ..   23 lb. $\times$ 0·750   =   17 lb.

                                              2137 lb.*

(vi) Metalloids in the metal

The metal contained:
Manganese reduced from manganous oxide (MnO)
$$2240 \times 0·0092 = 20·6 \text{ lb.}$$
Silicon reduced from silica (SiO_2)
$$2240 \times 0·007 = 15·7 \text{ lb.}$$
Phosphorus reduced from phosphorus pentoxide (P_2O_5)
$$2240 \times 0·0127 = 28·4 \text{ lb.}$$

(vii) The decomposition of compounds

The sinter † contains 0·5 per cent. of combined water in the form of hydrated ferric oxide (Fe_2O_3 H_2O). This compound is decomposed with the evolution of

$$5654 \text{ lb.} \times 0·005 = 28·3 \text{ lb. of water.}$$

---

* The Fe required for iron and slag is:
        For iron 2240 $\times$ 0·93326 = 2090 lb.
        For slag 2770 $\times$ 0·011   =   31 lb.
                                —————
            Total   = 2121 lb.

The 16 lb. error is not large and this amount might easily be lost as shot in the slag and would not appear in the slag analysis.

† In the calculation of the moisture in the top gas it was assumed that the moisture and combined water of the flue dust were evaporated in the furnace. It is also assumed that the flue dust leaves the furnace before it has had time to lose its carbon dioxide. The combined water is therefore that contained in the whole of the sinter charged and the carbon dioxide is from the net sinter.

The 0·37 per cent. of CO_2 in the net sinter † is present as calcium carbonate. This is decomposed in the furnace, releasing into the gas

$$5414 \text{ lb.} \times 0·0037 = 20 \text{ lb. of } CO_2.$$

The 28·4 lb. of phosphorus in the iron is present in the sinter as calcium phosphate. This is first decomposed in the furnace to P_2O_5 and lime (CaO). The reduction of the P_2O_5 to P has already been dealt with.

The blast moisture and that part of the burden moisture providing hydrogen in the gas are decomposed to hydrogen and oxygen in the furnace. The quantities, 40·9 lb. of blast moisture and 9 lb. of burden moisture, have been shown in the calculation for moisture in the top gas.

All the material weights necessary for the thermal balance having been calculated, they can now be tabulated for easy reference:

TABLE XI

	lb.
Iron produced	2240
Slag produced	2770
Coke burnt	1671
Dry blast blown	6408
Moisture in blast	40·9
Dry gas produced	8628
Moisture in gas	125·4
Fe reduced from Fe_2O_3	1444
Fe reduced from Fe_3O_4	29
Fe reduced from FeO	647
Fe charged as Fe	17
Total Fe charged	2137
Mn reduced from MnO	20·6
Si reduced from SiO_2	15·7
P reduced from P_2O_5	28·4
Carbon dissolved in the iron	84
CO_2 from decomposition of calcium carbonate ($CaCO_3$)	20
H_2O from decomposition of hydrated ferric oxide	
($Fe_2O_3 \, H_2O$)	28
H_2O decomposed to H_2	
from blast moisture	40·9
from burden moisture	9·0
Carbon oxidised to CO_2	400
Carbon oxidised to CO	941
Hydrogen in the gas	11
Nitrogen in the gas	4935

† See note p. 135.

CALCULATION OF THE THERMAL BALANCE

HEAT GENERATED

All the heat in the furnace was supplied by:
(a) The oxidation of carbon to carbon dioxide.
(b) The oxidation of carbon to carbon monoxide.
(c) The heat of solution of silicon and phosphorus in the iron.
(d) The sensible heat of the moist blast.

> (a) The oxidation of carbon to carbon dioxide 400 lb. of carbon at 14,550 B.Th.U. per lb. = 5,820,000 B.Th.U.
>
> (b) The oxidation of carbon to carbon monoxide 941 lb. of carbon at 4407 B.Th.U. per lb. = 4,146,987 B.Th.U.
>
> (c) The heat of solution of silicon in the iron 15·7 lb. of silicon at 1832 B.Th.U. per lb. = 28,762 B.Th.U.
> The heat of solution of phosphorus in the iron 28·4 lb. of phosphorus at 2858 B.Th.U. per lb. = 81,167 B.Th.U.
> (Manganese is also dissolved in the iron but its heat of solution is almost nil.)
>
> (d) The sensible heat of moist blast.

The heat capacity of a gas is the quantity of heat required to raise its temperature by 1°, but this heat capacity changes with temperature. For example, 0·2275 B.Th.U. is required to raise the temperature of CO_2 from 400° to 401°F.; from 800° to 801°F., 0·25 B.Th.U. is required.

The values of mean heat capacities of the constitutents of the air blown (and of the top gas) are based on equations from Hougen & Watson's *Industrial Chemical Calculations*.[2]

HEAT CONTENT OF THE DRY BLAST AT 1235°F.

The mean heat capacity of the dry blast between 60°F. and 1235°F. is 0·2491 B.Th.U. per lb. per °F.; this is a total heat capacity of

$$1175 \times 0·2491 = 293 \text{ B.Th.U. per lb. of air.}$$

The dry air blown was 6408 lb. and its total heat content was

$$6408 \times 293 = 1,877,544 \text{ B.Th.U.}$$

The blast water vapour at the temperature of the blast has a heat capacity of 0·4922 B.Th.U. per lb. per °F.; a total heat capacity of

$$1175 \times 0·4922 = 578 \text{ B.Th.U. per lb.}$$

The water vapour in the blast was 40·9 lb. and its total heat content was

$$40·9 \times 578 = 23,640 \text{ B.Th.U.}$$

HEAT CONSUMED

The heat was used in the furnace to satisfy the demands of:

(*a*) The production of the metal.

(*b*) The heating of the slag.

(*c*) The evolution of volatile matter.

(*d*) The sensible heat of the dry gas.

(*e*) The decomposition of the blast moisture.

(*f*) The heat loss in the cooling water.

(a) *The production and heating of the metal. The reduction of oxides*

The weight of materials in Table XI and the heats of formation in Table V will give the figure of heat required for the reduction of oxides.

Constituent	Wt. lb.	Reduced from	B.Th.U. per lb. of product	B.Th.U. per ton of iron
Fe	1444	Fe_2O_3	3,162	4,565,928
Fe	29	Fe_3O_4	2,870	83,230
Fe	647	FeO	2,051	1,326,997
Mn	20·6	MnO	3,012	62,047
Si	15·7	SiO_2	13,468	211,448
P	28·4	P_2O_5	10,451	296,808

Total for reduction of oxides   6,546,458

The P_2O_5 was produced in the furnace by the decomposition of calcium phosphate

$$28·4 \text{ lb.} \times 4761 = 135,212 \text{ B.Th.U.}$$

The carbon dissolved in the iron amounted to 84 lb. The heat required for the solution of carbon in iron is 1800 B.Th.U. per lb. of carbon

$$84 \text{ lb.} \times 1800 = 151,200 \text{ B.Th.U.}$$

The iron left the furnace at a temperature of 1415°C. The heat capacity of iron at this temperature is 547 B.Th.U. per lb.[3] The heat required to raise one ton of iron to 1415°C. was

$$2240 \text{ lb.} \times 547 = 1,225,280 \text{ B.Th.U.}$$

(b) *The heating of the slag*

The formation of the compounds contained in slag is accompanied by an evolution of heat and, in ore/limestone burdens, the "heat generated" side of the balance sheet contains an item of 230 B.Th.U. per lb.

of slag. When formed, the slag has to be heated to free-running temperature and the heat required must appear on the debit side of the balance sheet.

In sinter practice, the slag has already been formed in the sintering process, as mentioned earlier in this chapter. No credit is therefore shown for this item. The average temperature of the slag was 1440°C. at which the total heat content is 740 B.Th.U. per lb.[4]

$$2770 \text{ lb.} \times 740 = 2,049,800 \text{ B.Th.U.}$$

(c) The evolution of volatile matter

1. Calcium carbonate in the sinter was decomposed with the evolution of 20 lb. of carbon dioxide. At 1738 B.Th.U. per lb. of CO_2 the heat expended was

$$20 \text{ lb.} \times 1738 = 34,760 \text{ B.Th.U.}$$

2. The 28 lb. of water in combination with iron oxide was driven off with the expenditure of 137 B.Th.U. per lb. of water

$$28 \text{ lb.} \times 137 = 3836 \text{ B.Th.U.}$$

3. 9 lb. of burden moisture was decomposed, the resulting hydrogen going into the gas. The heat required was 6832 B.Th.U. per lb. of water

$$9 \text{ lb.} \times 6832 = 61,488 \text{ B.Th.U.}$$

4. The remaining burden and coke moisture was evaporated and left the furnace as gas moisture at a temperature of 435°F. The water is assumed to have entered the furnace at 60°F. In raising the temperature to boiling point (212°F.) 1 B.Th.U. per degree per lb. of water was required; a total of 152 B.Th.U. per lb. At 212°F. the water would evaporate, requiring 977 B.Th.U. per lb. (the latent heat of evaporation of water). To raise the water vapour from 212°F. to 435°F., *i.e.* 223°F., the heat required was 223 × 0·452 (the mean specific heat of the water vapour) = 101 B.Th.U. per lb. The total heat required was therefore

$$152 + 977 + 101 = 1230 \text{ B.Th.U.}$$

The 126 lb. of water evaporated required

$$126 \times 1230 = 154,980 \text{ B.Th.U.}$$

(d) The sensible heat of the dry gas

The mean heat capacities of the gas constituents are again taken from Hougen and Watson[2] and their weights have already been calculated.

The gas temperature was 435°F. and the heat required was the amount necessary to raise the temperature from 60°F. to 435°F.

Gas constituent	Wt. lb.	Heat capacity B.Th.U./ lb. per °F. from 60°F. to 435°F.	Total B.Th.U. per °F.
CO_2	1486	0·2193	326
CO	2196	0·2507	551
H_2	11	3·4975	38
N_2	4935	0·2507	1237

Total for dry gas 2152

The heat in the dry gas was

$$2152 \times 375 = 807,000 \text{ B.Th.U.}$$

(e) The decomposition of the blast moisture

The 40·9 lb. of blast moisture was decomposed in the furnace hearth with the expenditure of 5780 B.Th.U. per lb. of water vapour

$$40·9 \text{ lb.} \times 5780 = 236,402 \text{ B.Th.U.}$$

(f) The heat loss

A large proportion of the heat loss is in the cooling water; smaller losses occur by conduction of heat to the ground and by convection and radiation—principally in the upper part of the stack. These smaller losses have been calculated by Taylor[1] and Marshall[5] and their methods are clearly shown in the works referred to. Both authors found that the loss in cooling water was about 84 per cent. of the total loss. Marshall gives a figure of 3 per cent. lost to the ground by conduction. The proportion of heat lost from the stack by convection will naturally differ from furnace to furnace, according to the proportion of the surface exposed to the wind. The furnace under discussion is spray cooled from just below the top deck to the bottom of the bosh. Internal cooling staves are used in the tuyere belt and the hearth is spray cooled. The cast house covers 60 per cent. of the surface area of the stack. It is evident that the loss in cooling water represents a large percentage of the total loss. This figure has therefore been taken as the total loss, thus sparing the labour and expense involved in avoiding the small error.

The total water used in sprays, stave coolers and all the tuyeres and slag notch tuyeres and coolers was 4500 gallons per minute. The average

temperature difference between the ingoing and outgoing water was
10·8°F. One B.Th.U. raises the temperature of 1 lb. of water by 1°F.
and therefore 4500 gallons, *i.e.* 45,000 lb. of water raised by 10·8°F. will
require

$$45,000 \times 10\cdot8 \times 60 = 29,160,000 \text{ B.Th.U. per hour.}$$

The furnace produced iron at the rate of 8907 tons per week, *i.e.*
53 tons per hour, and the heat loss per ton of iron was

$$29,160,000 \div 53 = 550,189 \text{ B.Th.U.}$$

REFERENCES

[1] "A Materials and Thermal Balance of a Modern Blast Furnace", by
J. TAYLOR, R. P. TOWNDROW, and J. D. GILCHRIST. *W. of Scot. Iron &
Steel Inst.*, 1950.

[2] *Industrial Chemical Calculations,* by O. A. HOUGEN and K. M. WATSON.
J. Wiley & Sons, 114.

[3] "Basic Open Hearth Steelmaking", by S. MUDD, *A.I.M.E.*, 1951, 786.

[4] *Technical Data on Fuel,* by H. M. SPIERS, 172.

[5] "The External Heat Loss of a Blast Furnace", by D. F. MARSHALL.
J. Iron & Steel Inst., 1933, *127*, 127.

Chapter XI

MODIFICATIONS TO ORTHODOX OPERATION

MODIFICATIONS TO ORTHODOX OPERATION

I T HAS BEEN DEMONSTRATED that the furnace production rate can be substantially increased by the use of all-sinter burdens, but this is not the only method of achieving such increases.

HIGH TOP PRESSURE OPERATION

In the last decade a number of American furnaces, the majority of Russian furnaces and three furnaces in Great Britain have adopted a practice which has become known as high top pressure operation and certain advantages have been claimed for this method of working.

In normal operation, the gas leaves the furnace top at a pressure of about 2 lb. per sq. in. In high top pressure operation, the top pressure is increased by the use of a valve restricting the flow of the outgoing gas. Most operators use a top pressure of about 10 lb. per sq. in.

THE THEORY OF HIGH TOP PRESSURE OPERATION

One of the limits imposed on the amount of air blown in a given practice is the amount of flue dust made and the increasing irregularity of stock descent with increasing blast volume. The greater the velocity of the ascending gases, the greater is their upward thrust on the burden, and the greater is the tendency for the gas to find the easiest path through the stock. Having found an easy path, more and more gas travels through it with increasing velocity, doing little work of reduction, until the velocity is so great that gas laden with dust is forced out of the furnace top and, ultimately, slips of varying degree occur. This "channelling" results in some proportion of the burden reaching the furnace hearth in a poor state of preparation.

It was demonstrated by C. C. Furnas[1] that the pressure drop through a bed of broken solids can be reduced by increasing the overall pressure of the system. If the pressure is doubled, the density of the gas is doubled and it follows that the resistance to flow is reduced. Thus, by increasing the overall pressure of a blast furnace, the difference between top and bottom pressure is reduced. The result of increasing the top pressure from 2 to 10 lb. is an increase of about 6 lb. in the blast pressure.

T. L. Josephs[2] calculated that an increase of top pressure from 2 lb. per sq. in. to 10 lb. per sq. in. reduces the gas velocity in the stock and at the furnace top by about 32·5 per cent. Thus, with top pressure, a substantial increase in the air blown can be made without increasing the gas velocity. If such an increase of air blown is unaccompanied by a rise in the coke rate the output capacity of the furnace is increased.

At some Russian plants the top pressure has been raised to 13 to 15 lb. per sq. in. and it is claimed that production has been increased by 6 to 7 per cent. and the coke rate reduced by 3 to 4 per cent. American and British furnaces rarely operate with more than 10 lb. per sq. in. top pressure. The operators of these furnaces derive benefits from reduced flue dust losses and greater production but are hesitant about claiming any reduction in coke rates.

It appears that no appreciable benefits are obtained by pressure operation until top gas pressure is about 5 lb. per sq. in. Indeed, it may be that most of the benefits are obtained at this level of operation without running into the troubles associated with top gas pressures of 10 lb. per sq. in. or more.

It would appear that high top pressure operation can be of special advantage to furnaces working on badly prepared burdens as it reduces flue dust loss and permits increases in furnace output.

For a careful and impartial study of high top pressure operation, the reader is referred to the published work of Towndrow and Banks.[3, 4, 5]

ENRICHMENT OF THE BLAST WITH OXYGEN

The enrichment of the blast with oxygen has been much discussed during the past few years, but has not been widely adopted. Experiments are being carried out at Russian plants, and at one plant in the United States the blast is enriched, but no British plant engaged in the production of basic iron has yet changed to this practice.

The air blown in normal blast furnace practice (moisture neglected) consists of oxygen heavily diluted with nitrogen, the proportions being 21 per cent. of oxygen and 79 per cent. of nitrogen by volume. Any increase in the oxygen content is at the expense of the nitrogen and has the effect of increasing the amount of carbon burnt per cu. ft. of blast air. Table XII shows the effect of various degrees of oxygen enrichment on the blast air required to burn 1 lb. of carbon, and on the composition of the tuyere gas.

A 4 per cent. enrichment of the blast, i.e. an increase of oxygen from 21 to 25 per cent. by volume, results in a decrease of 16 per cent. in the volume of blast per lb. of carbon burnt and the tuyere gas contains an

TABLE XII

COMBUSTION DATA—100 CUBIC FEET OF DRY BLAST

(a) By volume				
Oxygen, cu. ft.	21·00	23·00	25·00	27·00
Nitrogen, cu. ft.	79·00	77·00	75·00	73·00
Carbon monoxide produced, cu. ft.	42·00	46·00	50·00	54·00
Tuyere gas produced, cu. ft. ..	121·00	123·00	125·00	127·00
Carbon monoxide %	34·7	37·4	40·0	42·5
Nitrogen %	65·3	62·6	60·0	57·5
(b) By weight				
Oxygen, lb.	1·78	1·95	2·12	2·28
Carbon burnt to CO, lb. ..	1·33	1·46	1·59	1·71
Carbon monoxide produced, lb.	3·11	3·41	3·71	3·99
Nitrogen, lb.	5·85	5·70	5·55	5·40
Tuyere gas produced, lb. ..	8·96	9·11	9·26	9·39
Blast required per lb. carbon, cu. ft.	75·00	68·50	63·00	58·50
Tuyere gas produced per lb. carbon, cu. ft.	90·70	84·20	78·60	74·40

additional 5·3 per cent. of carbon monoxide and has therefore greater reducing power. The temperature of combustion is increased because the heat generated is used to heat a smaller weight of gas. The temperature increase is not proportionate to the decreased gas weight because the sensible heat of the blast used is less by reason of its lower volume per lb. of carbon burnt.

Because the temperature of the gases in the hearth is substantially increased it must not be thought that more heat has been generated. Oxygen is not a fuel and will not add to the heat generated from 1 lb. of carbon. The quantity of heat produced by burning 1 lb. of carbon to carbon monoxide is 4407 B.Th.U.'s, whether the blast used contains 21 or 50 per cent. of oxygen.

The principal change in furnace conditions is that the hearth temperature will be higher but less heat will be carried into the stack by the smaller volume of gas. The stack temperature will be lowered and it follows that the top gas temperature will fall. All the reaction zones in the furnace will be altered and it is possible that the temperatures at the furnace top may be low enough to condense moisture and retard reduction.

It is now generally accepted that oxygen enrichment will bring great-er benefits to ferro-manganese production than to basic iron production as the former requires a much higher hearth temperature and normally works with a higher top gas temperature.

To sum up, the effects of oxygen enrichment are:

(a) A higher combustion temperature at the tuyeres and therefore a more rapid heat exchange in the furnace hearth.

(b) Less blast per pound of carbon. The blast therefore requires less stove power, but introduces less sensible heat in the blast.

(c) Less gas produced per ton of coke. The gas velocity is therefore lower than in normal practice and operation should be smoother and flue dust losses less. The stack temperature is reduced.

(d) A more reducing tuyere gas, and a top gas of higher calorific value.

For a full theoretical appreciation of this subject the reader is referred to the published work of Charles, Chater and Harrison.[6]

HUMIDIFICATION OF THE BLAST

Adding steam to the blast air is largely practised in Russia but has not yet been widely adopted in this country. It is claimed that the use of blast with constant moisture content of the order of 8·75 to 11 grains per cu. ft. (2·5 to 3·3 per cent. by volume) gives an increase of 3·7 to 7 per cent. in production and a reduction of 1·5 to 2 per cent. in the coke rate, provided that the heat used in the decomposition of the steam is compensated for by a corresponding increase in blast temperature.

As steam contains 88·9 per cent. of oxygen by weight and dry air only 23·3 per cent., one of the effects of steam addition is to enrich the blast with oxygen. A further effect is to increase the hydrogen content and reduce the nitrogen content of the tuyere gas. Table XIII gives a

TABLE XIII

	Air containing 11 gr. moisture/ cu. ft.	Air containing 3·4 gr. moisture/ cu. ft.
Oxygen, % by weight	24·68	23·73
Hydrogen, % by weight	0·23	0·07
Nitrogen, % by weight	75·09	76·20

comparison of the composition of air containing 11 grains of moisture per cu. ft. with air containing 3·4 grains per cu. ft.—about the average figure for this country.

If these figures are applied to the quantity of air blown shown in the calculation of the heat balance, viz. 6449 lb. of moist air, the comparisons in Table XIV can be made:

TABLE XIV

	Air containing 11 gr. moisture/ cu. ft.	Air containing 3·4 gr. moisture/ cu. ft.
Oxygen present, lb.	1,592	1,530
Carbon burnt, lb.	1,193	1,147
CO produced at tuyeres, lb.	2,785	2,677
Hydrogen produced at tuyeres, lb. ..	14·9	4·5
Nitrogen produced at tuyeres, lb. ..	4,842	4,914
Total weight of gas, lb.	7,641·9	7,595·5
Weight of gas per lb. of carbon, lb. ..	6·41	6·62
Tuyere gas		
CO % by volume	35·55	34·97
H$_2$ % by volume	2.65	0·82
N$_2$ % by volume	61·80	64·21
Heat produced		
C to CO, B.Th.U.	5,258,000	5,055,000
Less H$_2$O to H$_2$, B.Th.U.	775,000	234,000
Net heat, B.Th.U.	4,483,000	4,821,000

In considering the use of steam in the blast the following facts must not be overlooked:

(a) Every pound of carbon burnt produces 3·2 per cent. less tuyere gas, but this contains 2·5 per cent. more reducing gas.

(b) The extra steam results in the blast burning 4·0 per cent. more carbon per cubic foot and producing 7·0 per cent. less heat per cubic foot.

(c) The flame temperature of the carbon is lowered by about 60°C. owing to the endothermic $H_2O + C = H_2 + CO$ reaction.

(d) The loss of hearth temperature resulting from the smaller amount of heat generated per pound of carbon at a lower temperature must be compensated for by additional blast heat.

These facts are of course well known to the users of blast humidification, but they claim great benefits from:

(a) The increased reducing power of the gas.

(b) The increase in hydrogen content of the tuyere gas, hydrogen being a more active reducing agent than carbon monoxide.

(c) Greater regularity of operation owing to more constant moisture content in the air.

REFERENCES

[1] *Flow of Gases through beds of Broken Solids*, by C. C. FURNAS. U.S. Bureau of Mines, Bulletin 307, 1929, 28.

[2] "Blast Furnace Operation under Elevated Top Pressure", by T. L. JOSEPH. *Iron & Steel Engineer*, Feb. 1946.

[3] "Blast Furnace Operation at High Top Pressure", by R. P. TOWNDROW. *W. of Scot. Iron & Steel Inst.*, 1950–51, *58*.

[4] "Further Operating Experience with the Blast Furnace at High Top Pressure", by R. P. TOWNDROW and W. BANKS. *W. of Scot. Iron & Steel Inst.*, 1951–52, *59*.

[5] "Some British Aspects of High Top Pressure Operation", by R. P. TOWN-DROW and W. BANKS. *A.I.M.E.*, 1953.

[6] *Oxygen in Iron and Steel Making*, by J. A. CHARLES, W. J. B. CHATER, and J. L. HARRISON. Butterworths Scientific Publications.

Chapter XII

AUXILIARY PLANT

BLOWERS

Between four and five tons of air are required for each ton of pig iron and this must be delivered to the furnace in volumes of up to 120,000 cu. ft. per minute and at pressures of up to 35 lb. per sq. in. Reciprocating blowers, driven either by steam or blast-furnace gas, were once popular alternatives to steam turbine driven centrifugal blowers, but blowing duty today usually requires so much power that the latter type of machine is standard equipment for all furnaces built in recent years. Turbines developing up to 20,000 horse-power have been installed for driving blowers. Such a blowing set, designed to deliver 160,000 cu. ft. per minute at 35 lb. per sq. in. is shown in process of erection in fig. 47. The future may see a change to gas turbines and to axial flow compressors but the great reliability of the steam turbine ensures its place in the industry for many years to come. Failure of the air supply to a furnace can be disastrous; so much so that the operator places more emphasis on complete reliability than he does on maximum efficiency. When it is realised that this reliability is required over a wide range of duty, the reluctance shown by many operators to adopt the more efficient axial blower, which has a comparatively narrow stable working range, is explained.

The orthodox set—a steam turbine driving a centrifugal blower, will usually operate continuously for many months. The necessity to clean condensers and inspect boilers is usually taken as an opportunity to look at the turbine and blower, but where steam and water conditions have been favourable, many instances are known of turbo-blowers operating continuously for some years. Fig. 48 shows an installation of five turbo-blowers.

Usually, a blower is designed to match an individual furnace. Because of the continuing improvements in furnace operation, this design basis has tended to entail one of two disadvantages. Either the blower has to be over capacity, which means operation below optimum efficiency, or pig iron production becomes limited because insufficient air is available at the furnace.

(Courtesy of C. A. Parsons Ltd.)

Fig. 47. A 20,000 horse power steam turbine driving a centrifugal blower rated at 160,000 cubic feet per minute at a pressure of 35 lb. per square inch. Photograph taken during shop erection.

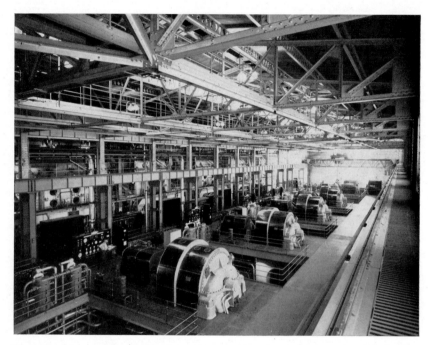

Fig. 48. A blowing house containing four 75,000 c.f.m. blowers and 160,000 c.f.m. blower in rear. Boilers are to the left of the blowers.

The development of "split wind" blowing rather alters this situation. So-called "common blowing" was practised many years ago at several works but the lack of suitable control instruments prevented such systems being perpetuated as furnaces increased in size. The regulation of air volumes by manual adjustment of a gate valve in either hot or cold blast lines was an almost impossible task. "Split wind" operation means the accurate division of air from one blower to the mains feeding two or more furnaces, with or without the aid of individual blowers already delivering air to those furnaces.

A schematic arrangement of split wind controls is shown in fig. 49.

The following extract is from a paper by Potter and Duffy which is recommended reading to all who are interested in blowers.[1]

"The blower is of the centrifugal type with a measuring Venturi in the intake and the air discharge is through a non-return valve to a header main which is connected through motor-operated sluice valves to each individual main. Each main also includes a flow orifice, impulse pipes, and a flow-control butterfly valve. In split-wind blowing the header-main pressure will be operated at a minimum differential above the furnace with the highest operating pressure, and the speed of the turbo-blower will be governed by a regulator to maintain this pressure constant. Conventional Askania volume regulators with impulse connections taken from the flow orifices in the cold blast mains will be used to control the butterfly valves in each separate furnace main by means of hydraulic crank-type cylinders. The regulators will be equipped with volume-setting adjustment capable of manual operation at the regulators or push-button operation from the control panels of the existing blowers. Provision is also made for manually-operated hydraulic adjustment of the butterfly control valves should the volume regulators be out of commission. Flow, as measured by each orifice and corrected to standard conditions, and the pressure in each main are recorded and indicated on a panel adjacent to the booster blower. Arrangements are also made whereby the increased flow to any line is indicated on the panel of the existing blower also feeding into that particular line, together with the total air flow to the furnace. For normal operation the booster blower will deliver its full rated volume distributed over the four furnace mains so that in conjunction with the existing machines it will be possible to deliver the maximum volume required to any furnace. All adjustments to flow rates and pressure will be made on the individual units feeding each furnace, with the booster blower working as a base-load machine."

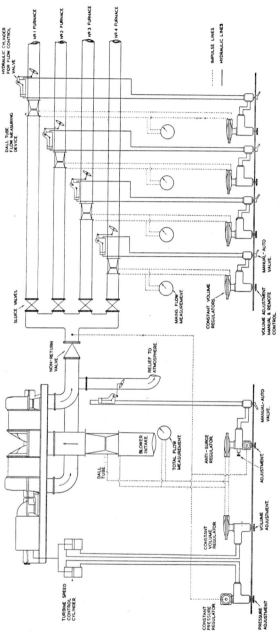

(Courtesy of C. A. Parsons Ltd).

Fig. 49. Schematic arrangement of controls for split wind blowing.

PIG CASTING PLANT

As is well known, pig iron is so called because of the fancied resemblance of iron cast in open sand beds to pigs suckling from a sow. Sand casting, of course, is now a matter of history but the name survives.

For disposal in the solid state, pig iron is cast into pieces of convenient size by means of a pig casting machine. The majority of such machines are of the stationary wheel type (*see* fig. 50). A normal-sized machine is 200 ft. between centres and contains approximately 420 moulds per strand. The speed of operation is variable, not only to deal with variations in the rate of flow but to permit the casting of different weights of pig in the same mould. Most machines can be varied in speed from about 6 ft. to 20 ft. per minute.

The ladle containing the iron is tilted in a crane-operated cradle. The iron first passes to a pouring box whence it flows down a brick-lined runner and launder to the moving moulds. The mouth of the launder should be fairly wide and carefully maintained to give good distribution of the metal into the moulds. Where twin machines are installed, both strands can be fed from one ladle of metal by means of a 'T'-shaped launder.

About one-third of the way along the machine, say 8 ft. from the pouring point, water is sprayed on to the moulds to solidify the metal before the pigs are discharged over the head pulley. Water control is extremely important. Sufficient water must be used to ensure solidification but sufficient heat must be left in the moulds to ensure that the lime sprayed on to them as they return to the pouring point is thoroughly dried out. The dangers of cold moulds are obvious. High phosphorus iron on a pig casting machine tends to splinter, making water control even more important. Ferro-manganese behaves in a rather similar manner. The moulds are mechanically sprayed with limewash to prevent the pigs from sticking to them. It has been found that limewash with a specific gravity of 1·20 is generally satisfactory in preventing "stickers". Constant agitation of the lime in the storage tank is necessary.

Moulds are normally made of hematite iron although, at some plants, steel moulds have been used with success. When the moulds are of iron, the castings should contain a steel reinforcement; this will usually prevent pieces of a broken mould falling into the moving machinery.

Pig machine duty is severe and a high standard of maintenance is essential if the pig caster is to be fully available when it is most needed.

GAS CLEANING

As mentioned in Chapter I, the dry dustcatchers remove about 80 per cent. of the dust carried from the furnace in the gas stream. It will be appreciated that the heavier and larger particles of dust will settle out first; the difficulties of cleaning gas increase as the particle size of the dust decreases. Efficient usage of blast-furnace gas demands that it should be cleaned to contain less than 0·005 grains per cu. ft. of dust. For under-firing coke ovens, the gas should be even cleaner if blockage of chequers is to be avoided, which is usually achieved by further cleaning of the gas at the coking plant.

Gas cleaning after the dustcatcher is always carried out in two stages, which should result in the removal of 95 per cent. of the dust not taken out in the dustcatchers. The first stage is almost always a wet process; many types of dry filters have been tried but none is as successful as any of the several types of washers or scrubbing towers.

Most of the recent installations of washers employ stationary baffles to break up downward falling water and at the same time evenly distribute upward rising gas. A typical arrangement of such a washer is shown in fig. 51. In this case, the baffles are made up of ceramic tiles.

Several types of plant are available for final cleaning. The Halberg Beth plant uses cotton filter bags to separate the dust. At intervals, the bags are automatically shaken to settle the dust into a collecting hopper below. Dry cleaners, however, have become less popular in the last few years.

Generally speaking, wet electric precipitation plants are now the most favoured type of equipment, having displaced the disintegrator type of cleaner because of the much lower power costs. A disintegrator consists of a high speed impeller which forces the gas through the jets of water moving in counter flow to the gas. This machine is a reliable piece of apparatus and capable of a high-cleaning efficiency, but requires a lot of power.

In electrostatic precipitation, the gas flows upwards through steel tubes or between parallel steel plates. A single wire located centrally in the tube, or a series of wires between the plates, act as the discharge electrode. The outer wall of the tube is connected to earth and acts as the collecting electrode. A high-voltage current (about 75,000 volts) passes along the discharge electrode. As the dust particles pass through the electric field between discharge and collecting electrodes, they are ionised and so attracted to the discharge electrode. As the dust accumulates on the tube, it is washed off by a film of water down to the bottom cone of the precipitator.

A typical tube-type precipitator is shown in fig. 52.

Dirty water from both primary washers and final cleaners is then passed through thickening ponds before the cleaned water is recirculated. The sludge extracted can be dewatered, usually in a filter press, and returned to the sinter plant.

(Courtesy of Ashmore, Benson, Pease & Company.)

Fig. 50. Double strand pig casting machine of the stationary wheel type. View of the strands from the pouring spouts.

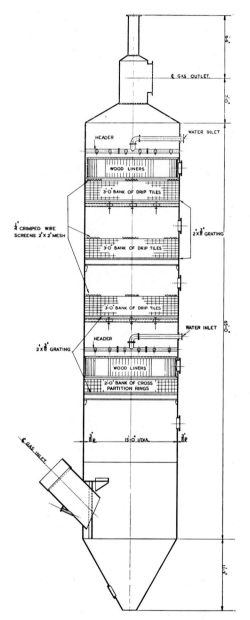

(Courtesy of Ashmore, Benson, Pease & Company.)

Fig. 51. Cross-section through a McKee gas washer.

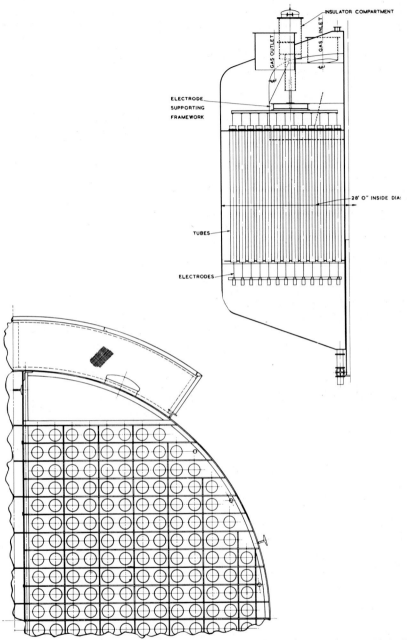

(Courtesy of Head Wrightson & Company Limited.)

Fig. 52. Half section through an electrostatic precipitator for final cleaning of blast furnace gas.

Fig. 53. Kling type hot metal ladle.

Fig. 54. Torpedo type hot metal ladle.

HOT METAL LADLES

It is hardly an exaggeration to say that a steel plant is designed around the hot metal ladles in use. It follows that in a new plant great care must be taken in the choice of metal ladles. If small ladles are used the cranes and tracks on the steelworks can be lighter than when big ladles are used. On the other hand, small ladles necessitate more iron spouts at the blast furnace and therefore an increase in the length of the iron runner and of the cast house.

Open ladles are rarely used at the blast furnace because of the unavoidable high skulling loss. The Kling type ladle is popular in sizes up to about 120 tons. It is almost spherical in shape and has a relatively small opening at the top for filling and emptying (*see* fig. 53).

Torpedo type ladles, of which several examples are manufactured, are roughly cigar-shaped and are built in several sizes to more than 200 tons capacity. The smaller type of torpedo ladle may be handled at the point of disposal by an overhead crane. In the larger type, the ladle itself is rotated about its long axis whilst in position on its carrying car. On occasion, this type of ladle may serve as a mixer at the steel plant. Fig. 54 shows a large torpedo ladle with self-contained tipping gear.

Almost all closed types of ladle will permit the retention of normal molten iron for periods up to 24 hours without severe skulling. Usually, hot metal ladles are lined with firebrick and should have a life of between 200 and 300 fillings.

If, owing to some mischance, iron does freeze in a ladle it can often be washed out by giving the ladle a rapid turn-round to a furnace manufacturing good hot iron. If this fails, it may be necessary to melt out the chilled iron by means of a gas or oil burner using oxygen. Such methods are somewhat slow and laborious but do avoid taking the ladle to pieces to remove the frozen skull.

REFERENCE

[1] "Blowers for use in Iron and Steelworks", by F. J. POTTER and L. DUFFY. *J. Iron & Steel Inst.*, 1956, *184*.

Chapter XIII

FURNACE OPERATION

BLAST-FURNACE OPERATION

THE LIFE OF A BLAST-FURNACE operator is filled with alarms and excursions. Too often, his day-to-day life is a constant progression from trouble to crisis and from crisis to trouble. No apology is made for reproducing words written in 1944.[1]

"Whilst there is no doubt that furnace managers are busiest when a furnace is in trouble, the maintenance of day-to-day operation requires close attention to numerous matters of details and close co-operation between the various members of the staff. Almost always, the operators of a blast furnace are choosing the lesser of two evils. Their path runs always between the devil and the deep, and the more economically the furnace is operating the narrower is the margin between good work and trouble. Raw materials and the weather are two factors which can bring serious trouble in spite of all the efforts of the men operating the furnace. In some ways, a furnace will stand a great deal of abuse before objecting, but in others, trouble is caused by very minor deviations from normal practice. There is no doubt that the furnaceman's biggest handicap is his ignorance. It is doubtful whether members of any other profession have to face their daily problems with a background of knowledge so incomplete as that of the furnaceman Thanks to the work of many furnacemen and scientific workers, knowlege of the furnace is steadily increasing, but there is still more to do than has already been done. The principal causes of this lack of knowledge are:

(1) The extreme complexity of the chemistry of the furnace and the rapid variations to which it is subject.

(2) The lack of visibility of the process. (When a furnaceman is looking into the tuyere glass of a furnace he is probably thinking that, even if he can understand what he sees there it represents only a peep at about one-thousandth part of the furnace and its contents.)

(3) The continuity of the process. When a furnaceman notices a change in slag composition, he cannot effect a correction to this change until about twelve hours of incorrect slag have been made.

(4) The cost of research work. It has still to be proved that models can faithfully reproduce what happens in a furnace, including all the diseases and mishaps to which a full-size furnace is subject in the course of a full campaign. This is not a condemnation of model work. On the contrary, it is the opinion of the Appleby-Frodingham staff that far too little use has been made of models, especially of models capable of making iron.

"The effect of the difficulties in gaining absolute knowledge is to place a premium on actual experience. A furnaceman who has successfully worried through a particular trouble is, therefore, apt to be regarded as an authority on that trouble, but the knowledge he gained is hardly ever shared with anyone except his colleagues in his own plant. If a furnaceman encounters a trouble which he has not before worried through it is almost certain that he can turn to no published work for assistance. The reluctance of furnacemen to admit troubles is a major cause of ignorance. In this paper fairly detailed accounts are given of two major troubles encountered at Appleby-Frodingham—scaffolds and hearth breakouts. The staff at Appleby-Frodingham had to face the scaffold trouble *de novo*, and while a search of the literature disclosed several general references, no direct information as to actual occurrences and no help as to curing or preventing these troubles could be found. It is believed that this is the first occasion upon which accurate description of scaffold removal and of the repair of a hearth breakout have ever been published. They will at least give ideas to a man who may be unfortunate enough to meet these troubles for the first time. The important point is that these two troubles at Appleby-Frodingham did not occur for the first, or last, time in the history of ironmaking. Such troubles are still too frequent in British ironmaking, and until there is a much freer interchange of experience are likely to remain too frequent. Far too often, the blastfurnaceman complains that the published work in connection with ironmaking is too academic. That accusation is true and will be true until furnacemen themselves alter it.

"It has been stated[2] that 'There are few situations in life where promptness and decision, forethought and good judgement, skill and experience are more needed than about a blast furnace in times of trouble'. This sentence would read, if written by a blastfurnaceman: 'There are few situations in life where the experience and example of others are so needed as round a blast furnace when a new kind of trouble is met'. Blast-furnace operation has suffered, and is still suffering, because no one man can live long enough to experience the full depths of depravity to which a furnace can sink. It has also suffered, and is still suffering, because of much confused thinking and opinions formed on incomplete evidence. This can be remedied only by a readier acknowledgement of troubles and failures."

These words were written fifteen years ago. In the intervening years, furnaces have increased in size and rates of production have gone up considerably. The whole tempo of ironmaking has speeded up so that the life of the operator is even less easy than it was. And it never was easy.

THE TOOLS OF THE OPERATOR

To tackle a job, the progress of which he can see very little, the blast-furnace operator has very few weapons in his armoury; he has a tremendous amount of plant at his disposal but there are only about six bases of operational control available to him day by day. These may be listed as:

(a) Blast volume.
(b) Blast temperature.
(c) Charging methods, including all aspects of distribution.
(d) Slag analysis.
(e) Slugs.
(f) Coke consumption.

Even these control factors have a restricted use in that the operator, as a rule, is attempting to blow with maximum blast volume and with maximum blast temperature. His slag analysis is usually dictated by the raw materials at his disposal and the analysis of the iron he has to make, and it is axiomatic that he must at all times be striving for minimum coke consumption. Perhaps the real skill in operating is knowing when to sacrifice or when to cut his losses; in knowing, for example, when to make a large temporary increase in coke consumption in order to recover normal operation as quickly as possible. Certainly, decisions of this kind are important factors in operation.

Consider what the operator is trying to do. Overriding all else, he is trying to make a taphole product at an economic cost. That generally means that he is pushing his furnace to produce every possible ton of iron per day. The harder he pushes the furnace the more likely is he to encounter mechanical troubles with his plant. With an increasing rate of production, wear and tear will increase.

He will attempt to produce iron with the lowest possible coke consumption. The lower the coke consumption, the lower is the margin of safety in regard to heat in the furnace. This inevitably means that metallurgical trouble is always nearer with low coke consumptions than when the furnace is normally operated with a high coke consumption.

Then the operator has to ensure the highest possible yield from the process, to avoid wastage of raw materials. This means emphasis on clean furnace work. Both dirty slags and dirty iron are wasteful. In conserving raw materials, flue dust production must be kept low. To have ample sintering capacity is no excuse for a high flue dust production.

Finally, iron quality must be satisfactory. The achievement and maintenance of this is by no means the easiest of tasks.

In striving to do all these things his principal difficulties are:

(a) The continuity of the process. In case of error, he cannot "empty out and start again".

(b) The time lag from charging to casting. An incorrect burden fills a furnace before the error can be detected.

(c) The lack of visibility of the process.

(d) The necessity to keep explosive gas, molten slag, molten iron and cold water flowing in their proper, but narrowly separated, channels.

(e) The ignorance of the operator about the process he is trying to carry out. However experienced a furnaceman may be, he will always admit that much of his "navigation is by guess and by God".

(a) BLAST VOLUME

If a furnace is normally being blown for a maximum production the only control which can be exerted by blast volume is downward. Reduced blast volume is helpful if a furnace is slipping, rolling, or hanging. If top gas temperature rises to a dangerous level reduced blast volume is the quickest way to restore normal conditions. Reduced blast volume, together with increased blast temperature, will help to increase hearth heat on a cold furnace before the life-saving coke blank (which is always charged as soon as the trouble is known to be serious) reaches tuyere level. And obviously, in all such troubles as slag breakouts, wild tapholes, etc., it is essential that blast volume be reduced to a minimum.

In other words, trouble occurs less frequently when the furnace is not being blown hard. Thus, the snort wheel station is the centre of operations. If a blast furnace can maintain a uniform unchanged blast volume for days at a time, that furnace is being under-blown.

When the stock is not descending (hanging), it can usually be settled by means of a sharp reduction in blast, which removes the upward support normally afforded by blast. As soon as the burden moves, blast should be restored to normal. This operation is known as "checking".

In some practices, checking is carried out as a regular routine at about 20 minute intervals.

(b) BLAST TEMPERATURE

Experience often imposes a limit to blast temperature much lower than that obtainable with the stove equipment at the disposal of the operator. This is especially true in basic iron practice based on ores and aiming at a freely moving furnace. In many districts, it is impossible to maintain uniform stock descent unless blast temperature is held at a comparatively low level. In general, the higher the slag volume, the lower this figure tends to become; for example, basic iron practice with British ores and little sinter will not permit a freely moving furnace with blast temperatures much in excess of 450°C. With lower slag volume, many basic iron furnacemen in the U.S.A. find that stock movement limits blast temperature to little more than 550°C. When this condition exists, blast temperature becomes an operating control both when it is increased and decreased. Obviously, any sign of chilling in the hearth of a furnace, as indicated by black slags or a reduced silicon content of the iron, should be offset by an immediate increase in blast temperature. It is more important to recover hearth heat than to maintain uniform stock descent.

If a furnace at normal temperature is hanging, a reduction in blast temperature is often efficacious in restoring stock movement; but such is the perveristy of the blast furnace that really persistent hanging may sometimes be overcome by a sudden and appreciable increase in blast temperature. If a furnace will not flush slag easily, a temporary reduction in blast temperature is often helpful. This does not of course apply when the slag will not flow because it is cold.

(c) CHARGING METHODS AND STOCK DISTRIBUTION

Manipulations of blast volume and temperature are usually effective in a matter of minutes. Changes in charging method cannot take effect so rapidly, although the effect of a change of charging may be felt in the way of furnace temperature and stock movement long before the charges concerned have arrived at the tuyeres. On a normally operating plant the operator will have decided on the most suitable charging cycle to be adopted and, in the light of experience, he will only depart from this if the furnace is suffering for more than a short time. On some furnaces, a built-in probe gives the operator information as to the gas distribution across the radius or diameter of the furnace. Unfortunately, these probes are very difficult to maintain in satisfactory condition.

Pyrometers situated in the inwall give almost as much valuable information and do so much more reliably. A change in the temperatures at this selected level can be brought about by changes in gas flow. If the temperatures increase without deliberate action by the operator, it is an indication that more gas is flowing up the wall of the furnace and, in some practices, this may not be desirable. The temperatures may be restored by such measures as reducing the amount of coke being charged or reversing the order of filling on to the big bell. If the temperatures fall at all points it is usually a sign that hearth temperatures will fall a few hours later. This warning of impending trouble can be extremely useful and can be offset by reducing blast volume, increasing blast temperature, or increasing the coke charged.

(For further remarks on the use of inwall pyrometers see the section on "Peripheral Distribution".)

If a furnace is making abnormally high amounts of flue dust without apparent cause, an increase in the size of the charge is often helpful. Big charges usually produce less flue dust than do small charges. Charging coke on the bell first usually produces a hotter furnace than charging ore first. It would be pointless to elaborate on the use of charging methods as an operating control: the best results can only be obtained as a result of experience. A method highly suitable to rich ore practice in one district may be completely unsuitable to lean ore practice in another district.

It is an almost universal experience to find that no single method of charging is always suitable. The self-aggravating effect of so many aspects of operation lead to the necessity for periodic correction. At many plants it is the custom to operate blast furnaces to a combination of charging methods, based on times dictated by experience. For example, C O C O for eight hours followed by O C O C for four hours.

If a furnace is using a burden low in volatile matter (rich, hard ore, or sinter) and is being pushed for tonnage, it may often be necessary to charge water in the skips in order to keep top gas temperature at a safe level. Varying the amount of water charged controls top gas temperature, and to a lesser extent, flue dust production.

(d) SLAG ANALYSIS

Bearing in mind that slag analysis is a function of the raw materials used and the iron quality desired, there are, nevertheless, occasions when the operator will deliberately alter slag composition to overcome furnace difficulties. For example, it is a very old trick to increase deliberately the lime content of a slag after a furnace has suffered a slag or iron breakout, although the efficacy of this is open to considerable doubt. On the other hand, if a furnace is working sluggishly or dirtily a change to more acid slags can often be of help. A more potent alteration in slag composition can be achieved by the use of slugs.

(e) SLUGS

A slug may be defined as an operating charge aimed at cleaning scabs or accretions from the lower stack and bosh wall. The most satisfactory slug in general use is coke and scrap (*see* next section). The other common types of slug consist of siliceous materials of low melting point—mill cinder, Bessemer slag, fluorspar, gravel and alkali salts have all been used on occasion. Perhaps the underlying consideration when using slugs of this nature is that wall accretions are usually of a high lime content; but this is not always the case (see section on "Scaffolds"). Nevertheless, many operators believe it to be good practice to charge a slug at regular intervals, more as a preventive measure than as a corrective of trouble.

(f) COKE CONSUMPTION

Variation in the method and amount of coke being charged is the most powerful aid to the operator in times of trouble. This is probably because coke has two main functions to perform:

(1) to provide heat,

(2) to provide voidage, or gas space.

If the furnace is cold and needs more heat, additional coke will provide it. If the furnace is tight and will not take blast volume, additional coke is again the certain corrective. When coke is relatively the most expensive raw material being charged, it requires experience to know when to make an addition to a furnace; failure to do so can, and often is, much more expensive than the troubles which can otherwise result.

Generally speaking, all furnace troubles other than purely mechanical ones (and the word "mechanical" includes such things as slag breakouts, tuyere losses, etc.) may be divided into the two categories mentioned above—lack of temperature or lack of voidage in the stock column. If the furnace is running cold it is best helped by increasing the weight of coke on every charge. If the furnace is suffering from lack of voidage, it is best corrected by introducing extra coke as separate and additional coke charges. These additions become more effective if clean heavy scrap is charged with the coke.

If extra coke is to be given to overcome trouble, let it be given freely. If iron is just a little off-grade and that persists, an increase in the coke charge—on every charge—of only one or two per cent. may be enough to correct matters. But if the furnace appears to be in trouble, or heading for trouble, an increase of one or two per cent. will be inadequate. In such circumstances, 30 or 50 tons should be given in one "blank". Aided by its own weight of heavy scrap, the coke will be even more effective. Of course, silicon will rise for a cast or two, but this coke and scrap blank, occupying several feet in depth in the furnace, will do two helpful things:

(1) It will increase the total heat available in the furnace.
(2) Because of its very high permeability, it will help to adjust distribution and thereby "straighten out the gas flow".

BURDEN DISTRIBUTION

Blast furnaces are charged by the opening of a cone-shaped valve, commonly known as a bell, within the reception hopper at the top of the furnace. Preliminary arrangements for gathering the charge on to this "big bell" may differ, but the final arrangement is almost always the same.

The blast furnace is charged with coke, a ferruginous burden which may or may not contain sinter or other prepared materials, and (usually) a fluxing material. Whatever the burden used, the bulk density and the angle of rest of the ferruginous and fluxing constituents are always radically different from those of the fuel. This means that the burden deposited at the stockline of the furnace must always undergo a certain amount of segregation, which can be influenced by the design and operation of the big bell.

The number of possible combinations to be obtained in charging is enormous but a few hard-and-fast rules can be laid down:

(1) As the diameter of the big bell approaches the diameter of the furnace throat the contour of the stockline will take on a more pronounced "V" shape. The more pronounced the "V", the more coke will segregate to the centre of the furnace, and the more ore will segregate to the walls.

(2) As the diameter of the big bell becomes smaller in relation to the diameter of the furnace throat the contour of the stockline will become a pronounced "M". Segregation with an "M" shaped stockline will lead to excess coke at the walls and centre of the furnace and to an ore-rich annulus below the lip of the bell.

(3) The greater the distance through which the burden is dropped from the big bell (that is, the lower the stockline) the more will the stockline take on an "M"-shaped contour. A low stockline will cause the exit gases to leave the furnace at a higher temperature.

The differences between "M" and "V" stocklines are important when they are considered in relation to segregation and bulk density.

In a charge of mixed particle size, the larger pieces will always tend to roll farthest. If a quantity of material of mixed sizes is dumped into a heap on the ground, the material at the foot of the slope will always be bigger than that at the top of the slope. It will be appreciated, therefore, that with a "V" stockline the centre of the furnace will be occupied by the larger material, which is usually the coke. With an "M" stockline, the larger pieces will tend to be distributed towards the wall and the centre of the furnace.

The segregation of sizes is further aggravated by the difference in the angle of rest of the materials. With unrestricted flow, furnace coke usually has an angle of rest of approximately 28°. Ores can range from 37° to 42°, but wet British ore may even be 44°. Sinter is usually about 35°.

In deciding whether an "M" or "V" stockline is required, many other factors must be considered; for example, an "M" stockline leads to a higher rate of gas flow up the wall and therefore to increased refractory wear. The amount of gas flow either up the wall or up the centre should be controlled to prevent it from becoming excessive. With an extremely pronounced "V" stockline, the condition may arise where the periphery of the furnace is relatively inactive and the gas is travelling at very high speed up the furnace centre. This will certainly lead to unsatisfactory operation, with a particular risk of the formation of adhesions to the wall (scaffolds).

Other things being equal, changes in furnace operation arising from altered distribution can be effected by varying the order in which materials are dumped on to the big bell. Practical experience alone can provide the answer to a particular problem, but one or two general principles may be expressed.

Charging ore on the bell first (*e.g.* ore, ore, coke, coke) gives a lower coke consumption than charging coke on the bell first (*e.g.* coke, coke, ore, ore). This latter method of charging is often found to be useful in cleaning a furnace with dirty walls, however, as it tends to encourage peripheral gas flow. Innumerable combinations can be employed, but one fairly well-established rule is that no single charging method will be suitable for continuous use, month in and month out. This statement will be better appreciated when it is realised that most of the effects of distribution are self-aggravating. For example, if the method of charging and the size of the materials is such as to encourage a "V" stockline, more gas will flow up the furnace centre. This in turn will mean that the centre of the furnace will work at a faster rate than the remainder of the cross-section and thus, the material in the centre will tend to descend at a faster rate than that at the furnace wall, so increasing the depth of the "V" stockline. (This principle can be applied to many aspects of blast-furnace operation.) Obviously, in the example quoted, the deepening "V" of the stockline will become unstable, and the burden will slip until stability is restored. A temporary change in the charging method will prevent this steady aggravation of conditions from developing to the point of trouble.

So far, consideration has been confined to distribution across the diameter of the furnace, that is, the radial distribution. However successful the operator may be in obtaining good radial distribution his efforts will be in vain unless supported by correct peripheral distribution. While there may be much argument as to the best type of radial distribution in a given practice, there can be no argument as to the desirability of correct peripheral distribution. Johnson,[3] was the first to describe means of controlling it and his classic work is worthy of study.

Fig. 55 shows a typical example of incorrect peripheral distribution. Once such a condition arises, the evils of self-aggravation operate only too often.

There are several causes of incorrect peripheral distribution in which the isotherms and iso-lines of CO_2 content of the gas depart from true circles described about the centre of the furnace. Some of these causes are:

(1) Uneven tuyering arising from plugged tuyeres or the use of tuyeres of uneven size.

(2) Lining wear. It is most unusual for the lining of a furnace to wear absolutely uniformly and towards the end of its campaign a mis-shapen furnace often results in incorrect peripheral distribution.

(3) A dirty bell caused by material adhering to it will lead to incorrect peripheral distribution.

(4) On furnaces equipped with revolving distributors trouble with, or incorrect operation of, the distributor, will soon lead to trouble with distribution. If for no other reason, the accuracy of the revolving distributor should be recorded charge by charge and also checked by visual inspection at frequent intervals.

Most furnaces are now equipped with at least one row of thermo-couples set in the brickwork and situated at 90° intervals some 20–25 ft. below the top platform. Providing the couples are efficiently main-tained they are a sensitive indication not only of correct peripheral distribution but of furnace conditions in general. Experience will soon indicate the desired temperature level which should be maintained on the inwall pyrometers. Generally speaking, if all four pyrometers show

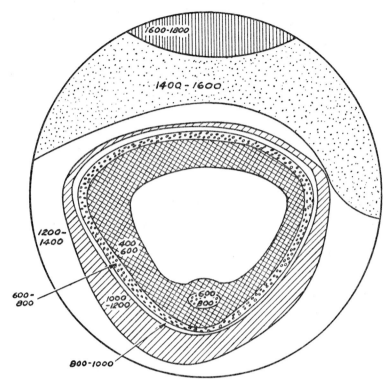

(Courtesy of American Institute of Mining and Metallurgy.)

Fig. 55. An example of incorrect peripheral distribution.

a fall in temperature, a fall in hearth temperature can be expected within a few hours. A fall in inwall temperature means that less heat is being transferred from ascending gas to descending stock, or less heat is being provided in the hearth for the ascending gas. If one thermocouple deviates from the others an obvious change in peripheral distribution is indicated, but an upward deviation is not as harmful as a downward one. The latter may be the warning of acretions forming on the stack walls. To counteract incorrect peripheral distribution the operator must make use of the controlling factors at his disposal. Some of these are:

(1) Altering the sequence of the revolving top to deposit either coarser or finer materials over a selected point.

(2) Altering the method of charging. This approach resembles the prevention of self-aggravating conditions, mentioned earlier.

(3) Varying the height of the stockline.

(4) Deliberately checking the furnace at intervals. (This only applies, of course, where checking practice is not followed.)

Generally, whatever material is being charged to the furnace and however closely graded that material may be, the study of distribution will always be important to the blast-furnace operator.

Perhaps the only effective way of controlling segregation is to adopt ore preparation to the greatest possible extent. It is undoubtedly true that the achievement of satisfactory distribution is easier with a fully prepared burden than with an ore burden which has not been efficiently screened. Sinter is almost invariably more closely sized than an ore burden. Alternatively, it may be that the achievement of the best type of distribution is not so important with a fully prepared burden.

It is virtually impossible to calculate scientifically the best type of distribution for a given practice or how to achieve it. Only by day-to-day operation can the necessary experience be obtained.

SIZE OF CHARGE

A further control in the hands of the operator is that of the optimum size of charge. At the risk of tedious repetition, experience is the only safe guide. The receiving hopper of a furnace will have a capacity (both in weight and volume) in excess of that needed to accommodate the size of charge normally employed. The minimum size of charge should be that which ensures that the material discharged from the bell will cover the whole area of the furnace. Because of the effects of segregation, it is always impossible to deposit a charge of uniform thickness over the furnace cross-section. But, especially with a "V" stockline, it is possible to put in a charge which does not cover the whole area (*see* fig. 56).

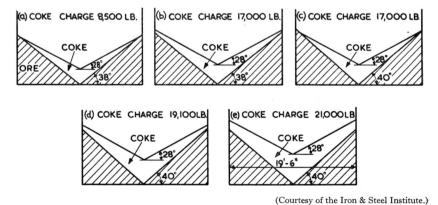

(Courtesy of the Iron & Steel Institute.)

Fig. 56. Theoretical stock lines.

Charges of this kind lead to high flue dust production and to irregular working.

BLOCK CHARGING

Mixed charging is the term used to describe the charging method when all the components of the burden are mixed in the charge and deposited on the bell as a mixture.

Example:	Coke	Ore	Coke	Ore	Stone	Dump
	Ore	Coke	Stone	Ore	Coke	Dump

Layer charging is the term used to describe the charging method when similar materials are deposited on the bell together and dumped separately.

Example:	Coke	Coke	Coke	Coke	Dump
	Ore	Ore	Ore	Ore	Dump

There are many theoretical reasons why layer charging should be preferable to mixed charging. Unfortunately, the results in practice are seldom convincing. An extension of layer charging is to separate the materials by size into separate layers.

Example:	Coke	Coke	Coke	Coke		Dump
	Ore	Ore ..	Ore	Ore	—all +1 in.	Dump
	Coke	Coke	Coke	Coke		Dump
	Ore	Ore	Ore	Ore	—all −1 in.	Dump

Again, results are usually not very convincing. The reason for this lies in the interface effects of the two sizes. This has been demonstrated when the raw materials have permitted the extension of layer charging to what is called "block charging".

Example:	Coke	Coke	Coke	Coke		Dump
	Ore	Ore	Ore	Ore	—all + 1 in.	Dump

Repeat for four hours

Then change to:

	Coke	Coke	Coke	Coke		Dump
	Ore	Ore	Ore	Ore	—all −1 in.	Dump

Repeat for four hours.

This cycle of eight hours is continued.

This method of charging is only possible when the ferruginous burden is a single ore or sinter and where facilities exist for size separation as near the furnace bunkers as possible. It has been proved in practice to be a highly satisfactory method, the success of which certainly lies in the reduction of interface effects between rough and fine materials.

The blast-furnace burden can be likened to a mixutre of sand and marbles and is well illustrated by fig. 57 after Josephs.[4] This analogy is

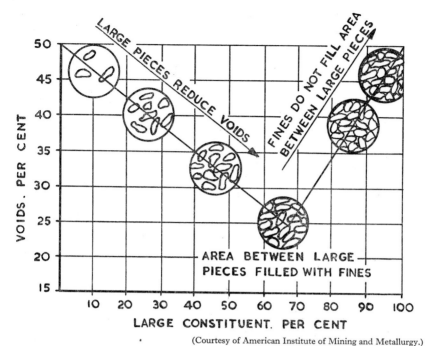

(Courtesy of American Institute of Mining and Metallurgy.)

Fig. 57. Voidage in a bed of broken solids of mixed sizes.

useful to explain the problem of permeability remembering that far too often it is stack permeability that determines the success or otherwise of the ironmaking practice. Providing the ore size is not too great for efficient reduction, the more permeable the stock column the easier it will be to blow air through the furnace, resulting in a greater iron output and a lower coke consumption.

Fill a glass jar with marbles and it will be evident that no difficulty would be encountered in blowing air through a stock column like this. Now loosely fill an identical jar with sand. There will be a lot of air space but it will be impossible to see it. Now gently pour the sand into the jar of marbles. A large amount of the sand will run through between the marbles with an obvious reduction in air space.

This simple experiment is a convincing demonstration of the difficulty of smelting a burden containing a lot of fines. Whether the fines originate from the coke, the flux, the ore, or the sinter, the result will be the same. Satisfactory furnace operation can never be achieved if the coke "marbles" are too small and the ore contains too much "sand". The only solution is to eliminate the sand before it enters the furnace.

When charging small layers of the two sizes, after size separation, it is impossible to avoid mixing in the furnace, so that the theoretical effect of layering is almost completely lost. But when block charging is possible, the chances of mixing are much reduced. The interface effect only operates at intervals of four hours in the examples given.

INSTRUMENTATION

A wide variety of instruments is available to help the blast-furnace operator. Instruments can be divided into two categories:

(a) *Operational instruments:* These are required for the minute-to-minute running of the furnace.

(b) *Inquest instruments:* These are so called because they help the operator, when looking back, to find the reasons for unusually good or bad results.

It is general practice to locate most of the instruments on a control panel, giving the operator only two or three essential indicators at the snort wheel position.

With the increasing scale of ironmaking operations, and the devastating speed with which trouble can occur, there is now some reason to regard the snort wheel station in the same way as the navigating bridge of a ship. A blast furnace represents a capital investment as great as that of a medium-sized liner. It would be criminal to send a ship to sea without a fully-equipped navigating bridge, and without having the bridge occupied at all times by a qualified officer of the watch.

The snort wheel station is as vital to the blast furnace as the navigating bridge is to the ship. The blast-furnace instruments should be located at this point, so that the "navigating foreman" has as much information as possible in front of him. Not only is it important for him to know what is happening at the moment (indicating instruments) but he should be able to see what has been happening some hours before (recording instruments). Recorders should be designed so that the immediate reading is clearly visible.

The following is a list of what are probably the minimum requirements in the way of instruments:

INSTRUMENTS FOR SNORT WHEEL STATION

1. *Blast volume:* recorder.

2. *Blast pressure:* recorder plus large indicator inside and outside the station.

3. *Stockline:* large movement visualiser and recorder.

4. *Top gas pressure:* recorder.

5. *Top gas temperature:* recorder.

6. *Hot blast temperature:* controller and recorder.

7. *Clean gas pressure:* recorder.

8. *Distributor:* recorder.

9. *Inwall temperature:* recorder. Inwall temperatures should be measured at four points (90° spacing) at each of two levels, 15-ft. and 25-ft. below the closed bell.

10. *Water pressure:* indicator.

STOVES AND STOVE PLATFORM

1. *Blast pressure:* Indicator showing pressure of the furnace on the cold side of the stoves. Blast pressure indicators showing pressure in each stove, located at each stove.

2. *Stove dome and chimney stack temperatures:* recorder. There should also be audible warning when these temperatures reach a predetermined limit.

3. *Gas flow to stoves:* recorder.

GENERAL—CAST HOUSE

1. *Blast pressure:* indicator on the horseshoe main in sectors where the blast pressure indicator on the outside of the snort control station cannot be seen. Blast pressure indicator in the hoist house.

2. *Stockline:* indicator in cast house.

3. *Water pressure:* indicators, with audible warning when pressure drops.

SCALE CAR PULPIT

1. Blast pressure indicator.

2. Stockline recorder and indicator.

3. Distributor indicator.

4. Skip cycle indicator.

5. Functioning of electrical relays to be indicated by lights.

6. Top gas temperature recorder.

COMMUNICATIONS AND SIGNALS

The importance of effective and rapid communication and signalling cannot be over-emphasized. The minute-by-minute operation of the blast furnace demands the co-operation of several people who are remote and invisible from each other. For example, an alteration in blowing rate affects not only the furnaceman but the man providing the air (*i.e.* the blower driver) and the man disposing of the gas. It follows, therefore, that each of these people should know what the other is doing. If a blast furnace is to be taken off wind the scale car driver should be warned by telephone and an isolating "stop charging" button should be fitted in the snort control station.

It is strongly recommended that furnace communications and signals comprise a completely independent system. Generally speaking, signals will be initiated at the blast furnace by the furnace operator. The following are considered to be the minimum desirable signals at his disposal:

(1) *"Stand by"*: this is to warn recipients of the signal that the furnace operator will shortly take some action affecting the blowing rate of the furnace.

(2) *"First ease"*: this is an instruction to the blower driver to reduce blast volume to a figure previously arranged.

(3) *"Second ease"*: a further instruction to reduce blast volume to an agreed lower figure than "First ease".

(4) *"Off blast"*: to notify recipients that the furnace is now off blast.

(5) *"Stove change"*: a general notification that a change of hot blast stoves is about to take place.

(6) *"Full blast"*: this is to notify all recipients that the furnace has now been restored to normal blast or operation.

These signals should be initiated by push button and they should be illuminated at the blast furnace, at the blower serving that furnace, at the gas cleaning plant, at the gas control station and at the charging pulpit. At the gas cleaning plant and at the blower, the visible signal should be augmented by an audible signal which will continue to sound until the recipient of the signal presses an acknowledgement button. This should stop the audible signal and illuminate a "signal received" panel at the blast furnace. A system such as this, modified to suit local conditions, ensures that the people who are intimately affected have a picture of what is happening at all times before them.

Signals alone are not sufficient; they must be reinforced by a system of spoken communication. A telephone system which is quite independent of any other system should serve the following points:

(1) Blast furnace.

(2) Charging pulpit.

(3) Blower.

(4) Gas cleaning plant.

(5) Gas controller.

(6) Shift maintenance office.

(7) Foremen's office.

(8) Manager's office.

(9) Boilers.

(10) Iron Controller.

(11) Traffic foreman.

This telephone system is used to inform a furnace foreman of what is happening at the other furnaces; queries can be made, and instructions given with the minimum delay.

A priority button should be attached to the telephone in each snort control station to enable the operator to cut in on any conversation.

Things can go wrong so quickly around a blast-furnace plant that it is essential for the operator to be absolutely sure of making contact with any man he needs, without delay.

The use of broadcasting systems is not recommended. Many people hear messages not intended for them and, in the course of time, tend to regard such broadcasting as merely background noise.

One further set of communications is required to cover the various levels of the furnace. It must be possible to speak from the top of the furnace to the bottom, to the hoist house, and to the charging pulpit. This is especially valuable during repairs and maintenance in order to keep in touch with personnel who may be on top of the furnace.

SCAFFOLDS

Of the more serious troubles which can beset a furnace, accretions on the walls of the stack are fairly common. Such growths are generally known as scaffolds and their incidence is reported in all practices. In their most severe form, they have been known to close the area of the stack almost entirely. Even growths of quite modest dimensions can and do cause serious deterioration in furnace results.

Scaffolds result from the downward moving burden adhering to the refractory walls. Growth may be so slow as to escape detection until it has achieved some degree of permanence. A scaffold such as the one accurately depicted in fig. 58 is by no means unknown and is extremely difficult to remove when of this size. Both structure and composition vary greatly, but in general all scaffolds have a hard working face and a soft powdery core and contain much deposited carbon.

A high concentration of alkali salts is usual in all scaffolds and some may contain tough leathery sheets of metallic iron. These accretions may occur at any level in the stack but they are rarely found in the region from 10 ft. to 15 ft. above the bosh, nor in the the top section containing the throat armour.

They are caused by many things, but can grow to a semi-permanent condition only if gas flow up the wall is at a low level. This will occur if the distribution of the materials being charged favours the segregation of fines to the wall of the furnace. If the burden contains no fines, the

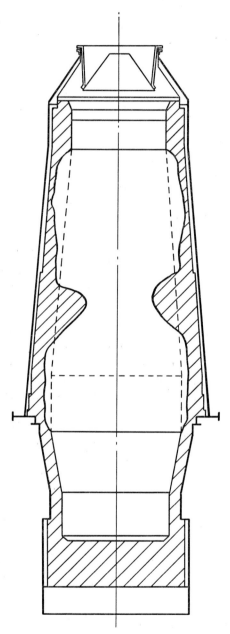

Fig. 58. A typical stack scaffold.

risk of scaffolding is much reduced. A burden of soft coke and fine ores with a low softening or melting range is more liable to stack scaffolds than one with hard ores and good coke. Sinter, because of its resistance to carbon deposition, is usually less troublesome in this connection than are the ores from which it is made. In a practice prone to scaffolds, the big bell should be smaller in relation to the throat than is usually the case. But if this is taken to excess, trouble with scaffolds may be replaced in a relatively short time by trouble from the cutting back of the lining. The correct ratio of bell to throat cannot be laid down—it is dependent on too many factors associated with a particular furnace and materials. But it can be stated with some confidence that several works have reduced the severity of scaffold troubles by improved coke quality, better and more complete ore preparation and by using a smaller big bell.

A scaffolded furnace will always be an erratic performer. The usual signs of trouble include the following:

(*a*) Increased coke consumption.

(*b*) Increased flue dust.

(*c*) Irregular iron quality.

(*d*) Higher blowing pressures which can be partly offset by a lowered stock-line.

(*e*) Difficulty in achieving uniform stock descent.

(*f*) Persistent incorrect peripheral distribution, as indicated by well maintained stack pyrometers.

Test drilling of the stack should be carried out to determine the location and amount of any accretion. If severe, explosives should be used to effect removal, but this is far from a certain cure. Even if the scaffold is removed, the lining may be left in such a shape that furnace operation remains poor. It will probably be desirable then to blow out the furnace so as to clean and repair the stack. Auxiliary tuyeres inserted under and into the scaffold and connected to the main blast supply have occasionally been used with success[5]—and also without success.

The removal of a scaffold is such a difficult and uncertain business, that it emphasises the importance of preventing a small, temporary accretion to the stack wall from growing into a large and permanent scaffold.

If the burden is really bad, scaffolds will occur in spite of all the operational controls which are applied—and changing a bell and hopper to a smaller diameter is too time-consuming to be regarded as an operational control. In all practices, the operator should keep the danger of scaffolds constantly in mind. Inwall thermocouples should be installed and efficiently maintained and continuously studied. A deterioration in peripheral distribution can usually be corrected if tackled immediately but can lead to scaffolding if ignored. Correction is effected by altered charging method, coke blanks, or manipulation of distributor and stockline height. Regular changes in charging method by changing the gas flow are undoubtedly of assistance in preventing scaffold growth and the regular use of "slugs" is also helpful.

REFERENCES

[1] *Iron and Steel Institute Special Report No. 30*, 1944, 171.

[2] *The Making, Shaping and Treatment of Steel,* by CAMP and FRANCIS. The Carnegie-Illinois Steel Corporation. Pittsburgh and Chicago, 1940.

[3] "The Peripheral Distribution of Gases, by H. W. JOHNSON. *Year Book Amer. Iron & Steel Inst.*, 126.

[4] "The Blast Furnace Process and Means of Control", by T. L. JOSEPHS. *A.I.M.E. Tech. Pub. 2021.*

[5] *Iron and Steel Institute Special Report No. 30*, 1944, 212.

Chapter XIV

OPERATING PROCEDURES – I

OPERATING PROCEDURES

THE HOUR BY HOUR OPERATION of a blast furnace demands that many jobs should be carried out as a matter of routine. It also demands that everyone concerned should have some knowledge of what to do when one of the less frequent, and therefore more troublesome, jobs becomes necessary. This is especially true for the man who has to work when his senior colleagues are asleep in bed.

For that reason, it is necessary to lay down agreed operating procedures to cover all foreseeable eventualities as well as the jobs which have to be done on every shift. What follows in this chapter is a series of instructions to cover some aspects of routine operation. It is by no means an exhaustive list but it is hoped that it will serve to indicate what is required on any well-managed plant.

The procedures are based on those applying at one British plant. They may not be directly applicable to all plants because of difference in plant design and layout, but the principles are the same everywhere. The procedures which follow have been tested over many years' operation at the plant in question.

But however well tried and proven such a set of standing orders may be, every opportunity should be taken to amend, improve and revise, as experience over the years dictates.

There are many occasions in blast-furnace operation when improvisation is necessary, but improvisation will always be more successful if applied against a background of generally followed and agreed procedure.

FILLING A FURNACE

1. Insert into the taphole a 6 in. diameter pipe in two sections. One section should be long enough to reach about one-quarter of the way across the furnace. The section outside the furnace should be about 6 ft. long so that when the furnace is lit, ignited gas may be blown down the pipe to dry the iron runner. The two sections should be joined in the taphole by means of a loose-fitting sleeve. The outer section should have

a hole about 1 in. diameter near its outside end so that a hook can be inserted to remove it when part of the runner is dry, thus allowing the furnace end of the runner to be dried. The space between the joining sleeve and the brickwork of the taphole should be packed with clay.

2. Fill the hearth to tuyere level with good quality coke. A few tons of selected foundry coke can be a good investment to ensure that taphole and notch are not buried in coke breeze. This should be hand-forked through a hearth cooler to avoid breakage. Select the largest lumps for the areas round the taphole and notches. Stack kindling wood round each tuyere inside the furnace. Lay wooden sleepers against the wall of the hearth to protect the tuyeres and to prevent the kindling from being flattened by the coke charged through the top of the furnace. Replace all goosenecks and copper coolers which have been left out for forking in the coke and laying the kindling.

3. Make sure that the distributor is working.

4. Charge sufficient coke to fill to the top of the bosh. Charge stone evenly throughout this coke blank to flux the coke ash.

5. Commence charging the burden. The ore/coke ratio of the burden directly on top of the coke blank should be approximately 0·5/1. Gradually increase the load until the ore/coke ratio is about 1·65/1 when the furnace is full. Burden the furnace to produce a slag rather more acid than normal.

Measure the burden as soon as possible to avoid over-filling and thus jamming the bell. Bring the automatic test rod into the electrical charging sequence when, by calculation, the furnace is approximately half full.

Do not fill to more than about 6 ft. below the normal full line. It is useful to be able to drop in a charge or two if the furnace should get "hot on top" shortly after blast is put on.

When filling is completed, go inside the furnace to check distribution. The angle of the crater should be measured to check that the big bell is exactly central in the furnace.

BLOWING IN

There are almost as many methods of blowing in a furnace as there are blast-furnace managers. At some plants, it is still the practice after filling the furnace to light wood in the taphole and to allow the furnace to draught naturally through open bleeders for twenty-four hours before putting wind on. At other plants, where wind is put on immediately after lighting, the lighting may be at the taphole, or as outlined later, at the tuyeres.

Blowing in usually follows a period of tremendous activity in preparing the furnace for blast, and for this reason, the importance of inspection before actually blowing in cannot be over-emphasised. Too many examples are known of such oversights as failure to turn on full water supply and to replace inspection covers. It is good practice to have two inspection crews to go round the whole of the plant concerned, separately and in opposite directions.

The detailed procedure is as follows:—

(1) Arrange a meeting of all directly concerned and inform all departments indirectly concerned.

(2) Fill the furnace, following the procedure given in "Filling a furnace" on page 181.

(3) Before lighting:

(a) Heat up the stoves to a pre-arranged programme, following instructions given in "Heating up a Hot Blast Stove" on page 210.

(b) Have instructions ready for:

(i) *The Scale Car Driver:*
These filling instructions should include the first 24 hours of blowing.

(ii) *The Stoveminder:*
The stove is to be on hand control—not automatic.
The position of the valves at starting will be:
Cold blast valves closed
Blow off valves closed
Chimney valves closed
Mixing valves closed
Hot blast valves closed.

(iii) *The Furnace Shift Staff.*

(iv) *The Blower Driver:*
These instructions should be given through the blast furnace shift staff.

(c) The furnace must be isolated from the gas main with the goggle valve shut. Close up all inspection covers and open any necessary purges. Before closing the dustcatcher inspection doors, dump sufficient sand (a few barrow loads) in the dustcatcher to make a gas seal. If this is not done, the area round the dustcatcher will be dangerously gas-laden for many hours. The discharge valve of a dust catcher is rarely gas-tight without the help of dust or sand. The gas washer must be isolated from the clean and dirty gas mains.

(d) Open the furnace bleeders.

(e) Close the furnace bells.

(f) Check the signalling system to all points, *viz.* blower, gas plants and furnace hoist.

(g) Open the snort valve to atmosphere and turn the blower into the cold blast main.

(h) Bott and clay up all slag notches.

(j) Check all furnace water and then recheck.

(k) See that instruments are working and checked.

(l) Turn on steam in the dustcatchers, furnace top and between the bells.

(m) Have a fire in the taphole runner and check that the taphole pipe (*see* "Filling the Furnace") is in position.

(n) Check the distributor.

(o) See that all personnel are off the furnace top. Rope off the furnace galleries and skip bridge staircase. If the installation includes a passenger lift, it should be isolated by removing the electric fuses, and these should be left in charge of the shift foreman.

(p) Have lighting equipment ready and paraffin-soaked cotton waste in each tuyere.

(q) Open all hearth gooseneck face pieces.

(r) See that the hot blast thermocouple is in position.

If the furnace is to be lit with hot blast, at least 600°C. blast temperature should be available. Gooseneck face pieces should be closed and blast put on in the normal way.

The lighting of a blast furnace is regarded as a somewhat ceremonial occasion and the application of visible fire to light the furnace is usually preferred to the mere turning of a valve.

(4) After lighting with torches:

(a) Make sure that all hearth tuyeres are ignited.

(b) Close the gooseneck face pieces.

(c) Warn the stoveminder to prepare for "on blast". He will open:

    (i) The cold blast valve.

    (ii) The cold mixing valve.

    (iii) The hot blast valve of the stove to be used first.

(d) Put blast on in the normal way.

(e) Check that the drop valve has lifted. If necessary, lift and fasten it in position, remembering to unfasten it when there is sufficient pressure in the main to keep it shut.

(f) Keep everyone away from the furnace area.

(g) Make sure that the gas at the taphole is ignited, by maintaining a large fire in the runner.

(*h*) Close the taphole after twelve hours, or when slag appears there, or when the taphole pipe becomes blocked. Use a light clay stopping.

(*j*) Try for slag frequently from four hours after closing the taphole.

(*k*) Open the taphole as soon as possible after slag has been flushed, burning horizontally and in the taphole roof. This will give a better chance of tapping iron as the bottom of the hearth will be chilled with viscous slag made from the large amount of coke ash in the furnace.

(*l*) If the furnace is one of several in normal operation, there should be no hurry about turning gas into the system, but if it is desired to use gas as soon as possible, as when starting up a whole plant, the gas should be tested for oxygen and hydrogen before opening the isolating valve. It is usually quite safe to do this two hours after putting wind on.

(*m*) Blow to the agreed programme. Check the blast volume with the amount of coke burned; a figure of 55 cu. ft. of air to burn 1 lb. of coke is near enough for this check.

The following is a guide for blowing in furnaces varying from 25 ft. to 30 ft. in diameter:

Start with a blast volume of 40,000 cu. ft. per minute which will probably give a pressure of $\frac{3}{4}$ p.s.i. at the hearth tuyeres. Do not increase this volume until the taphole is stopped, which should be about 12 hours later. Increase the volume by 800–900 cu. ft. per minute per hour to reach 60,000 cu. ft. per minute 36 hours from the start of the blow in. This volume will give a pressure of 8 to 9 p.s.i. The condition of the furnace will govern any further increase of volume over 60,000 cu. ft. per minute. Usually, slag should have been flushed after 18 hours and the first cast completed after a little over 24 hours blowing.

The log of the previous blow in of this furnace or of a similar furnace should be available to the operating staff throughout the blow in.

CASTING A FURNACE WITH MORE THAN ONE FURNACE ON THE GAS SYSTEM

One person only should be responsible for casting and no one must distract his attention unless really necessary.

Gas and metal controllers should be informed before starting to cast.

Give the "stand by" signal and make sure that the clay gun can be electrified.

It is desirable for the shift pipefitter to be in attendance whenever a furnace is being cast.

Check that the drill stand is in the correct position; it should be set to give a drilling angle of 25 deg. from the horizontal.

Check that slag ladles and metal ladles are in position.

See that the taphole is burned out with the lance at the angle of the drill and in line with the iron runner. Careless burning from a position wide of the runner side can result in burning a stave cooler or in damage to the taphole. The man burning through the taphole must wear protective clothing.

Maintain as high a blast pressure as possible, consistent with a reasonable flow of slag and iron. When a furnace is deemed to be "slag and iron dry" the gun should be plugged into the taphole at once. It is not advisable to blow the taphole unduly as slag and iron blowings will cut the internal brickwork round the taphole—brickwork that can never be replaced during the working life of a furnace.

There are, however, occasions when blowing a taphole may be done to advantage. If a furnace hearth has been chilled and at previous casts the taphole has been sealed immediately slag has been seen (in order to avoid the heavy work of cleaning up) a moderate blow will help to ensure a deeper penetration of the gun nozzle and so strengthen the taphole. In general practice, however, tapholes should not be subjected to blast when the furnace is considered to be dry.

Ensure that the power is on the clay gun just before the gun is inserted.

Increase the blast pressure as soon as the gun has sealed the taphole.

Leave the gun in the taphole at least five minutes to allow the clay to stiffen.

During this time, inspect all tuyeres and all cooler discharges.

Do not give the "Full Blast" signal until the gun is out of the taphole and the taphole is seen to be stopped.

During casting, the snort wheel must not be left unattended.

CHECKING A FURNACE

A furnace is checked for any of four reasons:
(1) To lower and settle the burden.
(2) To prevent the burden from slipping.
(3) To allow the passage of more gas up the furnace and therefore more blast into the tuyeres.
(4) To ensure that slag is not held up above the tuyeres.

For the first of these reasons, pressure is reduced by the snort valve control until the burden descends. When blowing at high pressure there have been many occasions when a slip has followed almost immediately after a check; it is therefore necessary to take the pressure as low as possible during checking.

If a furnace is blowing at maximum pressure for a low volume, more frequent checking is necessary, even if this is at ten-minute intervals.

When checking, the tuyeres must be watched to see that slag does not flow into the blast pipes.

After a check, maximum blowing conditions should be restored immediately.

TAKING A FURNACE OFF BLAST WITH OTHER FURNACES BLOWING

1. One man only must be responsible for taking the furnace off blast.
2. Give as much notice as possible to all concerned, namely:
   Gas controller
   Metal controller
   Blower driver
   Stoveminder
   Gas plant attendant
   Traffic foreman
   Dustcatcher operators
   Electrical foreman
   Fitter foreman
   Labour foreman
   Shift foreman at the other furnaces.

Some maintenance jobs can only be done in off-blast periods, so that riggers, platelayers, instrument maintenance and other departments concerned should also be informed. It is important that the furnace supervisor should estimate as accurately as possible the length of a stoppage and inform all departments of the time available.

3. Plan to dry the furnace at cast and have a hot stove ready through which to draught back.
4. Make all possible preparation for off-blast operations, such as the provision of tools, replacements and personnel.
5. Check that steam is turned on between and under the bells.
6. Give the blower the "stand-by" signal, cast the furnace in the normal way and fill to a full stockline.
7. Near the end of the cast, check the furnace at least once to below 5 p.s.i.
8. After casting, ease the furnace down as low as possible by means of the snort valve. Keep a close watch at the tuyeres to avoid slag flowing back down the blast pipes. Flush slag if necessary.

9. Increase the blast to 5–7 p.s.i. pressure and instruct the pipefitter to isolate the furnace from the gas system. As the isolating valve is closed, open the bleeders progressively with the increase of top gas pressure.

10. Receive word from the pipefitter that the furnace is isolated and that steam is in the dustcatchers.

11. Instruct the hoist driver not to drop in any more charges and check that there is at least one skip load on one of the bells. Inform the dustcatcher attendants that blast is off the furnace. Finally, operate the "no charging" button to isolate the hoist gear during the off-blast period.

12. Reduce the pressure on the furnace to zero by fully opening the snort valve. Fasten the snort wheel in the open position.

13. Instruct the stoveminder to isolate the stoves from the main to the snort valve, and the furnace from the stoves. When the stoveminder reports that this has been done, extract the hot blast thermocouple and give the blower the "Off blast" signal.

14. Instruct the stoveminder to draught back. On receiving his report, proceed with the maintenance work.

15. If the furnace is to be off blast for more than three hours, all tuyeres should be clayed up to prevent any slag and iron formation. Check every half-hour that all stoppings are effective.

16. Keep draughting back unless the blast pipes have been dropped or tuyeres clayed up and there is no connection between the furnace and the horseshoe main.

ISOLATING A FURNACE FROM THE BLOWER

I. JOBS WHICH NECESSITATE TAKING THE BLOWER OUT OF THE COLD BLAST MAIN

(a) Welding on the cold blast main. A steam inlet must be made adjacent to the welding.

(b) Changing cold blast valves, mixing valves and drop valves.

(c) Removing inspection covers on the cold blast main.

(d) Any furnace stoppage of sufficiently long duration to permit maintenance work on the blowing equipment.

Procedure when taking off blast

(i) Take blast off in the normal way (see previous section).

(ii) Clay up all tuyeres and drop all blast pipes.

(iii) Turn steam into the cold blast main at the furnace end and the blower end.

 (iv) Stop draughting back.
  (v) Isolate the blower from the cold blast main.
 (vi) Place danger boards in the blowing house on all valves to the
       furnace concerned.

Procedure when putting on Blast
   (i) Check that all the work which necessitated the stoppage has
        been finished.
  (ii) Inform the blower driver that the furnace is ready for the
        blower.
 (iii) Turn the blower into the cold main up to the open snort valve.
  (iv) Start draughting back at the stoves.
   (v) Remove the clay stoppings from the tuyeres and replace the
        blast pipes.
  (vi) Take steam out of the cold blast main.
 (vii) Fasten all the face pieces.
(viii) Put blast on in normal way.

2. JOBS WHICH NECESSITATE DROPPING THE BLAST PIPES

 (a) All occasions when the blower is to be taken out of the cold main.
 (b) The changing of hot blast valves and seats.
 (c) The removal of inspection covers in the hot and cold blast system.
 (d) Any work which involves men working near an opening in the
      hot blast main.

Procedure when taking off blast
   (i) Take blast off in the normal way.
  (ii) Clay up all tuyeres and drop all blast pipes.
 (iii) Stop draughting back.

Procedure when putting on blast
   (i) Start draughting back.
  (ii) Remove the clay stoppings from the tuyeres and replace the
        blast pipes.
 (iii) Put blast on in the normal way.

3. JOBS WHICH REQUIRE THE CLAYING UP OF TUYERES BUT NOT THE DROPPING OF BLAST PIPES

 (a) Changing bleeders.
 (b) Working between the bells.
 (c) The removal of dustcatcher valves.

(*d*) Stoppages of three hours duration or more (tuyeres are clayed up in order to prevent the formation of slag in front of the tuyeres).

Procedure when taking off blast
   (i) Take blast off in the normal way.
  (ii) Clay up all tuyeres and keep draughting back.
 (iii) Leave the tuyere face pieces open.

Procedure when putting on blast
   (i) Remove the clay stoppings from the tuyeres.
  (ii) Close the face pieces.
 (iii) Put blast on in the normal way.

LOSS OF COPPER COOLING MEMBERS

All copper cooling members should be examined after each cast and at intervals between casts.

(*a*) BLOWING TUYERES

Examine the water discharge pipe. If no water is flowing through this pipe, it should be assumed that all the water is going into the furnace. If this is the case, the tuyere will not be bright; slag may be showing in front of the tuyere, water flames may be showing in the vicinity and water may be showing in the hearth cooler bottom.

Fix a semi-circular water spray to play on the back of the tuyere and turn off the feed water. Change the tuyere at the first opportunity.

If the leak in a blowing tuyere is only slight it may be indicated by the following signs:
   (i) A "water flame" in the vicinity.
  (ii) Bubbles in the discharge water.
 (iii) Water appearing round the hearth cooler.
 (iv) Water "kicking" in the discharge pipe.
  (v) Moisture inside the tuyere or blowpipe.

Under such conditions, the feed water should be reduced and the tuyere may continue to work satisfactorily until there is a suitable opportunity to change it, but it should be examined more frequently than the others.

Whenever a blast pipe has been removed from a tuyere that has been cooled externally by water, it should be examined for cracks before re-use.

(b) TUYERE COOLERS

The most frequent cause of failure of hearth coolers is by slag and/or iron burning through the blast pipe and burning the bottom of the hearth cooler.

If the leak in a cooler allows water to flow into the furnace, ease the feed water and turn the discharge water pipe down into the trough below, thereby creating a slight suction.

If water still flows into the furnace, take the furnace off blast, plug the tuyere tightly with clay, turn water off the cooler, remove the feed and discharge pipe and insert brass plugs.

Change the cooler at the first opportunity.

In service, a heavy skull builds up in front of a tuyere cooler. This affords a considerable measure of protection so that changing may safely be postponed for some hours.

(c) PLATE COOLERS

Plate coolers are often coupled together in groups of three or four. If the first cooler of a group has a serious leak the remaining coolers in that group may be deprived of water and consequently be burned. It is therefore essential to separate any leaking plate cooler from all other coolers in the group. The discharge pipe from the affected cooler should be "turned down" and the feed water reduced.

If the furnace continues to take water from this cooler, it should be changed at the next cast.

(d) SLAG TUYERES, SLAG INTERMEDIATE TUYERES AND SLAG COOLERS

Slag should not be flushed through the slag notch copper cooling members when the water is off, except in cases of emergency (*see* section on "Iron over the Notch").

Water may have to be turned off these cooling members, however, when a furnace has a chilled hearth. Whenever this happens, the copper should be replaced as soon as conditions allow.

(1) *Slag tuyeres*

When a slag tuyere is found to be leaking during a flush, ease the water. This may prevent the slag from foaming. If a lot of foam is being made it may be necessary to turn off the water momentarily while the notch is being "botted up".

If a slag tuyere is found to be leaking when slag is not flowing through it, the water should be eased to a minimum and the tuyere changed at the first opportunity. It may be necessary to turn the water off completely. In such a case, make sure that the notch is left botted to prevent slag from breaking through.

(2) *Intermediate slag tuyeres*

Slag may be flushed through leaking intermediate slag tuyeres if the leak is slight and the water is escaping out of the furnace, but the water should be eased to a minimum. If too much water is escaping to allow normal flushing, ease the water to a minimum and change the member at the first opportunity.

Do not turn off all the water unless it is certain that it is entering the furnace.

(3) *Slag coolers*

Slag may be flushed through a leaking slag cooler if the leak is slight and the water is escaping out of the furnace, but here again the water should be reduced to a minimum. If too much water is escaping to allow normal flushing it should be reduced as far as possible and the member changed at the first opportunity. Do not use this notch until the cooler is changed.

Do not turn off all the water unless it is certain that it is entering the furnace.

If the water has to be turned off, fix a plate in front of the notch and rope off the area.

When slag coolers have been changed they should not be flushed (except in an emergency) for the next 24 hours, thus allowing a slag scab to form at the cooler nose and minimising the risk of slag flushing between the members.

The slag cooler, intermediate and tuyere are held in the furnace by means of cottered "keeps" which securely anchor the feed and discharge pipes to the furnace casing. In addition, the slag cooler is anchored to the furnace casing by means of steel "keeps" bearing directly on the back of the cooler and welded to the furnace casing. Whenever the furnace is off blast these holding arrangements should be inspected and any slackening rectified.

GENERAL REMARKS ON COPPER COOLING MEMBERS

All discharge pipes should be visible.

Feed cocks should be turned occasionally when the furnace is off blast, to ensure that they can be turned off in an emergency, and to familiarise furnace workers with the exact whereabouts of vital cocks.

To mark all the cocks round a furnace can be confusing but it is important that cocks for tuyeres and slag notch members should be marked. All cocks should be located so that they are not in front of the member they serve; it may be dangerous to pass in front of a damaged cooling member.

Hearth and slag coolers should be flushed out through the bottom plug hole as frequently as possible, but only when the furnace is off blast. On these occasions, manifolds should be flushed, preferably before flushing the coolers they serve.

Tuyere feed pipes should be at the bottom of the tuyeres and the discharge pipe at the top.

The life of all blowing tuyeres and slag notch members should be recorded. A stoppage may be averted if old tuyeres are changed during a planned stoppage.

Tuyere coolers and plate coolers are anchored by means of "keeps" to the furnace casing. These "keeps" should be examined once a month, or when an individual member has been changed.

Protection plates to guard against "flying" tuyere plugs should always be in place. Whenever a tuyere is changed, make sure that the protection plate is replaced before going on blast.

Water does not necessarily show itself near the point from which it is leaking; it has been known to travel half-way round the furnace before making itself visible.

The lower portion of tuyere coolers should be protected by a thin refractory lining to prevent damage to the cooler by molten iron or slag. In case of damage to this lining, it should be replaced as soon as possible.

SPRAY COOLING

1. No water sprays on the hearth and bosh should be taken off with blast on the furnace.

2. Any sprays not working properly must be immediately repaired. The cleaning out of spray holes should be a routine job for the pipe-fitter.

3. On no account must the sprays on the hearth jacket be stopped until there is an alternative method of water-cooling the jacket. This is most important in the taphole area.

4. If welding has to be done on a hearth or bosh jacket, the jacket temperature must not rise beyond about 60°C., *i.e.* a temperature at which it is possible to keep one's hand on the jacket.

5. If hot spots develop on parts of the furnace which are not spray cooled, sprays should be fitted to give extra cooling, care being taken that the water does not enter slag or iron runners.

6. Wherever spray cooling is employed, water collection and discharge troughs must be inspected and cleaned out regularly. An accumulation of slag, sand, waste or similar substances will result in a serious loss of cooling at that point.

Routine inspection of spray pipes is essential and must be carried out at least once each shift.

Water sprays should play at an angle on to the surface to be cooled, but this angle should be less than 90° to avoid unnecessary splash and mess.

STAVE COOLING

The temperature of the feed water and discharges from each stave must be taken and recorded every shift.

With a new or relined furnace, cooling water temperatures should be steady after about ten days' operation.

There must be a regular practice of back flushing staves with high pressure water, a record being kept by the pipefitter. The complete cycle of flushing all staves should not take more than two weeks.

If there is an increase in pick-up temperature on a stave, it must be inspected and the temperature taken more frequently.

If the rise in temperature is 1°C. above normal, the furnace should be taken off wind and the tuyeres in this area plugged with clay. The water feed must be tested to make certain that there is no obstruction in the manifold.

After three or four days, the plugged tuyere may be opened if the water temperature of the suspected stave has returned to normal or to subnormal. Careful observation of the affected area must be maintained.

If it is found that a stave cooler is leaking, the furnace should be taken off blast with all possible speed and an external spray prepared immediately. If possible, the furnace should be cast and emptied of iron and slag. If water is visible at the discharge, ease the feed to a minimum; if not visible, turn off completely and use the external spray. It may be possible after locating the leak to fill up the "U" tube with refractory cement and to operate the stave cooler again, using torpedo tubes in the undamaged section with the addition of external spray cooling.

A torpedo tube is a tube of smaller diameter than the stave cooler pipe. It has a closed bottom and is fitted inside the damaged stave cooler pipe, the space between being grouted to obtain surface contact. A pipe of yet smaller diameter, with an open end, is inserted inside this pipe. Water flows down the small pipe and returns around it to the top. A T-shaped closure is used to discharge to the normal trough.

When a stave pipe is cracked, without intrusion of iron, a satisfactory repair may be effected by leading a flexible copper pipe of suitable diameter through the length of the damaged pipe, connecting it up in the normal manner. The space between the flexible pipe and the damaged tube should be pressure grouted. To convey the necessary messenger wire round the sharp radius bends of stave "U" tubes, a ball of paper carrying a light string can be blown through the pipe by means of compressed air.

The seriousness of losing a stave cooler through contact with liquid iron cannot be overstressed.

The discharge pipes of all stave coolers should be visible from the cast house floor so that a stoppage of water is easily detectable.

CARE OF TUYERE SPRINGS

The purpose of a tuyere spring is to allow movement of the blast pipe and gooseneck with changes in temperature. It is therefore essential that the tuyere spring should never be over-tightened and must never be tightened up solid.

Pay particular attention to the springs in the area of the taphole and slag notches, *i.e.* in hot surroundings. Prolonged exposure to heat will lead to loss of temper in the spring. Change springs at the first sign of softening.

When burning out a tuyere, make sure that a portable launder is used over the spring bar to protect it from slag or iron.

The top of the spring should normally be protected from burning by an external casing which permits free access to the spring from below.

All springs should be examined weekly.

CARE OF TAPHOLES

It is not unusual for as much as 300 tons of iron and 60 tons of slag to pass through a furnace taphole at intervals of four or five hours, the actual period of flow averaging about 40 minutes. This duty is obviously heavy and places a premium on good taphole practice. A weak taphole is usually the precursor of serious trouble, unless the weakness can be quickly corrected.

Wear and tear caused at each cast must be made good, and it is essential that the clay gun should be allowed to plug the taphole with as much clay as the gun can feed at a charge.

1. Furnaces should be dried at every cast if at all possible. Tapholes should not be blown violently.

2. The taphole must be kept as clean and as near the original shape as possible.

3. A drill stand must always be used when drilling out the taphole prior to casting, and must always be set in the correct position against the drill stops. This is all the more important on a furnace in which there are stave coolers in the hearth construction.

4. No drill or oxygen lance must be used on the taphole unless ladles are set and runners drawn up ready for any iron which might be tapped.

5. An oxygen lance should always be used to tap iron, following the angle of the drill (25°). On no account must anyone, staff or workmen, burn out a taphole without wearing protective clothing.

6. When cleaning up in the taphole area, the protection plate must be dropped over the taphole as a protection against a possible breakout.

7. Water must never be turned off the sprays in the taphole area unless alternative cooling is ready.

8. The nozzle of the clay gun should be protected by a wash of thick spent oil. If the mouth of the taphole is large, a thick (1–2 in.) clay coating on the gun nozzle is of some help in preventing overtravel.

9. If it is known that the clay gun will not be available for use at cast, care should be taken to have as many iron and slag ladles as possible in position to ensure that the furnace is completely dry at the end of the cast. As soon as the furnace is dry, take the blast off. Prepare a cone of clay about 12 in. long and 6 in. diameter at the base. Cover the iron runner with corrugated sheets or steel plates about 4 ft. from the taphole. The cone of clay should be introduced to the taphole by means of a suitable long shovel and forced into the hole by the furnace keeper and crew, using a tool which consists of a circular disc about 1 in. thick and approximately 5 in. diameter set at right angles on the end of a 12 ft. pipe handle. Having sealed the taphole, as much clay as possible should be forced in to strengthen it.

If the gun fails at the end of cast, take the furnace off blast at the earliest moment and allow all the slag and iron to drain out. Taphole stopping should be carried out as explained above. A handstop should never be attempted while iron is running because of the dangerous splashes it might cause.

TAPHOLE CLAY

It is important that taphole clay should be made and kept carefully. Weak tapholes may often be traced to improperly handled or badly prepared clay.

Experience indicates that aluminous clay from the Bonnybridge area is satisfactory. It should be purchased in the "as mined" condition and ground and pugged at the furnace plant.

This raw clay should be mixed for 20 minutes in a pan mill with new firebrick, coal and water. Second-hand firebrick should only be used if its history is fully known; it must be free from contamination, especially by alkalis.

The approximate quantities used should be:

40 per cent. raw clay,
40 per cent. firebrick,
20 per cent. coal.

When the mix is complete, the water content should not exceed 15 per cent.

The pugged clay should not be stored for longer than 48 hours before it is used at the furnaces. It should be stored in a place free from heat, frost and water.

BLOWING OUT

This is one of the blast-furnace manager's most worrying operations, the history of the industry containing many examples of serious explosions during the blowing out of a furnace.

Formerly, it was general practice to continue blowing but to stop charging until the stockline fell to somewhere in the bosh; water was then turned into the furnace for cooling down. This is now considered an extremely dangerous practice. The introduction of water to the bed of incandescent coke is accompanied by the generation of water gas which, with indrawn air, can cause a serious explosion. The danger, of course, has been aggravated as furnace size has increased. In effect, the empty space above the burden is a potential explosion chamber and the bigger the chamber, the bigger the explosion.

It is now the general practice to maintain the furnace full of solids, so reducing the space left above the burden when blast is taken off. Many variations of full furnace blowing out have been successfully practised. In some districts, no ferrous materials are charged but the furnace is kept full with coke nuts until most of the ferrous burden has been smelted; in other cases, the charging of coke is discontinued and nothing but ore is used. In the former method, water is turned into the furnace after blast is taken off and pressure water is often used to wash out the coke nuts through the cooler holes. In the case of an ore blowout, no water is charged and the solid ore is drawn through the cooler openings.

It is believed that both these methods can be improved, however, the following technique having been found satisfactory on many occasions. In this method, the charging of both ferruginous materials and coke is discontinued and washed quartzite pebbles, screened to a size range of 1 to 2 in., are used. These pebbles have a high melting point and are much less reactive under blowing out conditions than either ferruginous materials or coke.

A detailed procedure which has been found to be satisfactory is set out below, the first step being to hold a meeting of all supervisors concerned and to draw up the programme.

1. The last cast before charging pebbles should be planned so that there are at least three hours of daylight during which to fix sprays and necessary gear on the furnace top. The following equipment will be needed:

(a) A water pump to supply at least 300 gallons of water per minute at the furnace top.

(b) Spray pipes to fit in two of the test rod holes. These sprays should not be fitted with rubber connections. A third test rod hole can be used for the pipe supplying steam under the large bell. Sprays should be marked to indicate the direction of delivery, in order to avoid spraying water on the furnace walls. Control valves and sprays must be checked before installation to ensure that they are free from blockages. The sprays should be approximately 20 ft. long, the bottom 10 ft. being slotted for spraying.

(c) Two semi-circular sprays to fit between the bells and round the large bell rod.

(d) A control valve and water meter at ground level for the water supply.

(e) Thermocouples in two uptakes and a suitable recorder at ground level.

(f) Sufficient pebbles and breeze in the furnace bunkers.

(g) Brick-lined troughs for running the iron from the bear taps, where this practice is followed.

2. Thirty-six hours before taking off blast, remove all scrap and miscellaneous materials from the burden.

3. Before charging coke breeze:

(a) Empty the dustcatcher and any dust hoppers on the dirty gas main.

(b) Empty the bunkers of coke, sinter and ore.

(c) Cast the furnace and take off blast.

(d) If longer tuyeres are normally used above the taphole, change them to normal sized tuyeres to shorten the taphole.

(e) If bosh tuyeres are used, plug them securely.

(f) Close the goggle valve in the dirty gas main, positively isolating the furnace from the gas plant.

(g) Insert thermocouples in the uptakes and connect to a recorder.

(*h*) Clear the furnace top of all inflammable materials and clean down thoroughly.

(*i*) Put the furnace on blast at reduced pressure. (As all the blast-furnace gas must now go through the furnace and dustcatcher bleeders, there would be a danger of gassing men in the cast house if full pressure were blown.)

(*j*) Have fires in bear tap runners, metal ladles in position and pie holes ready.

(*k*) The log of a similar previous blow out should be available to the operating staff.

4. THE BLOWING OUT BURDEN

Approximately fifteen hours before the planned last cast, charge coke breeze ($1\frac{1}{2}$ in. nuts). The volume of breeze should be sufficient to fill the hearth and bosh. In calculating the volume of pebbles, it should be assumed that the original stack lining is still present, but it is nevertheless prudent to add 10 per cent. to the calculated tonnage. (A useful check can be obtained by using one or two tracer charges a few days beforehand. Converter slag or similar siliceous material can be used for this purpose.) As the breeze blank approaches the tuyeres, the stockline should be allowed to move down to 8 ft. below the normal "full" level, so that there is sufficient depth for the water sprays to be fitted when the furnace is finally off blast. During the charging of breeze and pebbles the top gas temperature must not exceed 200°C.; control it by easing the blast and, if necessary, adding water with the pebbles in the skips.

If there is a possibility that the burden is hanging, ease the pressure slowly and maintain the lower pressure. The furnace should not be checked if stock descent can be promoted by other means, as the distribution of breeze and pebbles may be upset, the pebbles arriving at the hearth before the breeze and becoming fritted into a solid mass.

5. THE LAST CAST

Burn out the taphole at the lowest possible point and at as steep an angle as possible. After casting, draught back and drop all the blast pipes. Clay up all the tuyeres; brick them up inside the hearth coolers and fix a steel plate by means of a cross-bar and cotters over each opening.

6. Before taking the furnace off blast for the last time, two skips of pebbles should be dumped on the large bell. This is both a safety precaution and a convenience when doing the off blast jobs, such as fitting bell sprays and spacers.

7. BEAR TAPS

It is desirable to have two bear tapholes, one below the other. The top one will drain a large part of the bear into a metal ladle; the bottom one is taken at the lowest level at which iron is estimated to be molten, and can only be tapped into pie holes on the floor. A convenient way of dealing with the iron is to run it into three-or-four ton pigs underneath the cast house. Plenty of sand should be used between each pig.

If there are stave coolers in the hearth, the coolers through which the bear is tapped must previously be drained of water, blown through with compressed air, and filled with dry sand. There is a danger to personnel if liquid iron should penetrate a "U" pipe full of water, so that the area must be roped off wherever possible. As soon as iron is running from the bear, all personnel must keep well away from the hearth.

The above procedure may err on the side of caution, but it undoubtedly speeds up the subsequent cooling and emptying operation.

COOLING DOWN AFTER BLOWING OUT

As soon as blast is off after blowing out, four spacers made of 2 in. diameter round steel should be fixed with chains to the lugs at the top of the large bell so that when the bell is lowered the spacers drop into position between the bell and hopper. This ensures that the bell will remain slightly open when raised again. The water from the bell sprays will thus spread evenly over the area of the furnace throat. Nothing must be thrown on the bell after the spacers have been fitted, as this could cause water to accumulate in the hopper. If such an accumulation of water were suddenly released into the furnace a serious explosion could occur, with possible damage to plant and to personnel.

Check that there is plenty of steam under the bell. With the spacers, bell sprays and test rod sprays fitted and inspection doors closed, check that the valves for all the sprays are in the open position. Free passage of water through the valves and sprays should have been checked previously. The water supply for the bell sprays and test rod sprays should be on separate controls, both at ground level. Check that the high pressure water pump is running with the by-pass valve slightly open.

Care must be taken to prevent the bell being subjected to a high temperature; for this reason use only the bell sprays when first turning water into the furnace.

See that everyone is off the furnace top.

Slightly open the control valve for the bell sprays to give about 25 gallons of water per minute. Maintain this rate of flow for about three hours and then open the control valve for the test rod sprays, increasing the flow to about 75 gallons per minute. When water appears at the tuyeres, the flow can be stepped up again substantially. Care should be taken that the temperature in the uptake does not exceed 200°C. High temperature can be caused by adding too much water at the start, or by shortage of steam under the bell, or by a syphoning effect of the bleeders, *i.e.* one bleeder drawing in air which burns with gas under the bell and then goes up the other bleeder. A complete record of the rate at which water is going into the furnace and any other incident or change must be kept throughout the whole cooling operation.

During cooling down, no person must go to the furnace top or do any work round the furnace. Supervisory staff should only go to the furnace top in an emergency, such as a suspected water stoppage, and should always be accompanied by at least two other people.

Cooling down a furnace usually needs at least half a million gallons of water and the time required to apply the water is about 48 hours. Time spent in cooling down thoroughly is well spent because it promotes more comfortable conditions when wrecking operations begin, enabling the work to progress more rapidly.

The log of a previous similar cooling down should be available to the operating staff.

Chapter XV

OPERATING PROCEDURES – II

BURNING OUT TUYERES WITH OXYGEN

A BLOCKED TUYERE should be burnt straight through the centre of the tuyere into the furnace; the hole may then be enlarged. Slag will drain away in two directions—into and out of the furnace. Burning must be continued into the furnace until air is being drawn into the tuyere and all slag is draining away.

To protect the hearth cooler against slag and iron from the tuyere, sand or clay should be laid on the cooler. The launder normally used when dropping the blast pipe should be left in position so that slag and iron do not run round the tuyere spring and bind it.

Protective clothing and eye protection must be worn while burning out.

The lance must not be withdrawn from the tuyere until the oxygen supply has been turned off because of the danger of flying sparks.

When burning out a slag tuyere no one must stand directly in line with the notch in case slag should suddenly burst through the skull in front of the tuyere.

All lance pipes should be blown through immediately before use. A blocked pipe is dangerous. Only the man using the lance should give instructions to the person controlling the oxygen supply.

CHILLED HEARTHS

There are several causes of blast-furnace hearth chills. Inferior coke, undetected water leaks, excessive lime, charging mistakes leading to a deficiency of fuel, or an incorrect blast temperature pyrometer are some of the possible causes. The effect in each case is much the same. The furnace becomes steadily colder, increasing difficulty is experienced in flushing slag and casting iron, and tuyeres remorselessly close with slag against any blast pressure. A slip, which precipitates cold unprepared stock into the hearth, can cause these things to take place within minutes.

In the early stage of the trouble, water should be turned off a slag tuyere in an attempt to assist flushing. (In the subsequent efforts it is almost certain that the slag tuyere itself will be burnt.) If this measure is unsuccessful, the furnace can be regarded as chilled.

The closure of tuyeres may affect every tuyere in the furnace or only some of them, depending on the severity of the chill. If the tuyeres around the slag notches and taphole are closed and the tuyeres remote from these areas are open, there should be no hesitation in closing the open tuyeres at the earliest possible moment; to make slag and iron at one side of the furnace and to be unable to remove it at the other side will only aggravate the trouble.

The furnace should now be taken off wind and efforts made to open the tuyere nearest the slag notch. If the furnace is equipped with more than one slag notch, that nearest the taphole should be selected. Burning through the tuyere with oxygen will probably be a slow laborious job, accompanied by intermittent flushing of slag through the tuyere. The flow of slag should not be prevented; rather should it be encouraged and every effort made to burn through the chilled annulus to the still hot core behind.

While burning at the tuyeres has been taking place, lance burning should be carried out at the slag notch in a similar manner. It is a difficult job, but efforts should be made to burn upwards to establish communication between the slag notch and the tuyere. When this is achieved, the slag notch should be closed with a clay stopping, the blow pipe replaced as quickly as possible and a small volume of blast put on the furnace. With blast on the furnace, close watch should be kept on the one tuyere operating. The highest possible blast temperature should have been ordered already.

If the tuyere remains open, the slag notch should again be opened in a short time. The time can only be determined as the result of experience, but as a general rule, it should not be more than 45 minutes to 1 hour. If the operators have been fortunate, the one tuyere will remain open and, on opening the slag notch, a liquid with a distant resemblance to slag will run from the furnace. In this fortunate event, the furnace should then be taken off blast and the slag notch closed. The procedure outlined for opening the first tuyere should now be repeated at the tuyere on the other side of the slag notch. Again, as soon as communication is made with the inside of the furnace, the blow pipe should be put back and blast put on the furnace. Now two tuyeres will be working.

If all goes well, more slag will be flushed when the slag notch is opened. Remember that during this period the slag tuyere itself, if not burnt away, will probably have been pulled out and it may be that the intermediate will also have been burnt. The important precaution here is to ensure that the big slag cooler has a firm lining of clay or coke tar ramming so that the iron accompanying the dirty slag from the slag notch will not burn the cooler.

Assuming that all has gone well, the furnace should now be taken off wind again and two tuyeres opened, one on each side of those already working. This laborious process should be repeated until the major part of the tuyeres are open. When the tuyeres covering the taphole are working satisfactorily then, and only then, should attempts be made to open the taphole. The taphole should be pierced at as high a point and at as flat an angle as possible. Once the taphole is open and iron flowing, recovery is usually fairly rapid and the last three or four tuyeres may be opened together. But if, after opening the first tuyere the slag runs back and closes it, the whole process must be repeated.

The great temptation is to proceed too quickly in the early stage of the trouble. Do not attempt to open the second tuyere until you are sure of the first tuyere. Do not attempt to open the third and fourth tuyeres until the first and second tuyeres are working satisfactorily.

In extreme cases, great difficulties may be met and many hours may elapse before iron will flow at the taphole. This will indicate that the bottom of the furnace has solidified for some distance above the taphole and, in these circumstances, iron will certainly pass through the slag notch. A rough separation of iron from slag should be made by introducing a sand dam or a "bleed" in the slag runner.

A chilled hearth is one of the most laborious and heart-breaking experiences that can occur round a blast furnace. To quote Johnson,[1] "The furnace in this condition is said to be in a mess" and anyone who has seen a furnace at such a time will know that the phrase is literally true. With big furnaces, the procedure outlined above is usually sufficient to deal successfully with the most stubborn chill. With small furnaces, where the reserve of heat is much less, it may be necessary to resort to the use of a paraffin burner. It is very seldom that this is necessary today, but those who are interested should consult Johnson.

SLAG BREAKOUTS

If slag breaks out of a furnace the blast pressure must be eased and water used to cool the point of breakout. The slag level should be lowered immediately by flushing all available slag notches. If the breakout is serious the furnace should be cast and taken off blast; the weak point can then be repaired. If the hole can be repaired "down hill", or horizontally, the best material to use is carbon ramming tightened with carbon bricks. If the repair has to be done "uphill", then an unsatisfactory repair will be made with ramming because it will run before setting in place. In this case, the best material to use is pugged fireclay tightened with fireclay bricks. If the hole in the tuyere jacket is large, a steel patch should be welded on.

It is undesirable to allow blast to blow through carbon brickwork, or air to be drawn in, because of the danger of the carbon burning.

It is often undesirable to open up a big hole to investigate the damage as this may cause more damage than the original breakout, especially with carbon.

WHEN A FURNACE CANNOT BE CHECKED DOWN

1. Make sure that the furnace is "slag dry" so that there will not be a surge of slag into the tuyeres when the burden drops. Keep flushing slag at all available notches.

2. Reduce the blast pressure as low as possible and watch the tuyeres to avoid slag flowing back down the blast pipes.

3. Reduce the blast temperature to a minimum or increase to a maximum—either may have the desired effect.

4. If possible, cast the furnace, and so make the tuyeres completely safe from iron as well as from slag.

5. If the furnace is still hanging, increase the blast pressure to half normal for about five minutes and then check again. Continue to do this for as long as necessary. It is probable that a furnace in this tight condition will only be taking a small volume of blast.

6. Steam has occasionally been introduced into the hot blast main when a furnace would not check and has succeeded in dropping the burden.

7. Cases have been known where hanging persisted for many hours. When this happens, try leaving the furnace on a very low pressure for 15 minutes or so and then increase blast pressure to a higher level than has been tried so far during the trouble. After about 15 minutes of this harder blowing, check the furnace again.

8. Checking by the snort valve does not take all pressure off the furnace. Try opening the relief valve of the stove, which will bring pressure to zero when blowing small volumes of blast.

9. When the burden comes down, inspect all the tuyeres and copper cooler discharges.

BLAST FURNACE SLIPS

When a furnace slips, two serious things may happen:
  (1) The hearth may suddenly be chilled by semi-molten slag from the bosh or by partially reduced burden.
  (2) Hot gas may suddenly be released from the furnace stock, thereby increasing the temperature of the gas leaving the furnace top.

The slag in the furnace hearth may not have had sufficient time above the tuyeres to attain normal fluidity. In order to reach this fluidity, it must use the heat in the hearth, and if the amount of slag is large there may not be enough heat available. The notches may therefore freeze up and the tuyeres may blind because the viscous slag will prevent the coke from burning. If these conditions occur:

(1) Raise the blast temperature to a maximum.

(2) Attempt immediately to get slag to flow at any of the slag notches.

(3) Increase the coke charge if the trouble persists for more than an hour or so.

If slag cannot be made to flow, follow the procedure given in the section on "Recovering from a Chilled Hearth".

Excessively hot gas emerging from the furnace stack after a slip may seriously damage the furnace bell. To avoid this, reduce blast pressure as low as possible, taking care that slag does not flow back into the blast pipes.

Charge the furnace as rapidly as possible until the stockline is at its normal level.

IRON OVER AT THE SLAG NOTCH

The first sign of iron passing through the slag notch is either an unusual shower of iron sparks or a sharp bang as the slag tuyere melts, allowing liquid iron to come into contact with water.

It is dangerous practice to attempt to bott a leaking slag tuyere, unless water is turned off momentarily before inserting the bott. Water should be turned on again immediately the flow of slag has ceased. If water from the leaking slag tuyere is entering the furnace, it should be eased down to a minimum.

The commonest times for iron to run over a notch are after a "not dry" cast when the iron level is unknown, or when the furnace hearth is dirty. Care must therefore be taken after such casts and the subsequent cast should be made earlier. It may be advisable to reduce blast volume.

At no time should anyone stand in line with a notch that is flushing. This rule should be stringently applied if the furnace was "not dry" at the previous cast. No-one should even cross the runner.

If iron cuts any of the slag cooling members, blast pressure must be eased immediately and all men kept away from the front of the notch.

Reduce water flow to a minimum on the leaking members to avoid further damage.

The furnace must be cast as soon as possible and taken off blast to change the leaking cooling member.

If water has been turned off any copper cooler because of a chilled hearth, the feed and discharge unions should be broken to make certain that no water can possibly enter the furnace. A plug cock may not be shut completely even when apparently closed.

BURST BLAST PIPES

If a blast pipe is seen to be glowing due to the entry of slag and/or iron, water must not be applied to it as this could easily result in a fracture. Slag must be flushed immediately. If a blast pipe should fracture for any reason, blast pressure must be reduced to prevent unnecessary damage to the surrounding plant, slag flushed immediately and the furnace taken off blast as soon as possible.

Everyone should be warned to keep away from a fractured blast pipe. Water should not be allowed to play on blast pipes. If this has been unavoidable, the pipe should be examined as soon as possible. Cracked blast pipes must be scrapped.

DAMPING DOWN A FURNACE

1. Charge sufficient coke to ensure that when the furnace is finally taken off blast the hearth and bosh will contain only coke. The burden on top of this blank should be similar to a blowing-in burden, that is, the ore/coke ratio should be approximately one quarter of normal just above the blank, and half normal at the stockline.

2. Before the start of the last cast, empty both dustcatchers and any dust hoppers in the dirty gas main.

3. Check that all the safety steam valves are working and adjustable.

4. Cast the furnace and dry as completely as possible. This is one case when blowing at the taphole is permissible.

5. Isolate the furnace from the gas system. Turn steam in the dustcatcher and the dirty gas main.

6. Make sure that the furnace is full. The last charge should be sinter or fine ore (no coke) to help to seal the furnace. Sinter or fine ore (no coke) should be on both bells for the same purpose.

7. Take blast off the furnace in the normal way.

8. Draught back and drop all the blast pipes.

9. Clay and brick up all the tuyeres and slag notches. Stop draughting back and stop the blower. It is most important that no air should enter the furnace to burn coke. The usual practice is to point round all coolers and, for a long stoppage, to spray all the tuyere belt section with grout. This should be examined daily, so that contraction cracks can be

closed as soon as formed. A recent innovation is to cocoon the bottom of the furnace by spraying with a suitable plastic material.

10. Close the goggle valve which isolates the dustcatchers from the gas washers. Purge the dirty gas main of gas and leave it open to the air.

11. Reduce water on all the copper cooling members and on cooling sprays and stack coolers.

Any doubtful cooling member, or one which has been in service for more than average life, should be changed because the danger of water leaking in becomes more serious when there is no blast pressure in the furnace.

12. Turn off the water in the gas washers.

13. If the furnace is to be off for a long period, it will be advisable to tap the bear iron through the hearth jacket as in a normal blow-out. The furnace well will be deeper when starting up again and casting over the slag notch may be avoided. The bear should be tapped as the tuyeres are being closed and when the furnace bleeders are still open. The repair of the bear taphole made in the hearth wall can be done later. It should, of course, be plugged with clay as soon as possible to prevent air entering the furnace.

STARTING UP AFTER DAMPING DOWN

The following starting-up procedure is suitable after the furnace has been damped down for a period not exceeding fourteen days:

(1) Heat up the hot blast stoves with gas if available; if not, with fires in the combustion chambers.

(2) Increase all the cooling water.

(3) Check all the water flow, including that on the washers.

(4) Check that steam is in the dustcatchers, between the bells and under the large bell.

(5) Start the blower to the snort valve.

(6) Start draughting back.

(7) Remove all the bricks from the hearth tuyeres and put up the blast pipes.

STARTING UP AT THE SLAG NOTCH

1. Open out the slag notch nearest the taphole and open two tuyeres, one on either side of the slag notch.

2. Withdraw all the copper cooling members from the slag notch and make up with bricks or coke and tar ramming as there will probably be iron over the notch before the taphole can be opened. If it is necessary to open the tuyeres with oxygen, burn towards the slag notch and see

that clean coke is visible after using the lance. Burn upwards from the notch to each tuyere before bricking up the notch. Leave the slag notch open when blast is on and if no connection has been made between notch and tuyeres, continue to burn uphill from the notch.

3. Blast pressure should be about 5 p.s.i. The dustcatcher bleeder should be closed and the furnace bleeders open. Blast temperature should be as high as possible. When the first two tuyeres are working satisfactorily and slag is draining to the slag notch, the furnace can be taken off blast and one or two more tuyeres opened and blast volume increased as conditions allow. Work towards the taphole so as to have this section of the furnace active as quickly as possible. To avoid the risk of filling with slag the tuyeres which are already working, do not take the furnace off blast unless it is slag dry. Burden, coke and blast volume should be adjusted to the furnace condition.

STARTING UP AT THE TAPHOLE

The following is an alternative method recommended when the bear has been tapped or when the furnace has been damped down for more than fourteen days:

The taphole is dug out as far as possible until clean coke is reached. The coolers are removed from the nearest slag notch which is made up with bricks or carbon ramming in case it should be necessary to cast over the notch.

The skimmer is removed and the taphole made up with a 5 ft. length of 4 in. diameter pipe. One half of a ball joint is welded to the outer end of the pipe, the joint being flush with the outside of the taphole. An assembly of 4 in. pipe, starting from the flange on a gooseneck facepiece and finishing at the second half of the ball joint, is set in place so that blast can be drawn off from the gooseneck to blow at the taphole. The line should be made as flexible as possible with elbows to facilitate setting up and withdrawal, and a 4 in. valve should be inserted.

Start with a blast pressure of about 10 p.s.i. and as high a blast temperature as possible.

After blowing at the taphole for 5–6 hours, take the furnace off blast and open the two tuyeres nearest the notch, burning down to make a connection with the void at the taphole. With this connection made, put blast on the tuyeres and taphole pipe and maintain it until the taphole pipe is filled with slag.

Close the valve on the pipe and pull the pipe from the taphole. A flush of slag will follow. When the furnace is dry, take the blast off, seal the taphole and open the other taphole tuyere. Put the furnace on blast and cast again at approximately 2-hourly intervals, or before if slag shows at the tuyeres.

Open further hearth tuyeres as conditions allow, with the object of making the section of the furnace between the taphole and the notch active as soon as possible. Increase the blast volume as cleaning-up operations permit.

LIGHTING HOT BLAST STOVES WHEN NEW OR AFTER REPAIRS

1. Only stoveminders shall light hot blast stoves.

2. Smoking and naked lights are forbidden in the vicinity of the stove until it is purged and ready for lighting.

3. Check that all gas valves are shut, water seals overflowing and all inspection doors closed.

4. Open the chimney valves.

5. Set the burner in position for heating the stove.

6. Start the burner fan and blow air through the stove for at least five minutes.

7. Purging of the gas main up to the water seals must be complete before any further operations. The purges should be at the ends of the gas main. Empty the water seal and close the overflow valve.

8. Stop the fan, draw back the burner and light a good coal fire on the burner door sill.

9. Open the gas valve slightly and rack the burner to the stove. If the gas does not light, shut off the gas and withdraw the burner. Wait a least two minutes before attempting to light it again, so that the unburnt gas can be drawn up the chimney.

10. With the burner lit, slowly increase the gas and fan speed.

11. Do not leave the stove during the initial heating-up period, *i.e.* until the stove is hot enough to keep the gas ignited.

12. If there is any doubt whether the stove will light after being on blast, consider it as cold and act as above.

HEATING UP A HOT BLAST STOVE

The large amount of brickwork in a hot blast stove requires careful treatment when being brought into service. The following procedure has been found satisfactory:

During heating up, the temperature at the base of the chimney should not exceed 250°C. This table can be used with safety:

Day	Dome temperature	
1	150°C.	⎫
2	300°C.	⎬ The burner fan
3	400°C.	⎭ should not be used.
4	500°C.	
5	600°C.	⎫ Use burner fan
6	800°C.	⎭

When the dome temperature reaches 400°C. it can be used on blast with another stove; this practice will accelerate the drying out of the brickwork.

Holding down bolts at the base of the stove shell should only be tightened when the stove is empty of bricks. The purpose of the holding down bolts is to protect an empty shell against abnormal winds. The bolts should be slack before heating up the stove and always when the stove is in normal operation. During the heating up period the bolts should be examined twice daily to make sure that they are still slack.

As moisture is driven out from the brickwork it may be temporarily absorbed in the insulation. This may cause the shell plates to feel unusually warm in the early days of operation, but they should revert to normal in a few days.

SHUTTING OUT AND DRAUGHTING BACK

The stoveminder must only "shut out" a furnace when instructed by the supervisor. He should not draught back until the blower driver has been given the "off blast" signal and he has been given the instruction to draught back.

When the stoveminder is "shutting out" or draughting back, no one should distract his attention unless absolutely necessary.

PREPARATION

Take off gas the stove that is to be used for draughting back.

Check that the hot blast, cold blast, blow-off and mixing valves of this stove are completely closed.

Prepare the stove for draughting back by making sure that the chimney valves are open. Light a fire on the burner door sill and leave the burner door about 3 in. open. The stove must be sufficiently hot to ignite the gas drawn out of the furnace.

Open the steam valve to the Korting blower* to increase the chimney pull and to kill any unburnt gas which may reach the chimney.

* On modern stoves with small chequer openings, it is usual to fit a Korting blower in the stove chimney to ensure sufficient draught through the stove being used for back draughting.

TO SHUT OUT AND DRAUGHT BACK

When the pressure on the furnace is zero and the order to "shut out" is received:

Crack open the relief valve in the hot blast main. This is done by slightly turning the turn screw.

Shut the cold blast, mixing and hot blast valves of the stove that has been on blast.

Raise the turnscrew as soon as the relief valve has dropped.

Fully open the relief valve.

Take out the hot blast thermocouple. Exposure of the thermocouple to the hot burning gas being pulled away from the tuyere will lead to premature failure of the couple.

Check the opening of the burner door of the stove to be used for draughting back and make sure that the fire is burning.

Check that the chimney valves are open.

Open the hot blast valve.

Place safety chains to prevent people walking in front of the gas burner door.

Keep a gas-free stove with which to put blast back on the furnace; never use the same stove for blast as that which was used for draughting back.

STOPPING DRAUGHTING BACK AND OPENING OUT HOT BLAST STOVES AFTER WIND OFF

Put blast on through a different stove from the one through which the furnace has been draughting back. If this is impossible, burn gas on the stove for a few minutes to clear any unburnt gas and so avoid the danger of a gas "kick".

TO STOP DRAUGHTING BACK AND PUT BLAST
THROUGH TO THE FURNACE

1. Shut the hot blast valve on the stove used for draughting back and leave it ready for putting on gas.
2. Insert the thermocouple in the hot blast main.
3. Check that the blow-off valve on the stove to be used is shut.
4. Open the cold blast valve on this stove.
5. Open the hot blast valve.
6. Open the mixing valve.
7. Shut the steam off the Korting blower.
8. The furnace is ready for putting on blast. This is done by closing the snort valve to atmosphere.

INSPECTING, CLEANING AND REPAIRING HOT BLAST STOVES

Before men enter a stove for any reason:

(1) Clamp and lock the hot blast valve in the closed position. The valve is to be secured by a mechanical device.

(2) Close and lock the cold blast valve and the mixing valve.

(3) The keys for the locks are to be kept by the foreman in charge of the repair. They must be handed on from shift to shift.

(4) Close the gas valve and put in the water seal.

(5) Open the inspection door underneath the burner door. Purge through this inspection door and the chimney valves by allowing air to draught for twelve hours.

(6) A carbon monoxide detector is to be available.

(7) Fans may be used to maintain comfortable working conditions but care must be taken to ensure that they do not draw gas into the stove.

(8) Open the inspection door underneath the hot blast valve.

(9) A recognised means of communication is to be available between men inside and outside the stove. This may be either a telephone, a bell or simply visual communication between the men.

Men may have to enter the stove to work in any of the following positions:

(a) In the gas chamber well.

(b) On top of the checkers.

(c) Underneath the checkers.

Before men enter the stove to work in

(a) *The gas chamber well* the following manholes are to be opened:
Underneath the hot blast valve;
Underneath the gas burner door.

(b) *On top of the checkers* the following manholes are to be opened:
Stove top.

(c) *Underneath the checkers* the following manhole is to be opened:
Near the chimney valves.

Comfortable working conditions may be obtained by closing the chimney valves, opening the inspection covers under and above the checkers, and closing all other openings.

No matter where the men are working the following precautions are to be taken when men enter the stove:

(1) Danger boards are to be placed on the hot blast valve control, the cold blast valve control and the mixing valve control.

(2) A man must always be watching the overflow of the water seal at the gas burner. If the overflow stops, the men inside the stove must be withdrawn and the foreman informed.

(3) The means of communication between men inside and outside the stove must be regularly checked.

(4) If men are to work in the gas chamber well, a brick stopping is to be built in the hot blast exit as soon as possible.

SAFETY STEAM

Blast-furnace gas and air mixtures are explosive. If air contains any amount of gas between 35 and 75 per cent., the mixture will explode if ignited. When clean, the gas is odourless and invisible. In addition, it is highly poisonous. The toxic constituent is carbon monoxide, 0·01 per cent. of which is dangerous, while as little as 0·10 per cent. would be fatal in an hour. These hazards demand that every precaution should be taken in the handling of blast-furnace gas. So long as mains are under pressure little trouble should be encountered, but, as a rule, gas mains are most dangerous when gas is not flowing.

Steam should be used liberally on many occasions and in many places; for example, when a furnace is off blast, steam should be turned into the dustcatchers to prevent the formation of an explosive mixture by infiltrating air. It is good practice to maintain a slight pressure of steam between the large and small bells, as this space will fill with gas when the big bell is lowered. Cooling of this gas can lead to an indraught of air and the formation of an explosive mixture which may be ignited the next time the big bell is lowered. To maintain steam between the bells is a cheap insurance against explosion.

When a gas main or gas washer has to be purged of gas to permit men to work inside, a steam blanket is the safest means of dispelling the gas. Steam is also the safest means of displacing all air before gas is reintroduced to a main or washer. For this reason, all gas mains should be equipped with steam valves and with purge points.

When gassing through a length of main, etc., the principle is always the same—have the purge cock at the far end of the main open and turn in steam at the near end. Not until steam is issuing freely from the purge cock should gas be introduced. The principle also applies to cold blast mains.

If, for any reason, the blower stops, gas may work back into the cold blast main. On restarting the blower, a mixture of air and gas in the main will inevitably be formed. Before starting up the blower after any stoppage therefore, the cold blast main should be purged with steam.

The use of inert gases of combustion for purging purposes has been suggested. Steam is still preferred because of its highly expansible properties and visibility.

REFERENCE

[1] *Principles, Operation and Products of the Blast Furnace*, by J. E. JOHNSON, 354. McGraw Hill Book Company.

Chapter XVI

HOT BLAST STOVES

HOT BLAST STOVES

THE DESIGN OF hot blast stoves is perhaps the least controversial subject in ironmaking. After many variations have been tried and superseded, all stoves are now designed on the two pass, side combustion chamber principle. As uncleaned blast furnace gas is no longer used in stoves, all the many designs of chequer brick vary in detail only.

A blast-furnace stove is a heat storage device; it absorbs heat during the period gas is being burnt in the combustion chamber and gives up heat when the air blast passes through in the reverse direction. The fundamental requirement in stove design is the mass of effective brickwork which undergoes the heat-storage-heat-delivery cycle, thus converting cold blast to hot blast.

The mass of effective brickwork can be calculated and it has been so demonstrated that the interior of a brick more than $\frac{3}{4}$ in. from the surface being heated, is ineffective in heat exchange. All recent designs of chequer brick arise from this theoretical analysis. All aim at providing the maximum area of heating surface with as much of the brick as possible within $\frac{3}{4}$ in. of the surface. This obviously calls for bricks with fairly small holes, usually about 2 in. in diameter or section, and of such a shape that chequer spaces are provided where brick meets brick. Fig. 59 is a typical cross-section of a stove in which the shape of the brick is indicated. Fig. 60 is a section through a hot blast stove which is typical of modern design and has a heating surface of 164,000 sq. ft. As furnace size increases, demanding higher and higher blast volumes, the size of hot blast stoves must also increase. In recent years many stoves with a heating surface of over 300,000 sq. ft. have been built. The principles of design and the general relationships of the dimensions are unchanged.

It is usual to equip each furnace with three stoves. The normal operational cycle is for two stoves to be heating up and one stove to be on blast.

A correctly designed stove, properly operated, will have a useful life of around twenty years. This means that the brickwork must be stable

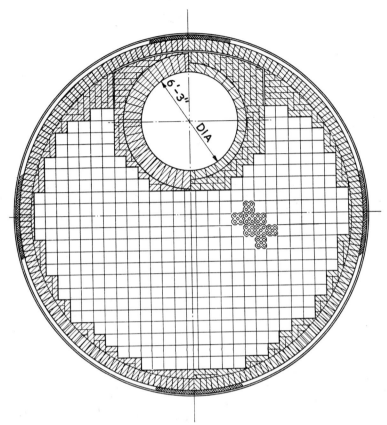

Fig. 59. Cross-section of a hot blast stove.

and to ensure this, it is usually necessary to depart somewhat from the ideal brick thickness set out above. It must also be remembered that the heating up and cooling down of a hot blast stove must be accompanied by considerable changes arising from expansion and contraction of the brickwork.

The chequer work itself should be free to expand independently of its containing brickwork; similarly the chimney-like combustion flue should be capable of independent movement. It is universal practice for the chequer work to be carried on steel or cast iron grids and columns.

In operation, the prime consideration is to rigidly limit the temperature attained in the dome of the stove. With correct conditions, the gas should be completely burnt at the top of the combustion flue. This means that the dome is exposed to maximum temperature and this should not be allowed to exceed 1150°C. For this reason a thermocouple

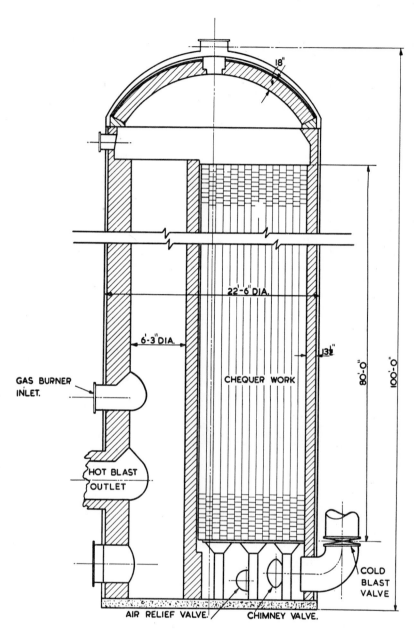

Fig. 6o. *Section through a hot blast stove.*

Fig. 61. Freyn stove burner.

is always inserted in the dome of the stove and is often connected to an audible signal set to operate when the temperature reaches slightly below the permitted maximum. It cannot be over-emphasised that an hour or so at an excessive dome temperature can do more damage to a hot blast stove than many years operation below 1150°C.

However clean the gas used may be, a certain amount of very fine dust is always present and much of this dust is precipitated on top of the chequer work. In most blast-furnace practices this very fine dust has a high alkali content and such dust will attack brickwork severely at temperatures little over 1200°C.

GAS BURNERS

Many designs of gas burner are now available. Fig. 61 shows a burner of Freyn design mounted independently of the stove. In many installations the burner is an integral part of the construction connecting the stove to the gas main. The burner shown in fig. 61, however, is positioned on top of the gas main connection and when retracted it automatically seals off the gas. This design is preferred by some operators because of its positive isolation from the stove, so that when it is necessary to work inside the stove there is no fear of the entry of gas through a leaking valve. Gas burners are now available capable of burning up to 1,000,000 cu. ft. of gas per hour.

The manipulation of a hot blast stove involves the use of several valves (see section on "Operating Procedures"). Because of the expected long life of the stove, ruggedness of construction is essential for all stove valves. The hot blast valve is always water-cooled and closes on a water-cooled seat. Mushroom type valves are usually used for this duty.

A constant blast temperature is maintained by allowing part of the blast to by-pass the stove after which it is mixed with the hot blast in the correct proportions to give the temperature required. The blast temperature is controlled automatically by means of a thermocouple inserted in the hot blast main. When a hot stove is first put on the blowing cycle, the temperature of the air leaving the stove is at its maximum and therefore the amount of cold air required will also be at a maximum. As the stove temperature falls, so does the amount of added cold blast decrease.

In recent years, especially on the Continent, many stove installations have been constructed with push-button control of the valves. This gives a more effective use of the stove in that the time for changing from one stove to another is reduced from approximately 10 minutes to about 5 minutes. This may be an important consideration when stoves are being used almost to capacity.

Chapter XVII

IRONWORKS REFRACTORIES

REFRACTORIES

UNTIL BLAST-FURNACE PRODUCTION attained the level of the last few years, refractories for ironmaking did not constitute a problem. It is little exaggeration to say that almost any fireclay brick was suitable for duty in any part of the ironworks. Perhaps it was in stoves that it first became necessary to pick and choose, especially as the use of clean gas for stoves became general practice. Then, as furnaces were pushed harder and harder, the shortcomings of the then generally accepted hearth refractories were uncovered. The solution of one problem is the formulation of the next one! As hearths stood up to harder duty, stack refractories became a problem. And as blowing rates increased still further, it was generally discovered that time-hallowed methods of lining hot blast mains, downcomers, dustcatchers, etc. were failing to withstand the more onerous duties imposed upon them.

Because of the long history of trouble-free service, and because of the insuperable difficulties of simulating service conditions in the laboratory, the rather sudden demand for better ironworks refractories found both the maker and the user of bricks somewhat unprepared. The long neglect of using "the stones of the field" had now to be paid for.

At the time of writing, there is a stronger demand for better refractories in the ironworks than ever before. Bricks of a quality proven by years of service two or three decades ago are unsatisfactory for the more arduous duties of today. In twenty or thirty years from now, the same may prove to be true of what is now recognised as the best available refractory.

For these reasons, what is now written about ironworks refractories should not be treated as the last word on the subject.

In general, refractories for stoves do not present many great problems but refractories for the furnace itself are the subject of much discussion and investigation. With furnace lives of up to six or seven years it will be appreciated that developments in blast-furnace refractories must, of necessity, be somewhat slow. The problem is not made easier by the conflicting evidence arising from attempts to simulate in the laboratory the conditions to which the bricks are exposed in service.

Progress has also been impeded by the understandable conservatism of furnace operators. With the smaller and more gently treated furnaces of some years ago, a satisfactory lining life could be obtained from comparatively low grade (and therefore inexpensive) bricks. That position has changed. The use of expensive "super" refractories is spreading. But it must always be remembered that with a campaign life of four to seven years, expenditure on bricks—however expensive they may be—is still a very minor item in the cost of pig iron. Under these circumstances, it is trite to observe that the best refractory is the cheapest in the long run. Time charges on a big furnace are so high that a short extension to lining life can quickly justify a greatly increased cost for the refractory installation.

STOVE REFRACTORIES

In the stove, bricks are subject to regular reversals of temperature but not to a very high maximum service temperature. This emphasises the need for such properties as resistance to thermal shock rather than absolute refractoriness. If a hot blast stove is built of good fireclay bricks and the correct safeguards in regard to operating temperature are observed, its useful life is about twenty years. Unless the stove is fired efficiently with gas containing not more than about 0·006 grains of dust per cu. ft., this will not apply. In the end, the slow accumulation of alkalis arising from the small amount of dust left in blast-furnace gas after even the most efficient cleaning, leads to "rotting" of the upper courses of chequers. With most designs of efficient chequering it is almost impossible to remove the upper courses without causing serious blockage of the chequers beneath, through falling debris. Most stoves built in the last twenty years or so are fitted with chequers which have an opening of only about 2 in. square. Because replacement of the upper courses often leads to blockage of the good chequers below, it becomes necessary to rechequer to a greater depth. This can be prevented by using newspaper to plug the top 2 or 3 ft. of each chequer opening before stripping off the defective brickwork. The procedure can be repeated at intervals of 2 or 3 ft. until sound brickwork is exposed. This simple procedure can prevent the unnecessary replacement of many feet of good chequers.

The maximum temperature in service arises in the dome of the stove where combustion of the gas is complete. It is bad practice not to limit the temperature of the dome, as measured by a recording thermocouple,

to 1150°C. If this limit is rigidly observed, the whole of the stove can be
built with two qualities of brick. A moderately high alumina brick
(42 to 50 per cent.) is recommended for flame flue and dome and for the
top 5 or 6 ft. of the chequer work. Properties of such bricks are set out in
Table XV. All other parts of the stove can be built satisfactorily in
ordinary 37 per cent. alumina fireclay brick, also given in Table XV.

Stove design and construction together with careful operating control
are much more important than the bricks used. If the gas to the stoves is
not sufficiently clean, however, trouble with refractories will be encountered whatever brick qualities are used.

MISCELLANEOUS

It is customary to line with brick such parts of plant as dustcatchers,
downcomers, uptakes and hot blast mains. The lining in these cases is
there as an insulation and as a protection to the steelwork. Temperatures are comparatively low in all these duties so that a high degree of
refractoriness is not required. What is required is accuracy of shape to
enable sound masonry to be constructed in the prevailing difficult conditions, and a high degree of resistance to abrasion by dust-laden gas.
The use of castable refractories is now achieving some popularity for
these duties. The major troubles in lining such a tube as a horseshoe
main arise from the necessity of using so many cut bricks. If really hard
dense bricks are used, the time and cost of lining becomes prohibitive.
Soft bricks are easier to cut but are much less resistant to abrasion; it
only requires one or two bricks to fall out of place, or for a joint to open,
for example, to allow the backing of insulating material to be swept out
by the air blast. For these reasons, a refractory lining consisting of layers
of "gunited" refractory cement has much to recommend it. This applies
similarly to such places as bends in uptakes and downcomers and to the
top cone of the furnace. It is believed that the future will see greatly
extended application of both gunited and castable refractories in the
ironworks. Conversely, unlined downcomers, or downcomers protected
by steel or iron wearing plates, are being increasingly used.

BLAST FURNACE

From top to bottom of the blast furnace almost every conceivable
duty for refractories can be encountered. At the top, temperatures can
and do fluctuate violently. Flash temperatures of 1000°C. are by no
means unknown. The charging of wet materials or even of water itself
aggravates the dangers of spalling brickwork. The dust content of the
gases varies enormously and a heavily dustladen gas stream is extremely

abrasive. At temperatures between 450 and 650°C. the well-known carbon deposition reaction can take place, the catalysts necessary for the promotion of this reaction being only too common, not only in most fireclay bricks but even in the gases themselves. The temperature gradient from working face to cool exterior means that at all levels there is a zone at a temperature suitable for carbon deposition. Abrasion and erosion occur throughout the height of the stack. In the course of a normal campaign, during which several million tons of raw materials are charged, trace amounts of injurious constituents in the raw materials may accumulate within the furnace to dangerous proportions from the viewpoint of refractories. Two such injurious burden constituents are alkalis and zinc.

In the lower stack, temperatures will not fluctuate as widely or as rapidly as in the upper stack, but temperatures will be high enough in this zone to lead to softening and melting of the raw materials. Depending on the raw materials and on the refractories used, this in turn may lead to slagging of the brickwork or to material adhering to the brickwork. The absorption of alkalis into the bricks will lead to a lowering of refractoriness. It follows, therefore, that the refractoriness of a fireclay brick, as measured in the laboratory, is not a sure indication of its probable refractoriness in service. Obviously, the less permeable or porous the brick may be, the less will be the possibility of penetration by these harmful constituents. On the other hand, the denser and less permeable the brick, the more prone it will be to damage by thermal shock. A dense brick will also be more prone to fracture because of the differential expansions which take place in a chimney of brickwork which has a considerable temperature gradient from the inside to the outside of the wall.

The design of the furnace—especially in regard to bell throat ratios— and the operating practice, may have profound influence on the behaviour of the lining. Going to one extreme, if the top design and top distribution are such that fines are segregated to the wall of the furnace, gas flow will be so low that action on the walls will be comparatively slight. In this case it can happen that the adhering or stationary raw material on the wall, rather than the actual brick lining, becomes the working face. At the other extreme, if the burden and distribution are such as to give a very permeable periphery to the stock column, gas flow and therefore attack on the refractory lining will be considerably increased. All these factors have to be considered and because of the long service life which is required it is difficult to assess before-hand the suitability of the brick. For example, a standard test to indicate the resistance of fireclay bricks to carbon deposition has been developed and is now widely accepted; but however well a test-piece may stand up to this laboratory test, the fact remains that no orthodox fireclay brick is free from carbon deposition after three or four years in service in a blast-furnace stack. This failure of tests to give a true indication of what will happen in the furnace places a premium on operating experience and on the interchange of service data. The problem is not eased by the time factor; even the most disappointing lining usually lasts for many months.

It has long been recognised that the same type of brick is not necessarily suitable for all parts of the blast-furnace stack. The lines of demarcation and the various qualities to be used are by no means generally agreed, nor can they be in the present ignorance of the location of the various zones of activity in the furnace.

For convenience, it is now proposed to divide the stack into three sections:

(*a*) Throat;

(*b*) Upper stack;

(*c*) Lower stack.

(*a*) *Throat*

It is universal practice to use a metal lining for as much as the top 10 ft. of the stack. This practice can be justified if the bell diameter is such as to lead to the burden impinging on the throat wall. Even if this is not so, extra throat protection is a reasonable precaution because moderately heavy scrap is charged from time to time in all furnaces.

The design of and materials employed for throat armour are outside the province of refractories and are discussed in the section on "Furnace Design".

(*b*) *Upper stack*

In the upper stack, service temperatures in themselves do not present a problem but it is in this zone that such factors as carbon deposition, alkali penetration, chloride penetration, and zinc deposition are usually at a maximum. This places a premium on a brick that is relatively dense and as immune as possible from carbon deposition. The general practice is to use moderately hard-fired medium alumina (35 to 38 per cent.) bricks in this part of the furnace. In recent years, American practice has moved towards the use of this type of brick, but fired much harder than was formerly the case. Test data for typical upper stack refractories are given in Table XV.

TABLE XV

Type of brick	37% alumina fireclay brick	42% alumina fireclay brick	50% alumina brick	73% alumina brick	American 'Super Duty' fireclay brick	Dense China clay brick	Carbon
Apparent porosity, per cent.	22·6	19·6	23·7	24·9	9·2	9·9	22·3
Bulk density, g./ml.	2·03	2·15	2·16	2·62	2·40	2·34	1·51
Apparent solid density, g./ml.	2·62	2·67	2·83	3·48	2·64	2·60	1·95
Permeability c.g.s. units	0·052	0·024	0·059	0·023	—	—	0·022
Percentage linear change on reheating:							
2 hrs. 1400°C.	nil	nil	nil	nil	nil	nil	nil
2 hrs. 1500°C.	−2·41	−2·85	−0·10	−0·2	−0·3	—	−1·0
2 hrs. 1600°C.	—	—	—	—	—	−1·0	—
Refractoriness under-load 28 lb./sq. in.: Initial softening	1440°C.	1360°C.	1450°C.	1560°C.	—	1560°C.	No deformation at 1700°C.
5 per cent. deformation	1580°C.	1620°C.	1600°C.	1690°C.	—	1715°C.	
Abrasion resistance index*	10·0	8·3	—	10·8	17·3	4·3	10·0

* The abrasion resistance index represents the percentage loss of volume after a standard shot-blasting treatment.

The development of hard-fired dense china-clay bricks is an interesting innovation of recent date. A big attraction of the china-clay brick is its immunity from carbon deposition because of its freedom from iron oxides.

Carbon has been tried in several installations throughout the world but it appears unsuitable for use in this part of the furnace. It is believed that attack by the moisture charged with the burden, infiltration of air into the furnace stack and solution by CO_2 are the reasons for the failures recorded.

(c) Lower stack

All the difficulties of service in the upper stack are encountered in greater or lesser degree in the lower stack (here defined as the bottom third of the blast-furnace stack). In addition, service temperatures can on occasion rise to levels approaching the under-load refractoriness of the brick. It is in the lower stack that the burden begins to melt and there is no doubt that with some types of raw material it is at least semi-molten before it enters the bosh. This can lead to slagging with or adherence to the brickwork. In addition, as mentioned in the section on design, there may be stresses arising from the differential expansion of bosh brickwork and stack brickwork.

Before considering the problem of refractories for this zone of the furnace it is pertinent to point out that the shape of blown out furnaces throughout the world exhibits a striking similarity. In every case, an upward extension of the bosh takes place in service. This means that the maximum diameter of the furnace in the orthodox profile is attained not at the top of the bosh, as designed, but approximately 10 ft. above this level. Whether or not this is an argument for returning to the high boshes of last century is discussed elsewhere, but this bosh extension is important in that it emphasises that refractory wear is at its maximum a few feet above the top of the normal bosh. By means of radioactive isotopes, it has been established that this wear normally takes place in the early months, or even weeks of a campaign.

The use of radioactive cobalt for measuring lining wear is an interesting development of recent years. Radioactive cobalt (Co60) has a half-life of five years and is stable under blast-furnace conditions. A small pellet of the isotope in an alumina envelope is inserted into a hole drilled into the brick at a predetermined distance from the working face Periodic inspection with a detecting instrument during the furnace campaign determines whether the pellet is, or is not, in place. When it has been lost iron samples can be checked for radio-activity and the

actual time of loss so determined within a few hours. The use of supersonic testing applied to steel rods inserted into the brickwork is another
means of detecting lining wear. Unfortunately, the reliability of this
method decreases at higher temperatures.

At one works, three furnaces were lined within a few months of each
other and pellets of radioactive isotopes were built in to detect lining
wear.

A 28 ft. 6 in. furnace was lined with normal stack quality bricks built
tight to the shell and with shower cooling on the shell from the time of
blowing in. A row of six pellets was installed 4 ft. above the mantle,
three being located 6 in. from the working face and three 13 in. away
from it. The furnace was blown in on May 27th, 1956 and by the end of
August, all the pellets at this level had been lost. Further pellets were
installed in this furnace at levels of 34 ft. and 52 ft. above the mantle.
In May 1957, not a single pellet at these levels had been lost, although
some of them were located only 6 in. behind the working face.

The next furnace to be blown in had a 31 ft. hearth diameter with a
stack lining of 73 per cent. alumina bricks. It was also built tight to the
shell and was shower cooled from blowing in; radioactive isotopes were
built in at exactly the same levels as in the 28 ft. 6 in. furnace. The
furnace was blown in on September 11th, and by September 24th, two
pellets had been lost at the lowest level. These were 4 in. behind the
working face. By January 7th, all pellets had been lost at this level,
corresponding to a loss of 13 in. of brick. In May 1957, all pellets at
higher levels were still present.

The third furnace was a 27 ft. 6 in. furnace with the lower 10 ft. of
the stack in carbon, the remainder being of normal stack quality firebrick. The brickwork was built tight to the shell but internal coolers
were incorporated to within about 10 ft. of the stockline. The furnace
was blown in on December 2nd and about 80 pellets were used,
designed in this case to detect wear on four vertical lines. By the end of
January 1957, up to 10 in. of brickwork at 12, 15, 18 and 21 ft. above
the mantle had gone. Nothing was lost above or below these levels.
In May 1957, between 5 in. and 9 in. were lost in the 10 ft. of carbon.
Nothing had been lost above the 21 ft. level.

In spite of different refractories and different methods of construction,
an appreciable amount of brickwork was lost in the lower stack of all
three furnaces very shortly after blowing in.

At this particular plant, very high sinter burdens are used and some
very short lining lives (approximately two years) have been obtained.
Confirmatory evidence was obtained in a German plant at about the
same time. The furnace, 21 ft. in hearth diameter, was lined with

35 per cent. Al_2O_3 bricks and was of orthodox design. At a level about 10 ft. above the mantle, approximately two thirds of the lining thickness was lost in the first forty days of operation. The burden being smelted contained only about 25 per cent. of sinter.

When it is realized that in other districts furnaces of similar size and of similar production rates have produced over 3,000,000 tons on a lining (representing a lining life of over seven years) there is some evidence that the type of burden being smelted dictates the refractories problem to be encountered. Again, this places a premium on experience. As with so many aspects of ironmaking, it is impossible to lay down hard-and-fast rules. It is a safe generalisation, however, to say that a normal brick lining resists an ore burden better than it resists a sinter burden. The points already discussed, slag action, carbon disintegration, alkali attack, etc. occur with both types of burden, but it is probable that the slagging effect is much greater in the case of a sinter burden.

Arising from experience throughout the world in recent years, there is a greater measure of unanimity regarding cooling. Whereas it has on the continent been normal practice for many years to cool the stack throughout the whole of its height, this practice was rarely followed in the rest of the ironmaking world. Up to about ten years ago, it was common to cool the lower two-thirds of the stack; then it became fashionable to reduce this amount of cooling to only about 10 ft. above the mantle. Now, there is more and more agreement that cooling should extend the full height of the stack.

The stack brickwork of a blast furnace is hardly an ideally-designed mechanical structure. There is some reason to believe that inset stack coolers afford some measure of support to the masonry, and in view of the severe wear in the lower stack, any additional support of the upper brickwork is to be welcomed.

It has long been said, in regard to hearth refractories that water is the best of them all. This hackneyed saying now appears to be equally true for the whole of the furnace.

HEARTH REFRACTORIES

A hearth breakout is one of the most serious disasters that can happen to a blast furnace. Apart from the immediate damage and loss of production, and the danger to personnel, all operators treat a furnace with suspicion after a breakout; to see many tons of molten iron flowing along the floor completely out of control is not a reassuring sight. Fortunately, breakouts were formerly much more of a problem than they are today.

Most operators today are agreed that carbon is the best refractory for the walls of a blast-furnace hearth. The carbon must be efficiently cooled, however. Under such conditions, iron may penetrate the joints between the brickwork but the high thermal conductivity of the carbon ensures that this iron is chilled and does not penetrate to the retaining steel casing.

It is believed that the change to carbon as a hearth refractory is a permanent one. Service conditions in the hearth are such that the best of fireclay bricks must be working near their temperature limit. The refractoriness of a good 42/44 alumina brick is about 1750°C. which is reduced to 1600°C. when the brick carries a load of 50 lb. per sq. in. Immediately before casting time, in a big furnace, the bricks at the bottom of the hearth wall are exposed to such a loading. Iron can and does penetrate into the pores of the bricks and this iron, when oxidised by the air which infiltrates through the foundations, will react with the firebrick to produce a low melting point layer behind the working face of the brick. This will lead eventually to a "slabbing-off" of the working face. It seems that pieces of brick about 1 in. are peeled off in this manner. The process will then be repeated until the final slabbing-off takes place, when liquid iron will come into contact with the retaining steel jacket. When this occurs it is extremely rare for water cooling to prevent a breakout. Steel is not a refractory material. With a carbon hearth wall, none of these reactions take place.

Carbon has not proved as successful in the floor of the hearth as in the wall. Of many furnaces examined after blowing out, none have retained any depth of carbon. It is believed that failure is the result of carbon solution in iron. Carbon refractories for the blast furnace are generally made of amorphous carbon. Under the conditions obtaining in the hearth of a blast furnace, this carbon will graphitize—and graphite is soluble in molten iron. However well the masonry of the hearth is constructed, liquid iron will penetrate the joints between the bricks and will dissolve graphite as it forms. Graphite in pig iron migrates to the hot face; that is, it will slowly float out, so rendering the iron capable of dissolving more graphite. This process will continue until sufficient of the brick has been dissolved to destroy any lock there may be in the jointing and then whole bricks will float out. It appears that the only way of preventing this is by under-cooling the hearth. In one or two places, especially in Sweden, under-cooling has been adopted. Except where foundation conditions are unusually difficult, however, it is doubtful whether under-cooling is worthwhile. The great majority of hearth breakouts are through the side of the hearth. Under-cooling will therefore only prevent the formation of a large-sized bear. If furnace construction is such as to permit tapping of the bear after blowing-out, under-cooling of the hearth becomes even less worthwhile.

When a blast furnace is blown out and the hearth brickwork is wrecked, it will often be found that the fireclay bricks used on construction have become completely vitrified at a level some feet below the original working bottom. It is recommended that this vitrified brick should not be disturbed unless absolutely necessary, because it has, in effect, been fired to service conditions. Cases are known where vitrified brick from the first hearth lining of a furnace showed no change nearly twenty years later. Unfortunately, the installation of a monolithic, zero porosity refractory of this nature is virtually impossible in practice.

TUYERE BELT REFRACTORIES

Carbon has not yet been universally accepted for use in the tuyere belt of a blast furnace. It has, however, been successfully used in several installations in this country. There is much to commend it—especially its resistance to the action of blast-furnace slag and its high thermal conductivity. When cooling is carried out by means of big cast-iron cooling plates (see "Hearth Construction" Chapter I) carbon is recommended, but if inset plate coolers are used, orthodox 42/44 per cent. alumina bricks may be better. It is extremely rare not to have slag breakouts round plate coolers at some time during a furnace campaign. It is equally rare for these coolers to remain leak-proof during a campaign. The ingress of air or of water into carbon brickwork, at the temperature of the furnace hearth, will lead to rapid destruction of the brick.

BOSH REFRACTORIES

When considering furnaces throughout the world, the commonest type of bosh construction is that in which a large number of inset copper coolers is used. The reasons for this are given in the section on bosh design. It is suggested that carbon is undoubtedly the best material for bosh refractories, where its high thermal conductivity makes it particularly attractive. It can only be employed to best advantage if an externally cooled welded steel jacket is used without inset coolers. If carbon is not used in the bosh, a high quality 42/44 per cent. alumina brick should be used.

GENERAL

Too often the furnace builder, or operator, chooses standard sizes of bricks and carries out a great deal of brick cutting during construction.

When relining has to be done in the shortest possible time, the use of special shapes is desirable; especially is this so for such parts of the furnace as cooler arches, tapholes, and slag notches. The sizes of square and tapered bricks normally used for blast-furnace construction are legacies from the days when furnaces were of much smaller diameter than is the case today. Ideally, all those parts of the blast furnace where the walls are not vertical should have a different shaped brick for each course. This, of course, would not be practicable but the combination of squares and tapers should be based realistically on the diameters under consideration. If, for example, the diameter under construction demands four or five squares to one key, the resulting masonry will not be as strong a job as if the ratio of squares to keys were reversed.

Chapter XVIII

BLAST-FURNACE SLAG

SLAG

I T I S H A R D L Y an exaggeration to say that the main preoccupation in blast-furnace operation is with slag. The furnace operator has to think all the time about slag. Is the furnace slag dry? Are the tuyeres free of slag? Is the slag too hot or too cold, too basic or too acid? Is the slag runner cleaned up ready for use? Are ladles available? If any of these and many other questions are answered unfavourably, action is called for. Again, the necessary action is dependent on many other factors. The character and quantity of slag has a profound influence on all aspects of ironmaking, from the layout of the plant to the operation of the furnace. Slag volume per ton of iron can and does vary within very wide limits—some fortunate plants working extremely rich ores may have a slag volume as low as 5 to 6 cwt. per ton of iron: at the other end of the scale, plants working British ores may have a slag volume of 26 cwt. per ton of iron. Plants can be found operating at all intermediate volumes. For rich ore practice 8 to 10 cwt. is a fair average and this, of course, represents the major part of the world's iron production.

EFFECT ON LAYOUT

From the furnaceman's point of view, the ideal way of disposing of slag is to handle it in a large pit adjacent to the furnace itself. The necessity for slag ladles is avoided, the slag being flushed directly from the furnace into the pit (*see* fig. 62). These pits are usually divided into two so that one half is being filled as the other half is being emptied. A capacity covering something like two weeks' slag make is desirable; that is, two sections each capable of taking seven days' make of slag. After a section is filled, a robust face shovel turns the slag over for cooling, and subsequently, the same machine loads the slag into vehicles for conveyance to the slag processing plant or to the slag dump.

This method has numerous advantages. On lean ore practice, however, the provision of pits may be impracticable because of the large tonnages to be handled. In certain British practices for example, as

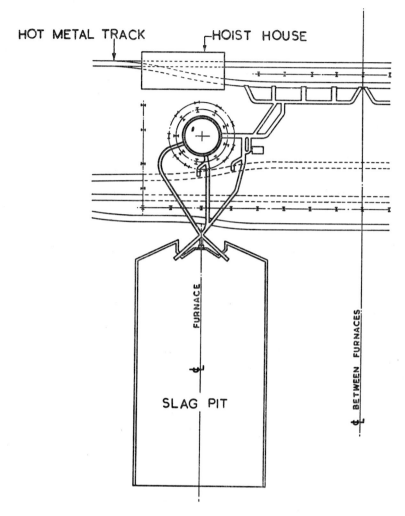

HOT METAL TRACK

HOIST HOUSE

FURNACE

SLAG PIT

BETWEEN FURNACES

Fig. 62. Slag pit at furnace.

much as 2000 tons of slag is made by each furnace in 24 hours. To allow for cooling and loading on the lines described above, the area occupied by slag pits would be enormous and, in a plant containing more than one blast furnace, it is doubtful whether a satisfactory layout could be made using such big pits. If a pit is impracticable then it becomes necessary to handle the slag in ladles. Even when slag pits are provided, however, at least one notch should be capable of delivering molten slag to ladles. This gives some insurance against unforeseen troubles with the normal pit arrangement.

Fig. 19 shows a typical layout for a high tonnage furnace where slag is being handled in ladles. It is desirable that slag traffic should be handled on the other side of the plant from iron traffic, so that the two systems do not interfere with each other. This means that in the original planning of a plant the slag side of the cast house should be on the same side as the ultimate disposal point of the slag. Only by obeying this rule can interference with other traffic be reduced to a minimum.

The size of the slag ladles obviously affects plant layout. The smaller the ladles the larger the number to be set at the furnace, entailing both longer slag runners and cast house. The correct choice of ladle size is usually a matter of compromise in which the merits of a large volume slag pot have to be considered against the disadvantages of a high tare weight and an increasingly expensive carriage. The distance to the tipping point and the track gradients and curves on the journey have an influence on the choice of ladle. Generally speaking, a 350 to 400 cu. ft. ladle is a good choice.

Slag ladles can be divided into two main types:
(a) Rope-tipped.
(b) Power-tipped.

(a) Rope-tipped ladles

This type of ladle is not very fashionable but has much to commend it. A typical example is given in fig. 63. The carriage is simple and inexpensive. The ratio of pay load to tare is more favourable than with power operated ladles. The main disadvantage is that pulling over the pot by means of a wire rope fastened to the locomotive whilst the ladle wheels are spragged may entail rather more wear and tear on the locomotive. With proper attention to pot maintenance there should be little difference in locomotive maintenance, and then the rope-tipped type scores heavily. Apart from renewal of tipping ropes there is less to go wrong than on a power-tipped ladle, with its necessary tipping gear. Tipping ropes are usually made from second-hand ropes (e.g. furnace skip and bell ropes).

A recent design of rope-tipped ladle as shown in fig. 63 has a capacity of 370 cu. ft. This carries, under normal conditions, a slag weight of nearly 20 tons and has a total loaded weight of 54 tons. Note that this pot is one of the very few which is not truly conical in shape.

Fig. 63. Rope tipped slag ladle.

Fig. 64. Steam tipped slag ladle.

(b) Power-operated ladles

Instead of pulling over the slag pot by means of a rope connected to the locomotive, the ladle may be tipped by means of compressed air, steam, or electric power. A typical arrangement of a steam or air-operated ladle is shown in fig. 64. In this case, steam or air is drawn from the locomotive and the slag pot is turned over without shock to the rolling stock. In the case of electrically-tipped ladles, a motor mounted on the slag ladle carriage performs the same duty, power for the motor being obtained by plugging into a trailing cable supply at the slag dump.

Power-operated ladles have a higher capital cost and a less favourable ratio of pay load to gross load. A typical steam-tipped ladle will have a capacity of 308 cu. ft. This means a pay load of 15 tons of slag and a gross laden weight of 47 tons. It is usual practice to fit roller bearings to the axles of power-tipped ladles, a practice with obvious advantages. This cannot be done with a rope-tipped ladle because of the shock necessarily imposed by the method of tipping.

At some plants, two pots are mounted in one carriage; this will shorten the distance between slag spouts and the cast house, but that appears to be the only advantage of such an arrangement.

SLAG LADLE POTS

In both types of carriage, the same pot may be employed. The commonest type of pot is a heavy hematite iron casting with a wall thickness of about 2 in. Steel pots are occasionally favoured, but it should be borne in mind that the more expensive steel pot can be burnt by molten iron as easily as a cheaper cast iron one. Corrugated slag pots have found favour in some places as they have greater resistance to cracking and warping.

Factors other than the material from which the pot is made have a bigger influence on the life obtained. It is most important, for example, that a bare metal pot should never be used. The usual method of achieving a satisfactory lining is to spray the hot ladle with lime wash. A certain amount of coal added to the lime wash has been found effective by some operators. Lime washing must be carried out before every filling of the ladle. The installation of a properly designed agitating tank and spraying gear is worthwhile if there are more than a few ladles in the fleet.

Slag pots are conical in shape to facilitate complete discharge of the slag on tipping. Between filling and tipping, a skull always forms in the ladle, the thickness of which depends on the time and temperatures involved. If the ladle is properly lime-washed, this skull will leave the pot without undue bumping provided that the ladle has been allowed to cool somewhat between fillings. When slag is poured into a cool, well-limed ladle the skull will form quickly and the pot will expand sufficiently to permit its free discharge, but with a hot pot, this expansion may not be sufficient. Whether rope or power-tipped ladle is used, the main cause of wear-and-tear on the slag ladle carriage arises from severe bumping to free skulls from the pot.

OTHER METHODS OF SLAG DISPOSAL

On some furnaces, particularly on the continent, slag is discharged from the slag notch into a granulating flume. A swiftly moving stream of water introduced through a specially designed granulating head, chills, granulates, and transports the slag to a settling pond some distance from the furnace. Grab cranes, or bucket elevators, are used to recover the granulated slag for transport in vehicles to a dump or to a processing plant. While this method has much to attract it from the viewpoint of convenience, it can be rather messy unless carefully operated and maintained.

At one or two works, a slag foaming plant is situated at the blast furnace so that slag from the slag notch flows immediately to the foaming system. This is not a desirable practice. Because of the limited amount of water used in foaming, the process is always accompanied by the copious evolution of steam and sulphurous fumes. Corrosion of structural work may be serious and working conditions are never pleasant. It is suggested that there are sufficient unavoidable problems around a blast furnace without adding to them by installing a foaming plant near the slag notch.

SCRAP RECOVERY

However well a blast furnace may be operated, a certain amount of shot iron will be contained in the slag. All furnaces run into trouble at some time or other and at such times comparatively large buttons of iron will settle out in the slag ladle from the dirty contaminated slags produced.

Much of the shot can be extracted if a jack runner or bleeder is used at the slag runners in the cast house, while the larger pieces can be recovered at the point of disposal. A routine for the recovery of "ladle buttons" is well worthwhile.

A special gang of four or five men and a small power loader can quickly justify themselves on this duty. Once recovered, iron tipped down a slag bank is just as valuable as iron poured over the pig caster.

EFFECT OF SLAG VOLUME ON OPERATING PRACTICE

The slag volume carried in any particular practice is dictated by the raw materials available; in the case of low slag volumes, it may be necessary to increase slag volume deliberately. This will be the case where the sulphur load is so high that the slag is saturated with sulphur to a degree which prohibits the production of a satisfactory low sulphur iron. For this reason, it is impossible to lay down a minimum slag volume. Cases are known of furnaces operating satisfactorily at less than 5 cwt. of slag per ton of iron. Generally speaking, however, the majority of practices require rather more slag than this. Some operators indicate that difficulty may be experienced in securing uniform stock descent below a certain minimum slag volume. It is suggested that this danger is not so real where the burden is correctly prepared. The maximum slag volume which can be carried by a furnace is purely a question of economics. Successful blast-furnace practice is carried out in some places with a slag volume as high as 26/27 cwt. per ton of iron but there is obviously a limit to the amount of slag which can be handled economically. It is suggested that anything over 30 cwt. of slag per ton of iron will be a prohibitive figure in any practice, because the higher the slag volume the more certain blast-furnace operating problems are aggravated. Copper losses, blinding of tuyeres, chilled hearths, etc. are all more prone to occur with high slag volumes than with low slag volumes. It requires more pressure to blow a given volume of air to a furnace carrying a high slag volume than to a furnace carrying a low slag volume. These considerations have led to the development of two different blast-furnace practices—"driving" practice and "checking" practice. With slag volumes of up to approximately 14 cwt. per ton, almost every blast-furnace operator throughout the world endeavours to maintain even stock descent at all times; so much so that in many places the necessity to check a furnace, or the occurrence of slipping, is looked upon as bad practice. There is considerable justification for this view. On the other hand, in districts where slag volumes of 22 cwt. per ton and more are usual, a freely moving burden is never found and indeed, is not wanted, by many operators.

In "checking" practice, stock descent is achieved by means of checking the furnace at regular and frequent intervals. On a furnace producing over 1000 tons of iron per day and a slag volume of 26 cwt. per ton, checking will take place every 15 minutes. Paradoxically, checking practice on high slag volumes, although wasteful from the viewpoint of blowing, can, and does, lead to an increase in the amount of air used per minute in the furnace. The main reason for checking practice is a high slag volume. In any furnace, slag formation probably commences some feet above the top of the bosh and slag is always present in the furnace from this level to the slag notch. As more slag is made, the pressure has to be raised, thus holding up a greater volume of slag. If the furnace slips, extra slag will be precipitated suddenly into the hearth. This precipitation is often accompanied by a general lowering of temperature, by slag flowing back into tuyeres, blow-pipes and goose-necks, and even by blow-pipes being burnt by contaminated slag. When checking practice is followed, the amount of slag held up above the tuyeres is considerably reduced. This enables more air to be blown because of the decreased pressure resistance and reduces the risk of the troubles mentioned above if a slip occurs. Of necessity, a high slag volume means a poor iron (Fe) content of the burden and a less favour-able ratio (by volume) of coke to burden in the stack of the furnace. As it is coke which usually provides most of the voidage in the stock column it follows that high slag volumes mean a tight burden, and therefore one more resistant to gas flow. Checking practice is of help in this direction, serving to move the burden at regular intervals of time.

Slag volume, then, determines which practice should be adopted: "checking" practice is almost certainly wrong and wasteful with low slag volumes, while "driving" practice with high slag volumes will never permit production figures as high as those obtainable with check-ing practice.

SLAG COMPOSITION

The composition of a blast-furnace slag depends on the raw materials used and the desired quality of the product. In practice, a compromise is usually necessary because the raw materials do not permit the use of the most suitable slag for the type of iron to be manufactured. Few operators would refuse the chance to increase deliberately the magnesia content of their slag, if this were possible without increased slag volume and increased cost of raw materials. Blast-furnace slags are members of the quaternary system—lime, silica, magnesia, alumina. These four constituents are found in all slags and rarely is any significant propor-tion of any other constituent present. Attention is directed to the classic work of Osborne, DeVries, Gee and Kraner[1] on this quaternary system.

It is not sufficient to consider the constituents of a slag in relation to its melting point. Johnson[2] explained the need for free running tem-peratures years ago. It is not sufficient to generate enough heat to make the slag. Enough heat must be generated to raise the slag to a tempera-ture at which it is fluid enough to run from the furnace. This places a premium on a slag which has a low viscosity at operating temperatures.

Fig. 65. Tipping and recovering from slag pits.

Fundamental studies of the slag system indicate how complex this problem can be, but one or two broad principles can be laid down.

There are two principal methods of slag control in the operation of a blast furnace. One is along orthodox lines, in which the slag is sufficiently basic to absorb enough sulphur for the iron to be immediately suitable for subsequent processing on leaving the taphole. The other method, acid burdening, ignores sulphur absorption and usually produces an iron so high in sulphur that further treatment is necessary after the blast furnace to reduce the sulphur to the required level. Orthodox burdening is therefore more of a compromise than acid burdening, because in the latter practice, no cognisance is taken of the sulphur content of the iron to be produced. The fundamentals of acid burdening have been described by Colclough.[3] Briefly, almost everything is subordinated to the production of a slag of low viscosity and low melting point. Where acid burdening is practised with British ores, a typical slag analysis is lime 34·3 per cent., silica 33·7 per cent., alumina 23·4 per cent., magnesia 6·7 per cent. and this slag gives a ratio of lime-silica of approximately unity. It will still be possible to control the silicon in the iron with such a slag, but it will not be possible to control the sulphur. Study of the fundamental work on slags (*see* Bibliography) shows that optimum conditions are only obtained in a very narrow range centred round this value. If the slag increases or decreases in basicity by comparatively small amounts, the viscosity increases appreciably. This increased viscosity will result in a higher coke consumption and a poorer blast furnace performance. In some ways, orthodox burdening gives more latitude in operation. Assuming a constant alumina and magnesia, the higher the ratio of lime-silica, the more effective a desulphuriser the slag will be. Generally speaking, this will be accompanied by an increase in melting point and viscosity which will demand increased fuel consumption. As this ratio rises to a point at which operation becomes difficult an increase in magnesia will do much to restore favourable conditions.

In the other direction, a decrease in lime/silica is to be aimed at under all circumstances until one of two limiting values is approached:

(*a*) The point at which desulphurisation is insufficient.

(*b*) The point at which viscosity increases.

It is impossible to lay down hard and fast values for these limits. Study of the fundamental work referred to earlier is extremely necessary before departing from known and established practice.

With self-fluxing burdens, little or nothing can be done in the way of magnesia changes, but where limestone is used as a flux the substitution of dolomite or magnesium limestone for limestone is always possible.

Broadly speaking, the effect of magnesia is to increase the fluidity of the slag at a given temperature. Table XVI gives typical slags employed in various blast furnace practices.

TABLE XVI

	Silica %	Lime %	Alumina %	Magnesia %
Magnitogorsk, Russia	34·5	41·5	14·5	8·0
Novo-Taguil, Russia	36·0	36·0	17·0	7·0
Home ores, acid burdening ..	33·7	34·3	23·4	6·7
Home ores, 100% sinter ..	34·0	40·5	17·3	3·9
Hematite iron, imported ores ..	31·4	45·2	10·1	6·1
Foundry iron, home ores ..	30·3	40·5	21·2	2·4
Basic iron, imported ores ..	32·2	39·5	20·9	4·2
Basic iron, U.S. Southern States	37·5	40·0	9·6	10·1
Basic iron, U.S. Northern States	34·8	45·6	12·8	3·8
Basic iron, Germany	32·0	43·0	13·8	4·6

SLAG UTILISATION

Blast-furnace slag can be used in several ways and in several forms. A brief catalogue of the more important uses are:

(a) Air-cooled slag

This is slag which has been tipped on to a dump or into pits, and loaded when cold. After crushing and screening, it can be a satisfactory substitute for natural stone for road-making and railways ballast. For such purposes, it is delivered in a range of sizes obtained by suitable screening, and either dry or tarred. Many slags are highly suitable as aggregate in concrete. An arrangement of slag pits which are situated away from the furnace is shown in fig. 65. Slag from ladles is dumped into the pit and after cooling, recovered for processing. In general, the quality of the slag is improved if the pit is wide. A pit width of 150 ft. means that the slag will flow without restriction.

(b) Granulated slag

This product is obtained by flushing molten slag into a considerable excess of water. After draining, the product is a glassy granulated material which may be used as a raw material in cement manufacture, as a sub-base for roads, as a stowing material in mining operations, or, in a few isolated cases, as a raw material for the manufacture of glass.

(c) Foamed or expanded slag

This material is obtained by running molten slag into a carefully controlled amount of water. In this case, instead of being completely quenched, as with granulate, the slag expands, or foams, to produce a cellular lightweight material. Generally speaking, only hot limey slags produce the lightest slag, which is commonly known as "foamed slag". Slags of medium temperature and basicity will produce a rather heavier material, usually referred to as "expanded slag". The bulk densities of the two materials are about 34 and 45 lb. per cu. ft. respectively. Both materials make a very good lightweight aggregate which can be used for both sound and thermal insulation, and the former is additionally attractive because of its fire-resisting qualities. In Britain, expanded slag is not yet generally accepted as a suitable material for these purposes.

(d) Slag wool

For the production of slag wool, a jet of high pressure steam is blown through a stream of molten slag. Satisfactory wool can be made from a wide range of slag compositions; the length of fibre produced is dependent on the woolmaking technique. Slag wool is an entirely satisfactory substitute for mineral wool as an insulating material.

GENERAL

By far the major part of the world's blast-furnace slag is disposed of in the air-cooled condition. It will be appreciated that the geographical situation has a considerable influence on slag disposal and its economics. For example, if a high lime, falling slag is being produced in a district where the local rock is granite, there will be very little chance of slag competing with granite as a material for road building.

REFERENCES

[1] "Optimum Composition of Blast Furnace Slag as Deduced from Liquidus Data from the Quaternary System $CaO-MgO-Al_2O_3-SiO_2$, by OSBORN, DEVRIES, GEE, and KRANER. *A.I.M.E., 1953 Proceedings.*

[2] *Principles, Operation and Products of the Blast Furnace*, by J. E. JOHNSON, 200. McGraw-Hill Book Co.

[3] "Constitution of Blast Furnace Slags in relation to Pig Iron Manufacture, by T. P. COLCLOUGH. *J. Iron & Steel Inst.,* 1936, *134,* 547.

Chapter XIX

DISTRIBUTION OF ELEMENTS

DISTRIBUTION OF ELEMENTS

SMALL AMOUNTS OF minor constituents are being proved to influence the properties of steel and iron, and it is becoming increasingly necessary to use new and strange raw materials. It is important therefore, that the ironmaker must know how these minor elements behave in the furnace.

1. MANGANESE

In the normal range of blast-furnace irons (not spiegel or ferromanganese) about 65 per cent. of the ingoing manganese is retained in the iron. The amount increases with temperature and with slag basicity.

2. PHOSPHORUS

All ingoing phosphorus is retained in the iron, which means that a desired phosphorus in the iron can only be attained by charging suitable raw materials.

3. SILICON

The amount of silicon passing to the iron increases with hearth temperature. Control of the blast furnace centres round silicon control, because generally speaking, the amount of silicon in the iron is a measure of the margin of heat being used in the process. Obviously, the operator making iron with 0·50 per cent. silicon has a smaller margin of safety than when making 2·50 per cent. silicon iron. Few furnacemen would care to work a furnace to produce silicons lower than 0·40 per cent., because at this figure, especially when normally low sulphurs are required, the furnace is either dangerously cold with a normal slag or dangerously limey with a hot slag. In either case, it requires little variation to cause trouble.

4. CARBON

For a given practice, the operator has little or no control over the carbon content of the iron. A fall in hearth temperature usually means a decrease in the carbon content of the iron.

5. ALUMINIUM, CALCIUM, MAGNESIUM, AND ALKALI METALS

Under all circumstances, these elements are retained as oxides in the slag.

6. SULPHUR

Except when working under conditions of acid burdening, not more than 6 to 7 per cent. of ingoing sulphur should be retained in the iron. Sulphur is lowered in the iron by increasing hearth temperature (and therefore silicon content) slag basicity, slag volume and manganese content.

7. ARSENIC

This element behaves in the same way as phosphorus and is entirely retained in the iron.

8. COPPER, TIN, AND NICKEL

These elements also pass into the iron.

9. VANADIUM

Most of the vanadium charged passes into the iron but a little, normally about 20 per cent., is held in the slag. This amount tends to increase with more acid slags.

10. CHROMIUM

In small amounts, virtually all the chromium in the charge will find its way to the iron, but with larger amounts as much as 30 per cent. will be held in the slag.

11. ZINC

This can be a nuisance, in that it will enter neither iron nor slag. When its compounds are reduced to form metallic zinc in the lower part of the stack one of several things may occur. The zinc metal may volatilize and seep through between a cooling plate and its socket so that slivers of the metal are sometimes found outside the furnace. The volatilised zinc may ascend with the gases and be oxidised. Zinc oxide is found in flue dust and is frequently found in the firebricks of the stack lining. If an appreciable amount of zinc is charged, deposits of zinc oxide may build up in the gas offtakes.

12. COBALT

Generally, all cobalt passes to the iron.

13. TITANIUM

All but a very small amount of titanium is retained in the slag. Titaniferous ores are notoriously difficult to smelt. Of the small amount which is retained in the iron, some combines with nitrogen (presumably from cyanides present in the hearth) to form titanium nitride. Large crystals of this copper coloured compound are frequently found in the boundary areas of a furnace bear or salamander.

BURDENING THE FURNACE

Everything that goes into the blast furnace, with the exception of a small amount of flue dust, must come out in the form of slag, iron or gas. The destination of some of the burden constituents, such as lime, alumina and magnesia is predetermined by the fact that they are irreducible even at the highest temperature of the blast furnace and they therefore pass into the slag as oxides in combination with silica. On the other hand, phosphates are reduced in the furnace and all the evolved phosphorus is dissolved in the iron. The partition of most of the other elements between slag and iron, depends on the furnace practice as described under the heading "Distribution of Elements" on page 248. In order to produce any desired grade of iron the furnace must not only be operated at the correct temperature but must be correctly burdened.

The first consideration in burdening the furnace is that the slag produced should be of such a composition that it will be fluid enough to run from the slag notch at the temperature normally attained in the furnace hearth, and be capable of absorbing enough sulphur to ensure that the sulphur in the iron is according to specification. What this composition should be is dealt with in Chapter XVIII, and Table XVI gives the analyses of typical slags made in various practices.

The next consideration is the production of iron of the correct specification. The specification for silicon and sulphur can be met by suitable operating practice but the phosphorus content of the iron, and to some extent the manganese content must be controlled by correct burdening.

The desirable phosphorus content of the iron varies with the purpose for which it is to be used. For basic open hearth steelmaking the phosphorus in the iron may vary from 0·2 per cent. to 1·7 per cent. depending on the ores used. In the basic Bessemer process it may be anything from 1·7 per cent. to 2·5 per cent. In the acid Bessemer and acid openhearth processes, all the phosphorus in the iron goes into the steel, and therefore, must not exceed 0·04 per cent. It is obvious that both the ores and the coke used for acid steelmaking processes must be chosen with a careful eye on their phosphorus content.

Most blast-furnace plants are connected with steel plants and the iron specification will be the same day after day. At some merchant plants, however, frequent changes of grade are called for and the greatest possible care and skill are required if off-grade iron is to be avoided. At one British plant, the grade of iron required may be changed two or three times in one week, the phosphorus content varying between 0·04 per cent. and 0·35 per cent.

The burdening of a furnace to produce iron of a given specification is simply an exercise in arithmetic. It is probable that every experienced operator has his own method of calculation but a specimen method is shown by the following examples.

It is assumed that the raw materials shown in Table XVII are available and that the grades of iron which will be required are:

Grade	1	2	3	4
Silicon %	2·0	3·0	1·0	0·7
Phosphorus %	0·04	0·30	1·0	1·3

Each ore must be evaluated, *i.e.* the amount of ore and coke required per ton of iron and the phosphorus content of the iron must be calculated. It may be necessary to control the manganese content of the iron, so this must also be calculated. The silicon content of the iron will be controlled by the furnace operation but it must be taken into account later when calculating the flux required and the slag weight.

EVALUATION OF ORE A

The percentage of Fe in pig iron depends on the amount of impurities, *i.e.* carbon, phosphorus, silicon, sulphur, and manganese. In this calculation it is assumed that the iron will contain 92·5 per cent. Fe, equivalent to 2072 lb. per ton and therefore the weight of ore required will be $\dfrac{2072 \times 100}{45 \cdot 0} = 4602$ lb. per ton of iron.

An estimate of the coke required per ton of burden must be based on the experience of the operator who will have a good idea of the ore/coke

TABLE XVII
RAW MATERIALS

	Ore A	Ore B	Ore C	Ore D	Ore E	Ore F	Limestone	Coke
Silica %	11·0	8·5	4·5	14·5	10·0	11·4	2·8	4·3
Alumina %	1·0	1·0	0·4	1·2	4·0	1·3	—	2·7
*Lime+Magnesia % ..	1·0	5·5	5·0	3·0	3·0	2·2	53·6	0·4
Manganese %	1·0	1·2	1·7	0·2	0·2	0·1	—	—
Phosphorus %	0·3	0·01	0·005	0·57	0·90	0·39	—	0·017
Iron %	45·0	42·0	48·0	44·0	52·0	46·8	—	—
Approximate slag forming materials %	14·0	17·0	12·0	19·0	18·0	16·0	57·0	10·0

* For simplification, lime and magnesia have been added together and will be referred to in the calculations as lime.

ratio in his practice. If it is assumed that this ratio is 2·5, the coke required will be $4602 \div 2 \cdot 5 = 1840$ lb. per ton of iron.*

The phosphorus in the iron comes from both the ore and the coke:

4602 lb. of ore at 0·03% P = 1·3806 lb. phosphorus.
1840 lb. of coke at 0·017% P = 0·3128 lb. phosphorus.

Total phosphorus in
   1 ton of iron   = 1·6934 lb.

This is equivalent to $\dfrac{1 \cdot 6934 \times 100}{2240} = 0 \cdot 076$ per cent.

The manganese in the iron comes from the ore charged and the proportion going into the iron depends on such factors as hearth temperature and slag basicity. If it is assumed that 65 per cent. passes into the iron, the percentage of manganese can be calculated as follows:

Manganese in 4602 lb. of ore at 1 per cent. = 46·02 lb. The weight passing into 1 ton of iron will be 65 per cent. of 46·02 lb. = 29·9 lb. The

manganese percentage is therefore $29 \cdot 9 \times \dfrac{100}{2240} = 1 \cdot 33$.

The five ores having been evaluated in this manner can be tabulated as follows:

	A	B	C	D	E	F
Ore required per ton of iron lb.	4602	4933	4316	4708	3984	4427
Coke required per ton of iron lb.	1842	1973	1727	1883	1593	1771
Phosphorus % in iron	0·076	0·037	0·023	1·21	1·62	0·78
Manganese % in iron	1·33	1·72	2·13	0·27	0·23	0·13

To produce iron with a phosphorus content of 0·04 per cent., ores A, B and C are suitable and ore B is so near to the specification that 100 per cent. could be used. Ores A and C can be used together, the correct proportions being represented by the equation:

$$0 \cdot 076A + 0 \cdot 023C = 0 \cdot 04(A + C)$$

which can be resolved as follows:

$$0 \cdot 076A - 0 \cdot 04A = 0 \cdot 04C - 0 \cdot 023C$$
$$0 \cdot 036A = 0 \cdot 017C$$
$$\frac{A}{C} = \frac{0 \cdot 017}{0 \cdot 036}$$

* If it is subsequently found that limestone must be added to the burden, the estimated coke rate will have to be increased. This will have little effect on the phosphorus in the iron, as 1 cwt. of coke contains only 0·019 lb. which in a ton of iron amounts to only 0·00085 per cent.

The proportions are therefore 17 parts of Ore A to 36 parts of Ore C, equivalent to 32 per cent. and 68 per cent. respectively.

Ore B, being so near to specification could be added, in any proportion, to a mixture of ores A and C in the proportions of 32 to 68.

Ore receipts may dictate that 20 per cent. of Ore A should be used.

Ore C would therefore be $20 \times \dfrac{68}{32} = 42 \cdot 5$ per cent. and the ore burden would be:

Ore A 20·0 per cent.

Ore B 37·5 per cent.

Ore C 42·5 per cent.

The weights of ores per ton of iron, the flux requirements and the coke rate can now be calculated and the iron analysis checked.

The iron in the burden will be:

Ore A 20·0 % at 45 % Iron = 9·00
Ore B 37·5 % at 42 % Iron = 15·75
Ore C 42·5 % at 48 % Iron = 20·40

$$\overline{}$$
$$45 \cdot 15$$
$$\overline{}$$

The weight of burden required will be:

$\dfrac{2072 \times 100}{45 \cdot 15} = 4587$ lb. and the burden will be composed of:

Ore A 20·0 % of 4587 lb. = 917 lb.

Ore B 37·5 % of 4587 lb. = 1720 lb.

Ore C 42·5 % of 4587 lb. = 1950 lb.

The coke required for this burden will be:

$4587 \div 2 \cdot 5 = 1835$ lb.

FLUX REQUIRED

It is assumed that it is desired to produce a slag with a lime/silica ratio of 1·3 (a fairly average figure) and therefore if the burden contains insufficient lime to produce such a slag, a material containing an excess of lime (or magnesia) will be needed as a flux. For the purpose of this calculation it is assumed that the flux available is limestone. To calculate the amount of limestone required it is necessary to know the lime deficiency of the burden.

The total silica input is:
From Ores:
Ore A 917 lb. at 11·0% silica = 101 lb.
Ore B 1720 lb. at   8·5% silica = 146 lb.
Ore C 1950 lb. at   4·5% silica =   88 lb.

    Total from Ores   335 lb.
From Coke:
1835 lb. at 4·0% silica   = 73 lb.

                408 lb.

The specification calls for iron containing 2 per cent. silicon equivalent to 45 lb. of silicon per ton of iron. Silica, from which the silicon is reduced contains 28/60 of silicon and therefore the 45 lb. is reduced from $45 \times \dfrac{60}{28} = 96$ lb. of silica. This silica will not need fluxing. The silica to be fluxed is:
$$408 - 96 = 312 \text{ lb.}$$
The lime input is:
Ore A 917 lb. at 1·0% lime =   9 lb.
Ore B 1720 lb. at 5·5% lime = 95 lb.
Ore C 1950 lb. at 5·0% lime = 97 lb.

                201 lb.

To flux 312 lb. of silica requires $312 \times 1 \cdot 3 = 406$ lb. of lime of which only 201 lb. is present in the burden. The difference of 205 lb. of lime must be added in the form of limestone.

EVALUATION OF LIMESTONE

Limestone contains both lime and silica (*see* Table XVII) and therefore part of the lime must be used to flux this silica and will not be available to flux the burden silica. The 2·8 per cent. of silica present in the limestone will require (at the 1·3 lime/silica ratio assumed) $2 \cdot 8 \times 1 \cdot 3 = 3 \cdot 6$ per cent. of lime and this deducted from the lime percentage leaves 50 per cent. available for fluxing. The conversion factor for lime to limestone is therefore $\dfrac{100}{50} = 2$.

When evaluating the ores, the coke estimated was that required to smelt the ores only. The addition of limestone to the burden will increase the coke required for smelting and this additional coke will introduce silica which will have to be fluxed. At the burden/coke ratio of 2·5 every pound of limestone will require 0·4 lb. of coke, containing 0·016 lb. of silica. This silica must be fluxed by $0·016 \times 1·3 = 0·021$ lb. of lime, equivalent to 0·042 lb. of limestone. The calculated quantity of limestone should therefore be increased by 4·2 per cent. to provide for this silica.

The limestone addition in the present case is therefore $205 \times 2 \times 1·042 = 427$ lb.

The calculation can now be checked to see that slag basicity, slag weight and iron quality are reasonably correct.

Burden	Ore	4587 lb.
	Limestone	427 lb.
	Total	5014 lb.

Coke at 2·5 burden/
    coke ratio   2006 lb.

Silica to be fluxed:

From ores—(previously calculated)	335 lb.
From 2006 lb. of coke at 4%	80 lb.
	415 lb.
Less 96 lb. for silica in the iron	96 lb.
	319 lb.

The lime required is therefore $319 \times 1·3 = 415$ lb.

Lime for fluxing:

From ores—(previously calculated)	201 lb.
From 427 lb. Limestone	214 lb.
	415 lb.

It is important that the slag volume should be adequate to remove the sulphur from the iron. Taking the figures of estimated slag forming materials from Table XVII the slag volume will be:

From Ore *A*   917 lb. at 14 % = 128 lb.
From Ore *B*   1720 lb. at 17 % = 292 lb.
From Ore *C*   1950 lb. at 12 % = 234 lb.
From Coke   2006 lb. at 10 % = 201 lb.
From Limestone   427 lb. at 57 % = 243 lb.
                                  ‾‾‾‾‾‾
                                  1098 lb.
Less 96 lb. silica for silicon in iron =   96 lb.
                                  ‾‾‾‾‾‾
                                  1002 lb.
                                  ‾‾‾‾‾‾

Phosphorus in Iron
From Ore *A*   917 lb. at 0·03 % P = 0·275 lb.
From Ore *B*   1720 lb. at 0·01 % P = 0·172 lb.
From Ore *C*   1950 lb. at 0·005 P % = 0·098 lb.
From Coke   2006 lb. at 0·017 % P = 0·341 lb.
                                  ‾‾‾‾‾‾
Total phosphorus in 1 ton of iron   = 0·886 lb.
                                  ‾‾‾‾‾‾

Phosphorus % in iron $\dfrac{0·886}{2240} \times 100 = 0·0396\%$.

The second grade of iron, *i.e.* silicon 3 per cent. and phosphorus 0·3 per cent. can be made from various mixtures of the ores available. All six ores can be used or mixtures of two, three, four, or five ores.

The correct proportions of the ores can be arrived at by trial and error but the simple formula used in the calculation for using two ores can be applied. The following example shows the use of this formula.

The correct proportions of ores *A* and *D* are represented by the equation: $0·076\,A + 1·21\,D = 0·3\,(A+D)$
which can be resolved as follows:

$$1·21\,D - 0·3\,D \;= 0·3\,A - 0·076\,A$$
$$0·91\,D = 0·224\,A$$
$$\frac{D}{A} = \frac{0·224}{0·91}$$

The proportions are therefore 0·91 parts of Ore *A* to 0·224 parts of Ore *D*, equivalent to 80·2 per cent. and 19·8 per cent. respectively.

Ores *A* and *B*, containing little phosphorus can both be used to balance the high phosphorus of Ores *D*, *E* and *F*. (Ore *C* is neglected in order to simplify the calculations.)

If the proportions of *A* with *D*, *E* and *F* and of *B* with *D*, *E* and *F* are calculated they can be tabulated as follows:

			_1_	_2_	_3_	_4_	_5_	_6_
_A_ ..	..	..	80·2	85·5	68·0			
_B_ ..	..	..				77·5	83·5	64·7
_D_ ..	..	..	19·8			22·5		
_E_ ..	..	..		14·5			16·5	
_F_ ..	..	..			32·0			35·3
Manganese % in iron produced ..			1·12	1·17	0·94	1·39	1·48	1·16

(The resulting manganese per cent. in the iron has been calculated and is shown in the tables because it has a bearing on the choice of ores used.)

It is obvious that by adding together any or all of the vertical columns the proportions of the different ores will be correct for the production of iron of the required phosphorus content. For example, columns _1, 3_ and _4_ give:

			%
_A_	80·2 +68·0	=148·2	49·4
_B_		77·5	25·8
_D_	19·8+22·5	= 42·3	14·1
_F_		32·0	10·7
		300·0	100·0

The phosphorus in the iron from this mixture of ores would be:
Ore _A_ 49·4% at 0·076% P=0·0375
Ore _B_ 25·8% at 0·037% P=0·0096
Ore _D_ 14·1% at 1·21% P =0·1708
Ore _F_ 10·7% at 0·78% P =0·0835

$$0·3014$$

It is also obvious that any multiple of any of the vertical columns can be used. Thus, if large quantities of ores _B_ and _F_ were available, a mixture could be arrived at by taking columns _1_ to _5_ and adding say three times column _6_. This would give:

			%
Ore _A_	80·2+85·5+68·0	=233·7	29·2
Ore _B_	77·5+83·5+(3×64·7)	=355·1	44·4
Ore _D_	19·8+22·5	= 42·3	5·3
Ore _E_	14·5+16·5	= 31·0	3·9
Ore _F_	32·0+(3×35·3)	=137·9	17·2
		800·0	100·0

If a shortage of say ore E occurred, the mixture could easily be changed by recalculating without columns *2* and *5*.

It may be necessary to keep the manganese content of the iron as low as possible. In that case columns *4* and *5* must be left out of the calculation. An average of columns *1*, *2*, *3* and *6* gives a manganese content of 1·10 per cent. (with the correct phosphorus content) and this can be reduced by using multiples of column *3*. For example, column *1*, *2* and *6* with three times column *3* would give:

$$\frac{1 \cdot 12 + 1 \cdot 17 + 1 \cdot 16 + (3 \times 0 \cdot 94)}{6} = 1 \cdot 04 \% \text{ Mn.}$$

However, this example would require:

Ore *A*	61·6%
Ore *B*	10·8%
Ore *D*	3·3%
Ore *E*	2·4%
Ore *F*	21·9%

and stocks may not allow the use of such a large proportion of Ore *A*. Use of the table will, however, enable the operator to keep to the correct phosphorus content, with the lowest manganese content consistent with the ore stocks.

When the ore mixture is decided upon, the amount of flux required and the slag weight can be calculated in the same way as was shown for the 0·04 per cent. phosphorus iron. It must, however, be remembered that the silica reduced and therefore not requiring fluxing varies with the different grades of iron, and the correct allowance must be made.

To determine the correct ore mixtures for the other grades of iron specified earlier it is only necessary to compile a table of proportions, similar to that on page 258 but calculated on a basis of the phosphorus desired. The mixture can then be chosen after taking cognisance of the slag volume and its alumina content, the manganese content of the iron and the state of the stockyard.

Chapter XX

BIBLIOGRAPHY

H UNDREDS OF ARTICLES have been written and papers presented dealing with various aspects of ironmaking—these are scattered over the technical press and scientific proceedings of various bodies in many countries.

In the following pages are references to various publications which can be recommended as useful reading in further study of ironmaking. It will be appreciated that the Bibliography does not pretend to be comprehensive; rather, it attempts to be selective. For obvious reasons the great majority of the references are to works published in the last fifteen years.

Anyone interested in a particular subject will find, in almost every one of the papers mentioned, further references to enable a more comprehensive study to be made of the information available.

BIBLIOGRAPHY I

THE BLAST FURNACE PLANT AND EQUIPMENT

"Redesigned Cooling Systems in the Stack and Bosh", by G. G. ORESKEN. *Metallurgy*, No. 3, March 1956, 1–7.

"Automatic Regulation of Blast Furnace Working", by I. A. RYLOV. *Stal*, No. 6, 1957.

"Construction of Blast Furnaces with Thin Wall Stacks", by S. CHERNOKN. *Stal*, No. 8, February 1956.

"Essential Consideration in the Design of Blast Furnaces", by A. L. FOELL. *A.I.M.E.*, April 1942.

"The Blast Furnace of Today. Part I", by W. R. BROWN, *I.S.I. Journal*, January 1947, 107–115.

"Specialised Rolling Stock for Iron and Steelworks", by H. STAYMAN and D. BROWN. *I.S.I. Journal*, October 1948, *160* (2), 197.

"A New Blast Furnace and Ore Preparation Plant at Seraing", by J. MILES and T. THOMPSON. *Iron & Coal Trades Review*, 16 May 1952, 1073–8.

"The Modern Blast Furnace", by T. J. Ess. *Modern Series Iron & Steel Engineer*, 1946.

"Tubular Construction Skip Bridge." *Engineering*, 5 December 1952, 722–3.

"Blast Furnace Controlled Split Wind Blowing", by W. O. BISHOP. *Iron & Steel Engineer*, 28 July 1951, 78–82.

"Rational Distribution of Stock in a Blast Furnace" by T. N. TESCH. *Iron & Steel Engineer*, December 1955, 125–6, 129–31.

"The Design History of the Blast Furnace Tuyere", by L. V. DILLON. *Blast Furnace & Steel Plant*, July 1954.

"Blast Furnace Instrumentation", by J. D. MAY. *Iron & Coal Trades Review*, 31 October 1952, 951–7.

"Gas Sampling Apparatus for Control of Blast Furnace Operation", by N. LOORZ. *Stahl u. Eisen*, 23 October 1952, 1325–8.

"Blast Furnace Instrumentation", by E. T. MORTSON and S. T. PAISLEY. *Blast Furnace & Steel Plant*, July 1951.

"The Development of Controlled Air Distribution for the Blast Furnace", by J. M. STAPLETON. *Iron & Steel Engineer*, July 1957.

"Design and Operation of a Blast Furnace with a Carbon Bosh Lining", by E. K. MILLER. *Iron & Steel Engineer*, April 1957.

"Automatic Stock-Level Control on Blast Furnaces", by I. KJELLMAN and B. GRONBLAD. *J.I.S.I.* 1956, *182* (2), 168.

"The Ironmaking plant at John Summers & Sons", by F. JONES and A. WALKER. *J.I.S.I.* 1953, *175*, 313.

"Belt-Charged Blast Furnaces of S. A. John Cockerill, Belgium", by G. HOOKHAM. *J.I.S.I.*, 1953, *175* (4), 409.

"A Gas-tight Device for Measuring Blast Furnace Stock Level", by D. R. BROWN and C. E. WILSON. *J.I.S.I.*, 1952, *170*.

"Evolution of the All-Carbon Blast Furnace", by J. H. CHESTERS and others. *J.I.S.I.*, 1951, *167* (3), 273.

"Radio-active Indicators for Blast Furnace Refractory Wear", by E. W. VOICE, *J.I.S.I.*, 1951, *167* (2), 157.

"Proposals for the Modification of a Blast Furnace Top to give Controlled Burden Distribution", by E. L. DIAMOND. *J.I.S.I.*, 1950, *164* (2), 173.

"A New Blast Furnace Stock Rod Gas Seal", by E. J. WALKLATE. *J.I.S.I.*, 1949, *163*, 432.

"The Maintenance of Blast Furnace and Ancillary Plant", by A. BRIDGE. *J.I.S.I.*, 1948, *159*, 193.

"No. 1 Blast Furnace at the Margam Works". *J.I.S.I.*, 1947, *155*, 289.

"Differential Pressure Control at Neville Island Blast Furnace", by L. W. ADAMS. *A.I.M.E.*, 1952, 31 March 1952, 24.

"Progress and Problems in Blast Furnace Design", by C. G. HOGBERG. *A.I.M.E. 1947*, 30 April 1947, 83.

"Blast Furnace Pre-Construction", by B. M. STUBBLEFIELD. *A.I.M.E.*, 30 April 1943, 74.

"Relining and Enlargement of No. 7 Blast Furnace at Bethlehem Steel Company", by E. W. TREXLER. *A.I.M.E.*, 30 April 1943, 98.

BIBLIOGRAPHY 2

BLAST FURNACE OPERATION

"The Operation of the Low Shaft Blast Furnace", by H. SCHUMACKER. *Stahl u. Eisen*, 26 February 1953, 257–66.

"Blast Furnace Field Tests." *I.S.I. Special Report No. 18*, 1937.

"Practical Side of Blast Furnace Management", by A. A. WALTON. *I.S.I.* 1940, No. II, 13P.

"Modern Blast Furnace Design and Operation", by J. DALE. *West of Scotland Iron & Steel Inst.*, 1943–4.

"Blast Furnace Operation under Elevated Top Pressure", by F. JANACEK. *Iron & Steel Engineer*, February 1946, 88.

"Some Questions on Inter-related Processes going on in the Blast Furnace", by B. M. LARSEN. *Technology*, February 1947.

"Further Operation Experience with the Blast Furnace at High Top Pressure", by R. P. TOWNDROW. *West of Scotland Iron & Steel Inst.*, 1952, 59.

"Relining and Enlarging No. 9 Blast Furnace at Appleby-Frodingham", by G. D. ELLIOT and others. *I.S.I. Journal*, June 1953, *174*, 143.

"The Making of Iron in a Blast Furnace", by G. D. ELLIOT. *Institute of Chemical Engineers*, 1953, *31* (1).

"Blast Furnace Operation with Controlled Differential Pressure", by L. W. ADAMS, *Journal of Metals*, April 1952.

"Bibliography on Explosions in the Blast Furnace." *Centre de Documentation Siderurgy*, 1956.

"Blast Furnace Practice at Appleby-Frodingham", by H. S. AYRES. *Iron & Coal Trades Review*, 25 December 1953, 1463–9.

"Examination of Blown Out Blast Furnaces", *I.S.I. Special Report No. 51*, October 1954.

"Blast Furnace Breakouts, Explosions and Slips", by F. H. WILCOX. *United States Bureau of Mines Bulletin No. 130*, 1917.

"Experience with Conditioned Blast at the Woodward Iron Company", by H. A. BYRNS. *A.I.M.E. 1952*, 31 March 1952, 41.

"The High Top Pressure Blast Furnace", by E. L. PEPPER. *Metal Progress*, February 1953, *163*, 71–3.

"Jet Caster Technique Explosive Methods of Opening Blast Furnace Tapholes".

"Ironmaking at the Appleby-Frodingham Works", by G. D. ELLIOT and others. *I.S.I. Special Report No. 30*, 1944.

"Problems in Blast Furnace Practice, Ore Preparations and Beneficiation". *Iron & Coal Trades Review*, 17 June 1955, 1397–1402.

"Typical Blast Furnace Practice on the N.E. Coast", by D. RIST. *Iron & Coal Trades Review*, 8–15 July 1955, 79–84, 135–41.

"Some Data on Russian Blast Furnace Operation". *Iron and Coal Trades Review*, 29 October 1954, 1035–7.

"Water Failures on Blast Furnaces", by H. GOLDFEIN. *Blast Furnace & Steel Plant*, February 1953, 209–12.

"Erection and Operation of Blast Furnace in Chile Plants." *Iron & Steel Engineer*, August 1955.

"Extending Blast Furnace Stack Life after Appearance of Hot Spots", by R. SUNDQUIST. *Iron & Steel Engineer*, June 1955.

"The Working of Blast Furnaces on Sinter and Lorraine Ores", by J. SZCZENIOWSKI and others. *Iron & Coal Trades Review*, October 1954, 857–60.

"Method of Blowing in Blast Furnace from Bank", by W. W. DURFEE. *A.I.M.E.*, 21 April 1953, 225.

"Some British Aspects of High Top Pressure Operation", by R. P. TOWNDROW and W. BANKS. *A.I.M.E.*, 21 April 1953, 246.

"The Use of Oxygen in the Iron and Steel Industry of Western Europe", by G. BULLE. *Blast Furnace & Steel Plant*, April 1954, 419–23, 427.

"Conditions for Good Distribution of Materials in the Blast Furnace", by J. Vibrac. *Iron & Coal Trades Review*, 16 and 23 April, 1954, 911–16, 957–62

"Experience in Salamander Tapping", by C. SQUARCY and E. H. BARE. *Blast Furnace & Steel Plant*, March 1954, 331–5.

"Experience in Indefinite Banking at Inland", by J. S. KAPITAN and M. G. SLIFKO. *Blast Furnace & Steel Plant*, May 1953, *41*, 497–502.

"The Efficiency of Blast Furnaces and the way to the Development of High Capacity Blast Furnaces", by E. SENFTER. *Stahl u. Eisen.*, 18 December 1952, 1633–42.

"Lessons from Hanging Blast Furnaces", by L. M. FULTON. *Journal of Metals*, March 1950.

"Blast Furnace Practice in California", by C. H. LENHART. *Iron and Steel Engineer*, July 1949.

"Reducing Delays in Blast Furnace Campaigns", by W. O. BISHOP and C. FRAME. *Iron & Steel Engineer*, January 1957.

"The use of Wet Blast at Constant Humidity in Blast Furnaces", Russian Experiences. *Steel Technology* 1955, *1*; *E.C.E.*, February 1956.

"Blast Furnace Oxygen Operations", by J. H. STRASSBURGER. *Blast Furnace & Steel Plant*. June 1956, 626–35.

"75 Years of Progress in Iron and Steel", by C. D. KING. *A.I.M.E.* Series, 1948.

"Studies of Blast Furnace Assessment", by J. M. RIDGION and A. M. WHITEHOUSE. *J.I.S.I.*, 1956, *184*, 249.

"Desulphurisation of Liquid Pig Iron by Blowing with Lime Powder", by B. TRENTINI, L. WAHL, and M. ALLARD. *J.I.S.I.*, 1956, *183*, 124.

"Investigations on Taphole Clays and Taphole Practice", by W. BANKS and F. D. RICHARDSON. *J.I.S.I.*, 1954, *178*, 138.

"Iron and Steel Making Processes used in Sweden", by S. FORNANDER. *J.I.S.I.*, 1954, 177, 1.

"Some Aspects of the Blast Furnace Situation in the U.S.", by O. R. RICE. *J.I.S.I.*, 1952, 170, 89.

"Desulphurisation of Pig Iron by Solid Lime", by V. GIEDROYE and T. E.
DANCY. *J.I.S.I.*, 1951, *169*, 353.

"Full Scale Blast Furnace Trials", by J. A. BOND and T. SANDERSON.
J.I.S.I., 1951, *168*.

"Measurement of Stockline Contours on Driving Blast Furnaces", by
E. W. VOICE. *J.I.S.I.*, 1950, *166*, 84.

"Analysis of Blast Performance", by R. F. JENNINGS. *J.I.S.I.*, 1950, *164* (3),
305.

"A Radio-active Technique for Determining Gas Transit Times in a Driving
Blast Furnace", by E. W. VOICE. *J.I.S.I.*, 1949, *163*, 312–15.

"Observations of the Stockline in a Driving Blast Furnace", by E. W. VOICE.
J.I.S.I., 1949, *163*,

"Investigations relating to the Scaffolds in Blast Furnaces", by G. R. RIGBY.
J.I.S.I., 1949, *161*, 295.

"An Examination of Blast Furnace Scaffolds and Scaffold forming materials",
by J. H. CHESTERS, I. M. HALLIDAY, and J. MACKENZIE. *J.I.S.I.*, 1948,
159, 23.

"Trends in Pig Iron Manufacture", by T. P. COLCLOUGH and I. S. SCOTT-
MAXWELL. *J.I.S.I.*, 1948, *159*, 186.

"Elimination of Sulphur in the Blast Furnace", by D. JOYCE. *J.I.S.I.*, 1948,
159.

"The Production of Iron and Steel with Oxygen Enriched Blast", by
R. DURRER. *J.I.S.I.*, 1947, *156*, 253.

"The Possibilities for the Extended Use of Oxygen in The British Iron and
Steel Industry", by M. W. THRING. *J.I.S.I.*, 1947, *156*, 285.

"Blowing out a Blast Furnace", by R. FOWLER. *J.I.S.I.*, 1947, *155*, 513–18.

"Ironmaking from High Sinter Burdens", by G. D. ELLIOT and others.
J.I.S.I., 1953, *175*, 241–7.

"The Use of Sinter at Dorman Long", by H. LEDGARD and others. *Iron & Coal
Trades Review*, 2 August 1957.

"Some Blast Furnace Experiences at Ijmuiden, The Netherlands", by
F. W. E. SPIES. *A.I.M.E.* 23 April 1947, 155.

"Effect of Sized and Sintered Mesabi Iron Ores on Blast Furnace Performance", by H. F. DOBSCHA. *A.I.M.E.*, 13 April 1948, 49.

"Some Factors Affecting Distribution of Stock in the Blast Furnace Top",
by J. H. WELLS. *A.I.M.E.*, 1944.

"A Tapping Hole Survey", by D. P. CROMWELL. *A.I.M.E.*, 26 April 1946, 60.

BIBLIOGRAPHY 3

BLAST FURNACE THEORY AND RESEARCH

"External Heat Loss of a Blast Furnace", by D. F. MARSHALL. *J.I.S.I.*, 1933,
127, 127.

"Distribution of Materials in the Blast Furnace", by H. L. SAUNDERS and
R. WILD. *J.I.S.I.*, September 1945, *152*, 259P.

"A Study of Blast Furnace Slags", by R. S. McCaffery. *American Iron & Steel Institute* 1938.

"Review of Work on Blast Furnace Reactions", by J. Taylor. *Journal of The Royal Technical College, Glasgow,* January 1950.

"Stock Distribution and Gas Solid Contact in the Blast Furnace", by C. C. Furnas and T. L. Joseph. *United States Bureau of Mines,* 1930.

"Simplified Construction of Heat Balances for the Blast Furnace Process", by S. Klemantaski. *J.I.S.I.,* July 1953, *174,* 236.

"Optimum Composition of Blast Furnace Slag as Deduced from Liquidus Data for the Quaternary System—Lime, Magnesia, Alumina, Silica", by E. F. Osborn and others. *A.I.M.E.,* 21 April 1953, 281.

"Solid Movement in Blast Furnace Models", by J. B. Wagstaff. *A.I.M.E.,* April 1953, 298.

"Considerations on Blast Furnace Practice", by T. P. Colclough. *J.I.S.I.,* October 1944, No. 2, 359P.

"A Materials and Thermal Balance of a Modern Blast Furnace", by J. Taylor and others. *West of Scotland Iron & Steel Inst.,* 1950.

"Further Studies of the Tuyere Zone of the Blast Furnace", by J. B. Wagstaff. *A.I.M.E.,* April 1953, 104.

"Solution Loss and Reducing Power of Blast Furnace Gas", by T. L. Joseph. *Journal of Metals,* January 1951, *191,* 37–43.

"The Carbon Deposition Reaction over Iron Catalysts", by J. Taylor. *J.I.S.I.,* 1956, *184,* 1.

"The Measurement of Gas Transit Times in a Blast Furnace", by T. W. Johnson. *J.I.S.I.,* 1956, *184,* 18.

"Rate of Desulphurisation of Carbon-Saturated Iron by Blast Furnace Slags", by C. E. A. Shanahan. *J.I.S.I.,* 1955, *180,* 140.

"The Enthalpy and Specific Heat of Iron and Steel. A critical Survey of the Methods of Determination", by J. R. Pattison. *J.I.S.I.,* 1955, *180,* 359.

"Use of a Thermal Model to Determine Temperature under Blast Furnace Hearths", by E. J. Williams and E. Burton. *J.I.S.I.,* 1955, *179,* 17.

"International Research Committee on the Low Shaft Furnace", *J.I.S.I.,* 1955, *179,* 36.

"Further Factors Influencing the Distribution of Solids in the Blast Furnace —Part III", by R. Wild. *J.I.S.I.,* 1952, *170.*

"Significance of Equilibrium and Reaction Rates in the Blast Furnace Process", by J. B. Austin. *J.I.S.I.,* 1951, *167.*

"Distribution of Materials in the Blast Furnace—Part III", by R. Wild. *J.I.S.I.,* 1950, *166,* 339.

"Thermo-Dynamics of Substance of Interest in Iron and Steel Making— II. Compounds Between Oxides", by F. D. Richardson, J. E. Jeffes, and G. Withers. *J.I.S.I.,* 1950, *166,* 213.

"The Influence of Gas/Solid Temperature Differences on Blast Furnace Operation", by J. A. Taylor. *J.I.S.I.,* 1950, *164,* 129.

"Distribution of Materials in the Blast Furnace—Part II. Compensated Charging", by H. L. SAUNDERS and R. WILD. *J.I.S.I.*, 1949, *163*, 61.

"Investigations on an Experimental Blast Furnace", by H. L. SAUNDERS, G. B. BUTLER, and J. M. TWEEDY. *J.I.S.I.*, 1949, *163*, 173.

"The Thermo-Dynamic Background of Iron and Steel Making Processes. I. The Blast Furnace", by F. D. RICHARDSON and J. E. JEFFES. *J.I.S.I.*, 1949, *163*, 397–420.

"Thermo-Dynamics of Substances of Interest in Iron and Steel Making from 0°C. to 2400°C. I. Oxides." by F. D. RICHARDSON and J. E. JEFFES. *J.I.S.I.*, 1948, *160*, 261.

"An introduction to the Inter-Action of Carbon and Iron Ore at Temperatures of up to 1450°C.", by H. L. SAUNDERS and H. J. TRESS. *J.I.S.I.*, 1947, *157*, 215.

"An Experimental Enquiry into the Inter-Actions of Gases and Ore in the Blast Furnace. Part 6—Influence of Limestone on the Reduction of Oron Ore at up to 850°C.", by H. L. SAUNDERS and H. J. TRESS. *J.I.S.I.*, 1946, *154*, 67P.

"The Distribution of Materials in the Blast Furnace—Part I.", by H. L. SAUNDERS and R. WILD. *J.I.S.I.*, 1945, *152*, No. 2, 259P.

"Blast Furnace Slag-Metal Reactions", by J. CHIPMAN. *A.I.M.E.*, April 1954, 193.

"Analysis of Factors that limit the Production Rate and the Coke Rate in the Iron Blast Furnace", by W. O. PHILBROOK. *A.I.M.E.*, April 1954, 248.

BIBLIOGRAPHY 4

THE SINTERING PLANT

"Some Design Problems of the 'Seraphim Plant'" by I. M. KEMP. *J.I.S.I.*, 1955, *181*, 61.

"A Method of Automatic Control for Sinter Plant Feeder Tables", by S. K. DEAN and others. *J.I.S.I.*, 1954, *177*, 220.

"The Ore Preparation Plant at The Workington Branch of the United Steel Companies Ltd. (Engineering)", *J.I.S.I.*, 1948, *159*, 73.

"Smidth Agglomerating Kiln Plant and Practice at Cardiff", by W. SIMONS. *J.I.S.I.*, January 1951, *167*, 1.

"Ore Preparation Plant at Margam", by K. C. SHARP and H. R. TUFNAIL. *Iron & Coal Trades Review*, 19 October 1956.

"Sintering Iron Ore", by R. A. KIPLING and N. D. MACDONALD. *Process Control*, January 1955.

"A Greenawalt Sintering Plant", by J. A. POLL. *A.I.M.E.*, 1952, 214.

"The World's Largest Sinter Plant", by W. J. URBAN., *Blast Furnace and Steel Plant*, March 1951, *39*, 339–42.

"Recent advances in Sintering Plant Design and Operation", by M. F. MORGAN. *A.I.M.E.*, April 1951, 91.

BIBLIOGRAPHY 5

SINTERING AND ORE PREPARATION

"The Role of Iron Ore Beneficiation. The Solution of the Taconite Problem in the U.S.A.", by W. A. HAVEN. *J.I.S.I.*, 1955, *180*, 144.

"Removal of Sulphur during Iron Ore Sintering", by V. GIEDROYC. *J.I.S.I.*, 1955, *180*, 129.

"Sinter Plant Operation at Appleby-Frodingham", by N. D. MACDONALD. *J.I.S.I.*, 1954, *178*, 51.

"Aspects on Pelletizing of Iron Ore Concentrates", by M. K. TIGERSCHIOLD. *J.I.S.I.*, 1954, *177*, 13.

"The Pelletizing of Northampton Sand Ironstones by Vacuum Extrusion", by A. STIRLING. *J.I.S.I.*, 1954, *177*, 25.

"The Development of a Pelletizing Process for Fine Iron Ores", by J. M. RIDGION, E. COHEN, and C. LANG. *J.I.S.I.*, 1954, *177*, 43.

"Sintering Practice at Domnarfvet, Sweden", by C. DANIELSSON. *J.I.S.I.*, 1953, *175*, 152.

"The Rating of Sinter Plants for Economic Output", by R. F. JENNINGS. *J.I.S.I.*, 1953, *175*, 248–56.

"Sinter Plant Assessment Trials at Dagenham and at Cleveland", by R. F. JENNINGS and others. *J.I.S.I.*, 1953, *175*, 267–77.

"Effect of Mineral Additions and Moisture Control on the Sintering of Sierra Leone Concentrates", by P. K. GLEDHILL and others. *J.I.S.I.*, 1953, *175*, 277–9.

"Measurement of Air Flow through the Strand in Sinter Plants", by F. JORDON and M. P. NEWBY. *J.I.S.I.*, 1953, *175*, 36.

"Sinter Making at Appleby-Frodingham", by G. D. ELLIOT and N. D. MACDONALD. *J.I.S.I.*, 1951, *167*, 261.

"The Sintering of Northamptonshire Iron Ore: A Production Plant Study of Factors Affecting Sinter Quality", by D. W. GILLINGS and others. *J.I.S.I.*, 1951, *167*.

"Agglomeration of Taconite Concentrate", by W. LUND. *J.I.S.I.*, 1949, *162*.

"Iron Ore Concentration at Sydvaranger, Norway", by J. K. JOHENSSON. *J.I.S.I.*, 1949, *162*.

"Quality of Sinter. Some Recent Technical Research on Improving the Product from Home Iron Ores", by D. W. GILLINGS. *Iron & Coal Trades Review*, February 1952, 303–9.

"Sinter Plant Operation at Appeby-Frodingham", by N. D. MACDONALD. *Cleveland Institute J.I.S.I.*, September 1954, *178*, 51.

"Output and Quality Ratings of the Appleby-Frodingham Sinter Plants", by B. L. ROBERTSON and others. *2nd International Symposium on the Agglomeration of Iron Ores. IRSID.* May 1957.

"The Making of Self-Fluxing Sinter and its use in the Blast Furnace", by C. DANIELSSON, *A.I.M.E.*, April 1955, 134.

"Blast Furnace Sintering Practice Surveyed", by R. E. POWERS. *Steel*, February 1951, *128*, 95.

"Sinter Plant Practice", by M. F. MORGAN. *A.I.M.E.*, 1944.

"Up-Draught Sintering at Port Pirie", by W. R. BURROW and others. *Australian I.M.M. Proceedings No. 180*, 1956.

"Experiment to Increase the Output of Iron Ore Sinter Plants", by H. WITTENBERG and K. MEYER. *Stahl u. Eisen*, *63*, 1943.

"Research on the Efficiency Increase of Moving Band Sintering Plants", by H. POHL. *Stahl u. Eisen*, June 1951, *71*, 597, 664.

"Smelting of a Fluxed Sinter made from Krivoi Rog Ores", by I. V. RASPOPOV and others. *Stal*, February 1957.

"Recent Results in Operating with Limey Sinter Process", by H. BOOS. *Report No. 242. Blast Furnace Committee and V.D.E.*, October 1956.

"Elimination of Sulphur and Other Elements During Sintering", by B. G. BALDWIN and L. F. BURGESS. *Iron & Coal Trades Review*, August 1957, 425.

"Mixed Firing to Save Solid Fuel in Sintering", by H. RAUSCH and K. MEYER. *Iron & Coal Trades Review*, August 1957. 389.

BIBLIOGRAPHY 6

SINTERING—THEORY AND RESEARCH

"The Reproducibility of Test Results in an Experimental Sinter Box", by C. LANG and J. M. RIDGION. *J.I.S.I.*, 1956, *184*, 172.

"A Laboratory Study of the Sintering Process", by E. W. VOICE and R. WILD. *J.I.S.I.*, 1956, *183*, 404.

"Reducibility of Iron Ore Lumps", by A. E. EL-MEHAIRY. *J.I.S.I.*, 1955, *179*, 219.

"The Mechanism of the Reduction of Iron Oxides by Solid Coke", by B. G. BALDWIN. *J.I.S.I.*, 1955, *179*, 130.

"The Nature of Ironstone Sinter", by E. M. McBRIAR and others. *J.I.S.I.*, 1954, *177*, 316.

"Factors Controlling the Rate of Sinter Production", by E. W. VOICE and others. *J.I.S.I.*, 1953, *175*, 97.

"Towards Faster Sintering of Ironstone", by M. A. K. GRICE and W. DAVIES. *J.I.S.I.*, 1953, *175*, 155.

"Sintering as a Physical Process", by H. B. WENDEBORN. *J.I.S.I.*, 1953, *175*, 280-8.

"Softening of Iron Ores at High Temperatures", by A. GRIEVE. *J.I.S.I.*, 1953, *175*, 1.

"Radiographic Studies of the Process of Sintering Iron Ores", by E. COHEN. *J.I.S.I.*, 1953, *175*, 160.

"Permeability Tests on Blast Furnace Raw Materials", by E. W. NIXON and F. R. MAW. *J.I.S.I.*, 1953, *174*, 331.

"The Chemical Constitution of Sinters", by R. WILD. *J.I.S.I.*, 1953, *174*, 131.

"The Permeability of Sinter Beds", by E. W. Voice and others. *J.I.S.I.,* 1953, *174,* 136.

"Investigation of the Effects of Controlled Variables on Sinter Quality. Part I.—Development of Experimental Sinter Plant and Preliminary Results using Northants Ore." by E. W. Voice and others. *J.I.S.I.,* 1951, *167.*

"The Reduction of Lump Ores", by R. Wild and H. L. Saunders. *J.I.S.I.,* 1950, *165,* 198.

"Magnetic Concentration Experiments upon Iron Ore used in North Lincolnshire Practice", by L. Reeve. *J.I.S.I.,* 1948, *159.*

"Sinters and Sintering—Part I", by H. L. Saunders and H. J. Tress. *J.I.S.I.,* 1945, *152,* 303P.

"How can Theory Help us to Make More Sinter?", by E. W. Voice and R. Wild. *A.I.M.E.,* April 1957.

"Determination of Optimum Water and Fuel Contents for Sinter Mixes", by H. Kosmider, E. Bertram, and H. Schenck. *Stahl u. Eisen,* 12 July 1956, *76* (14), 858.

"Reaction Zones in the Iron Ore Sintering Process", by R. D. Burlingame and others. *A.I.M.E.,* 1956.

BIBLIOGRAPHY 7

MISCELLANEOUS

"The Family Tree of the Blast Furnace", by J. W. Gilles. *V.D.E.,* November 1952.

"Foamed Blast Furnace Slag", by R. T. Parker. *I.S.I. Special Report No. 19,* 1937.

"Investigation Relating to Scaffolds in Blast Furnaces", G. R. Rigby. *B.C.R.A.,* July 1948.

"Iron Blast Furnace Slag Production, Processing, Properties and Uses", *United States Bureau of Mines, Bulletin 479,* 1949.

"Preparation and Utilisation of Blast Furnace Gas", by J. Szczeniowski. *Battelle Technical Review,* April 1953.

"Danger Zones in a Blast Furnace Lining", by R. B. Snow and others. *American Iron & Steel Institute Regional Technical Meetings,* 1953, 253.

"Blast Furnace Gas Cleaning Practice", by K. Guthmann. *Iron & Coal Trades Review,* 7 August 1953, 305.

"Carbon Hearths for Blast Furnaces", by E. W. Voice. *Iron & Coal Trades Review,* June 1952.

"Modern Blast Furnace Gas Cleaning Practices", by G. P. Burks. *Journal of Metals,* May 1950, *188,* 746.

"The Performance of Larger Hot Blast Stoves", by B. B. Frost. *Iron & Steel Engineer,* February 1945, *22,* 64.

"Changes Occurring in Blast Furnace Stoves Refractories During Service", by J. Mackenzie. *British Ceramic Society,* March 1948, *47,* 91.

"Blowers for use in Iron and Steelworks", by F. J. POTTER and L. DUFFY. *J.I.S.I.*, 1956, *184*, 331.

"The Gas-Turbo-Driven Blower for Blast Furnace Service", by C. E. SAYER. *J.I.S.I.*, 1955, *179*, 359.

"Reduction of Iron Ore Without Melting in a Rotary Furnace", by B. KALLING and F. JOHANSSON. *J.I.S.I.*, 1954, 177, 76.

"Blast Furnace Gas Cleaning Methods for Calculating the Motions of Particles in a Gas", by J. H. STRINGER. *J.I.S.I.*, 1950, *164*, 294.

"A Brief History of Electric Pig Iron Smelting in Norway", by H. CHRISTIANSEN. *J.I.S.I.*, 1949, *163*.

"A Note on the Varying-Turbulence Cowper Stove", by D. PETIT. *J.I.S.I.*, 1948, *160*, 131.

"Developments in the Use of Blast Furnace Gas at Port Kembla Steelworks", by H. ESCHER. *J.I.S.I.*, 1947, *156*, 1.

"Gas Turbine Applications in Iron and Steelworks, Part II.—Blast Furnace Blowing Applications", by various authors. *J.I.S.I.*, 1947, *156*, 104.

"Fuel Utilisation in Iron and Steelworks", by N. H. TURNER and F. H. GRAY. *J.I.S.I.*, 1946, *153*, (1) 183P.

"Aspects of Swedish Iron Ore Concentration", by P. G. KIHLSTEDT. *J.I.S.I.*, 1954, *177*, 63.

"Action of Inhibitors of Carbon Deposition in Iron Ore Reductions" by S. KLEMANTASKI. *J.I.S.I.*, 1952, *171*, 176.

"Disintegrators for Fine Cleaning Blast Furnace Gas", by O. W. RICE and Y. C. G. BIGELOW. *A.I.M.E.*, 1950, 111.

"Pig Machine Practice at Hanna Furnace Corporation", by A. J. MACDONALD. *A.I.M.E.*, 1950, 119.

"Pig Machine Practice at Wisconsin Steel Works", by R. P. WHEATLEY. *A.I.M.E.*, 1950, 127.

"Pig Machine Practice at Woodward", by H. A. BYRNS. *A.I.M.E.*, 1950, 130.

"Ferro-Manganese Gas Cleaning at Duquesne Works", by C. H. GOOD. *A.I.M.E.*, 1954, 169.

"Properties and Performance of Blast Furnace Hearth Refractories", by H. M. KRANER. *A.I.M.E.*, 1946, 40.

BIBLIOGRAPHY—TEXT BOOKS

BASHFORTH, G. R. *Manufacture of Iron and Steel*. Chapman and Hall, 1957.

BRANDT, D. J. A. *Manufacture of Iron and Steel*. English Universities Press, 1953.

CAMP, J. M. and FRANCIS, C. B. *Making, Shaping and Treating of Steel*. United States Steel Co., 1957.

CHARLES, J. A., CHATER, W. J. B., and HARRISON, J. L. *Oxygen in Iron and Steel Making*. Butterworth Scientific Publications, 1956.

CLEMENTS, F. *Blast Furnace Practice* (3 vols.). Benn, 1929.

GUMZ, W. *Gas Producers and Blast Furnaces*. Wiley, 1950.

HOUGEN, O. A. and WATSON, K. M. *Industrial Chemical Calculations*. Wiley, 1947.

HETZEL, F. V. and ALBRIGHT, R. K. *Belt Conveyors and Belt Elevators*. Wiley, 1911.

JOHNSON, J. E. *Principles, Operation and Products of the Blast Furnace*. McGraw-Hill Book Co., 1918.

KOREVAAR, A., *Combustion in the Gas Producer and the Blast Furnace*. Crosby, Lockwood, 1924.

MILLER, W. T. W. *Crushers for Stone and Ore*. Mining Publications, 1932.

SPIERS, H. M. *Technical Data on Fuel*. British National Committee World Power Conference, 1952.

SWEETSER, R. H. *Blast Furnace Practice*. McGraw-Hill Book Co., 1938.

TAGGART, A. F., *Handbook of Ore Dressing*. Wiley, 1945.

INDEX